London
Restaurant
Guide 1997

Evening Standard

London
Restaurant
Guide 1997

Fay Maschler   ESB

To REG GADNEY, MY DEAREST COMPANION

First published in Great Britain in 1993 by
Pavilion Books Limited
26 Upper Ground, London SE1 9PD

This fully revised and expanded edition published in 1996 by
EVENING STANDARD BOOKS
Northcliffe House,
2 Derry Street, London W8 5EE

Reprinted in 1997

Text copyright © Fay Maschler 1996
Maps and design copyright © Evening Standard Books 1996

Publishing Manager Joanne Bowlby
Editorial Manager Charlotte Coleman-Smith

Additional testing and reporting has been done by Charles Campion,
Dee McQuillan, Maureen Mills and Douglas Wregg.
Wine reviews are by Douglas Wregg.

Designed by Nick Cave
Typesetting by Jane Royston and Sally Blackmore
Production Manager Roger Hall

Jacket illustration by Brian Ma Siy

ISBN 1 900625 20 2

Printed and bound in Great Britain by Redwood Books Ltd, Trowbridge, Wilts.

This book may be ordered direct from the publisher
but please try your bookshop first.
Corporate editions and personal subscriptions of the *Evening Standard London
Restaurant Guide* are available. Call us for details. Tel: 0171 938 6774.

Also published by Evening Standard Books:

Evening Standard London Pub Guide by Angus McGill
Evening Standard Wine Guide by Andrew Jefford
Evening Standard London Fashion Guide by Mimi Spencer

Contents

Introduction

The feeding of the 9,000

A theory which has been doing the rounds is that in London the same 9,000 people eat out every night. They hurtle from the opening of the latest mega-restaurant to the newest pub which has discovered the greater profits buried in polenta than in pork scratchings, to the secret only they possess concerning the Portakabin serving jerk pork and rotis in a deserted car park. Distressing as the image is, there is an element of truth in it. By common consent, over the past decade, London restaurants have progressed by leaps and bounds. Now it is time for customers to change.

A meal out works most satisfactorily when reasonable and appropriate expectations are invested in it. The potential for bathos, disappointment and tears inherent in anniversaries and celebrations is a heavy burden for any restaurant to carry, yet often it is the somewhat trumped up 'occasion' that provides impetus for a meal out. Of course there are special restaurants for certain special – and usually expensive – rites of passage, but the interesting development that has been taking place in London is in the area of restaurants which cost not a great deal more than buying expensive pre-prepared dishes from a supermarket. When everyone pays for himself or herself – as is becoming commonplace even among courting couples – a restaurant meal can be put in perspective. This might also include comparing the cost to what is spent on other diversions in life. Happy will be the day when restaurants comparable in size to the big brasseries of Paris will be filled – as they are in that city – with a cross-section of society; when, as it were, duke sits down with dustman – and enjoys the same dishes.

The structure
The guide has a different format in this, its fourth edition. Reflecting the frenetic activity and volatility in the restaurant business, the longer reviews are, in the main, for worthwhile establishments which have opened since the previous edition went to press – the almost incredible amount of 69 (compared to last year's 40). Other long reviews simply got carried away with enthusiasm. Shorter reviews – and more of them – summarize the sort of experience you can expect at a wide range of established restaurants. A system of a plus and minus for each place aims to pinpoint its strengths and its weaknesses. Basic details are given for restaurants which were about to open when we had to stop writing, but should be open by the time you read this book.

Eros Awards

Unlike the other awards of most other restaurant guides, the *Evening Standard* Eros Awards recognize that London's restaurant culture not only is composed of many and varied elements — and that a South Indian vegetarian meal can be quite as thrilling as the efforts of a classically trained chef — but that it is built on shifting sands. A restaurant which performs brilliantly one year, may lose its chef to a higher bidder, may get complacent, may suddenly, perversely, decide that the way forward is Argentinian food. We have no compunction about changing the list each year, sometimes quite radically. However, there is no merit in change for its own sake and the greatest achievement of a restaurant is consistency and continuing vitality. There are restaurants which receive an Eros year after year and, despite the breathless excitement about change, drama and diversity in the restaurant business — which the *Evening Standard* newspaper covers so thoroughly — these are the bosoms we return to in times of happiness or when in need of comfort.

The 21st Eros – the reader's Eros

For the first time, we asked *Evening Standard* readers to vote for their own Eros Award. This year it goes to The Brackenbury, recipient of Eros Awards in the past and probably not co-incidentally the inspiration and nurture for an Eros of 1997, The Chiswick.

New restaurants are those which opened after August 1995.

Price

The price quoted, based on dinner à la carte, is an indication of the cost of a three-course meal for one including half a bottle of modest wine (or the equivalent), tax, but not service. It would be easier to spend more, but eating at lunchtime or from set-price menus will often be cheaper.

Telephone numbers

0181 numbers are prefixed. All others are 0171 numbers. Now, all that is needed is to pick up a phone and make a booking.

FAY MASCHLER

"'I rather like bad wine," said Mr Mountchesney; "one gets so bored with good wine."'

(SYBIL — BENJAMIN DISRAELI)

L ondon is a huge magnet attracting the best wines from throughout the world. Just as the 1990s have witnessed the evolution of a style of cooking known as Modern British, so too have wine lists assumed global aspirations. The eclectic menu is now being matched by the eclectic wine list. As Tim Atkin writes in *The Observer*: 'The wine business is faster, younger and more cosmopolitan than it used to be. Prices are keener, competition greater and the quality of what we drink especially at the cheaper end, much more varied and interesting'. With such beneficial saturation, it should be difficult, if not impossible, to construct a bad wine list and wine merchants in the capital must be given proper credit for encouraging the overall improvement of standards. Indeed, London is potentially the most exciting city in the world to drink modishly.

There is, however, for all the infinite variety, the danger of a 'stepfordizing' of wine lists, reinforced by a sense of 'déjà-bu' when you survey what is on offer. The usual French suspects have been given new accomplices: the obligatory anodyne Pinot Grigio, the ubiquitous oak-chippy Aussie Chardonnay, the token quaffing delegates from Chile, South Africa and Spain. What looks like a catholic selection is, on closer analysis, conservative. Modern wine-making techniques and equipment may have ensured that your bottle of wine is clean, fruity and technically correct, but have stripped the final product of real personality. Lists, moreover, tend to be largely varietal-dominated, formulated under the straitjacketed assumption that people will choose only what they have heard of, with Sauvignon and Chardonnay inevitably dominating the whites and Cabernet Sauvignon the reds. Choice then depends on more than merely girdling the globe for a dozen examples of the same grape variety.

The most stimulating, provocative and intelligent restaurant lists will incite you to experiment with more intrepid alternatives. The positive trends this year have been towards a recognition of Languedoc-Roussillon as a source of attractive, well-made wines, and Syrah, which has amply proven its unlimited potential, is my grape variety of the year. Austria, Switzerland and Hungary have arrived on the map and from further afield, Argentina has succeeded with grape varieties like Torrontès and Malbec, meanwhile boutique wineries in Australia and California are reinvigorating and reinterpreting Italian natives such as Charbono, Sangiovese and Barbera.

'I have a little list... '

A quick inventory for what makes a good wine list. 1. A representative cross-section of styles and grape varieties to reflect different moods and different tastes. 2. An intelligible format, one which gives more information than the name of the wine and its price; which, preferably, categorizes or groups wines according to criteria such as alcohol, fruit, oak, acidity, sweetness etc. or divides into sections of discrete grape varieties or regions, providing the customer with an entry point to the list, facilitating choice. 3. Concise and accurate tasting notes – these are a boon to those of us unfamiliar with the names of producers, the quality of vintages and with the intrinsic properties of certain grape varieties. Food and wine recommendations would also be helpful. Alas, very few lists get to grips with this thorny area. 4. A minimum of four wines should be served by the glass (excluding dessert wines). 5. At least 50% of the wines should cost less than the average price of three courses from the menu.

Cloudy Baywatch...

I have instituted a price index called Cloudy Baywatch, named after the buxom charms of New Zealand's finest Sauvignon, a wine which purportedly arouses the most primitive rapacious instincts in restaurateurs. What you will find at Ransome's Dock for an eminently reasonable £17.95, will command a range of wildly-differing prices across the West End, culminating in the eminently crazy £42.50 at The Dorchester, for which you can drink it out of a glass slipper (presumably). Whereas certain fluctuations and discrepancies in prices are understandable, I have tried to point out some of the grosser anomalies and would urge people not to buy where they suspect they are being expected to subsidise wholly unrealistic profit margins. Most restaurants in London mark up between 2.5 and 3 times the cost price of the bottle. Anything more is pure greed.

When ordering...

If you are unsure ask for advice. If you are unable to drink the bottle you have been recommended, don't suffer in British stiff-upper-lipped silence. Most restaurants will replace it without charging you. If you enjoy a wine, try to remember what it is, and what you liked about it. The more you learn about wine, the more you will want to learn, but don't take it too seriously – wine is for pleasure as well as being the natural accompaniment to food. There is no place for snobbery, mystification or ritualisation – why should there be? After all, go into any decent restaurant and you will see how good wine has become as much part of our culture as good food.

DOUGLAS WREGG

MAP 1 • Greater London

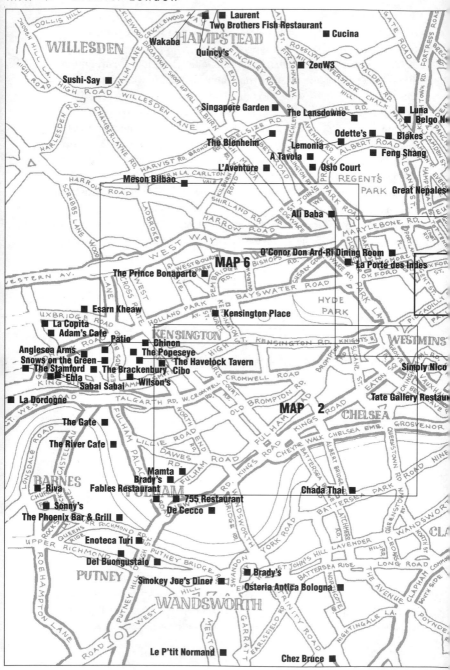

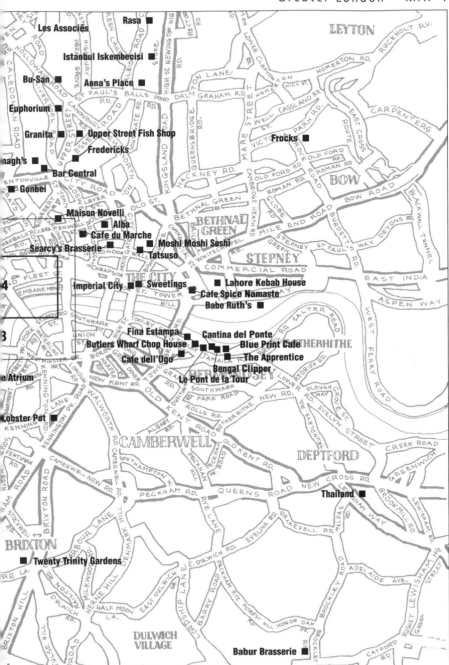

Rasa

Les Associés

Istanbul Iskembecisi

Bu-San

Anna's Place

Euphorium

Granita   Upper Street Fish Shop

Fredericks

Frocks

nagh's

Bar Central

Gonbei

LEYTON

CARPENTERS

BOW

Maison Novelli

Alba

Cafe du Marche

BETHNAL GREEN

Searcy's Brasserie   Moshi Moshi Sushi

Tatsuso

STEPNEY

THE CITY

EAST INDIA

ASPEN WAY

4

Imperial City   Sweetings   Lahore Kebab House

Cafe Spice Namaste

Babe Ruth's

3

Fina Estampa   Cantina del Ponte

Butlers Wharf Chop House   Blue Print Cafe

Cafe dell'Ugo   The Apprentice

e Atrium   Bengal Clipper

Le Pont de la Tour

HERHITHE

WEST FERRY ROAD

Lobster Pot

CAMBERWELL

DEPTFORD

CREEK ROAD

GREENWICH

Thailand

BRIXTON

Twenty Trinity Gardens

DULWICH VILLAGE

Babur Brasserie

11

MAP 2 • West London

- Mon Petit Plaisir ■
- Arcadia ■
- Bistro 190 & Downstairs at 190 ■
- ■ Royal Garden Hotel – The Tenth
- Wodka ■
- Launceston Place ■
- Ognis...
- ■ The Abingdon
- Stratford's ■
- Gilbert
- Bombay Brasserie ■
- Bangkok ■
- Hilaire ■
- SOUTH KENSINGTON
- Star of India ■
- Cambio de Tercio ■
- ■ Shaw's
- Lou Pescadou ■
- Il Goloso
- Kartouche ■
- Christoph's ■
- Bar Centra...
- Formula Veneta ■
- Aubergine
- La Famiglia ■
- ■ Montana
- Blue Elephant ■
- Chutney Mary ■
- WALHAM GREEN
- B Squa...
- The Canteen ■

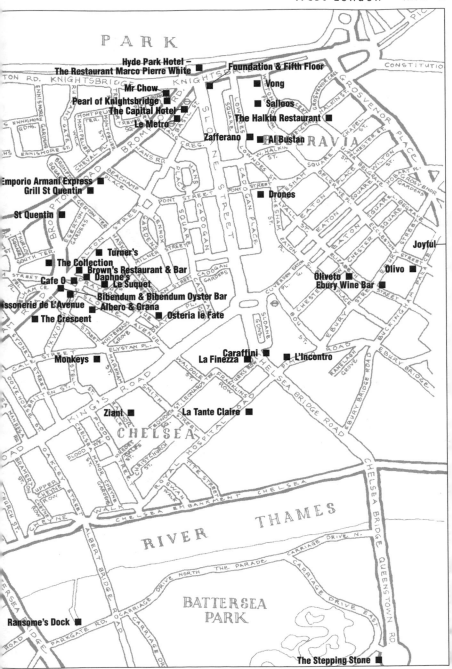

PARK

Hyde Park Hotel –
The Restaurant Marco Pierre White ■   Foundation & Fifth Floor ■

■ Vong

Mr Chow ■

Pearl of Knightsbridge ■   ■ Salloos
The Capital Hotel ■
Le Metro ■   ■ The Halkin Restaurant ■

Zafferano ■   ■ Al Bustan   BRAVIA

Emporio Armani Express ■
Grill St Quentin ■

■ Drones

St Quentin ■

Joyful

■ Turner's

The Collection ■   ■ Olivo ■
Oliveto ■
■ Brown's Restaurant & Bar   Ebury Wine Bar ■
Daphne's ■
Cafe O ■   ■ Le Suquet
Bibendum & Bibendum Oyster Bar ■
issonerie de L'Avenue ■   Albero & Grana ■
■ The Crescent   ■ Osteria le Fate

Caraffini ■
Monkeys ■   La Finezza ■   ■ L'Incontro

Ziani ■   La Tante Claire ■

CHELSEA

RIVER   THAMES

BATTERSEA
PARK

Ransome's Dock ■

The Stepping Stone ■

13

MAP 3 • Central London

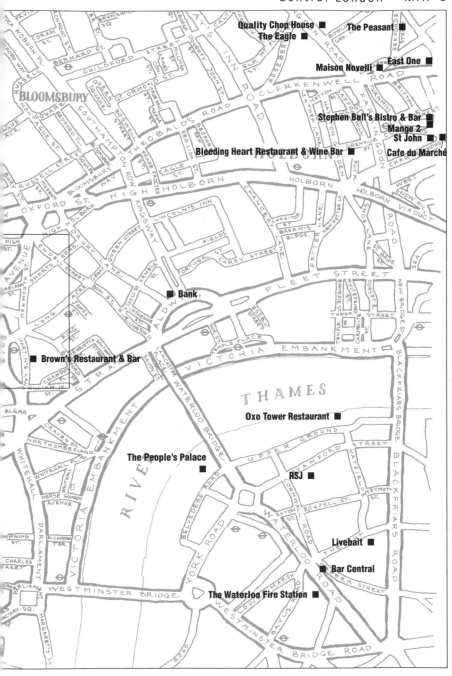

BLOOMSBURY

Quality Chop House ■
The Eagle ■
The Peasant ■
Maison Novelli ■
East One ■

CLERKENWELL

Stephen Bull's Bistro & Bar ■
Mange 2 ■
St John ■ ■
Bleeding Heart Restaurant & Wine Bar ■
HOLBORN
Cafe du Marché ■

HIGH HOLBORN

FLEET STREET

■ Bank

■ Brown's Restaurant & Bar

THAMES

Oxo Tower Restaurant ■

The People's Palace ■

RSJ ■

Livebait ■

■ Bar Central

The Waterloo Fire Station ■

MAP 4 • West End

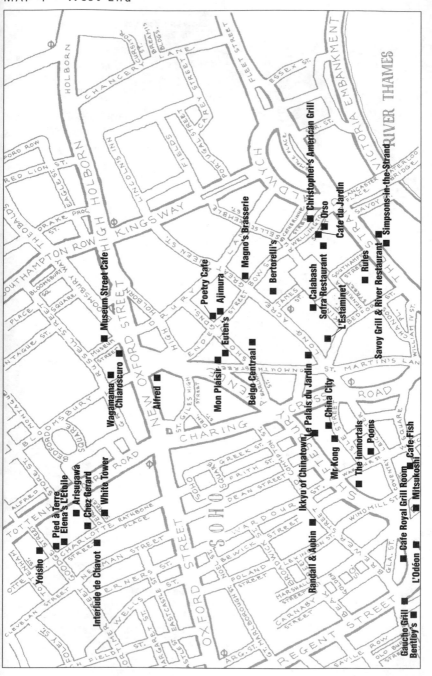

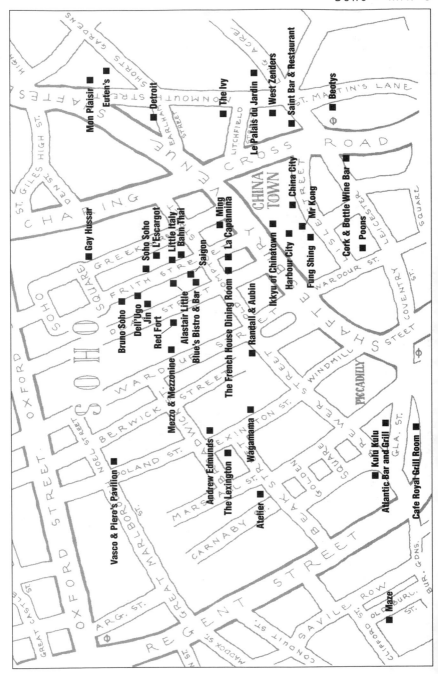

MAP 6 • Notting Hill Gate

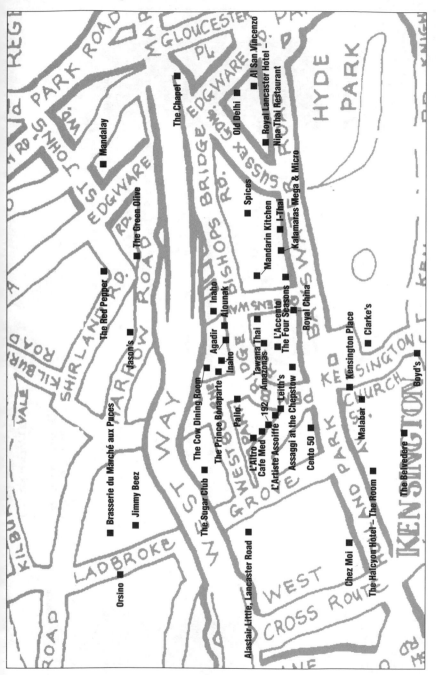

Eros Awards 1997

AUBERGINE SW10

BIBENDUM SW3

LE CAPRICE SW1

CAMBIO DE TERCIO SW5

CHEZ BRUCE SW17

CHEZ MOI W11

THE CHISWICK W4

THE CRITERION W1

FUNG SHING WC2

THE IVY WC2

LIVEBAIT SE1

QUAGLINO'S SW1

RASA N16

RIVA SW13

THE RIVER CAFE W6

STAR OF INDIA SW5

THE SUGAR CLUB W11

LA TANTE CLAIRE SW3

VONG SW1

ZAFFERANO SW1

THE 21ST EROS – READER'S EROS – THE BRACKENBURY W6

London's Top Wine Lists

BIBENDUM SW3

CLARKE'S W8

THE CRESCENT SW3

ENOTECA TURI SW15

THE FIFTH FLOOR,
HARVEY NICHOLS SW1

KARTOUCHE SW10

LEITH'S W11

ODETTE'S NW1

RSJ SE1

RANSOME'S DOCK SW11

Lavazza has developed a reputation for producing fine coffee since humble beginnings from a small grocery store in the heart of Old Torino in Northern Italy.

Luigi Lavazza, the founder of the company, had no idea that the business he started in 1895 would one day become Italy's number 1 coffee brand with growing interests around the world. Today, Lavazza remains family-owned and run by the latest generation of the Lavazza family — Mr Emilio, Alberto and Giuseppe (son of Emilio) Lavazza.

Lavazza for the

Coffee is the second most valuable trading commodity in the world — sales are only exceeded by oil. It's hardly surprising that people feel so passionate about the 'perfect cup of coffee' and that the discerning palate in the UK puts Lavazza, the real Italian coffee, at the top of their shopping list.

As 'Café Society' develops in the UK, along with our interest in good food and quality wine, so has the opportunity to serve authentic Italian espresso in the home. Lavazza's ground coffee makes the perfect cup of cappuccino or espresso and is suitable for all types of coffee-making equipment, from filters, cafetières, Italian mocha pots to electric espresso machines.

Lavazza's coffee produces an intense flavour, real aroma and a lasting taste that is truly distinctive.

LAVAZZA QUALITÀ ROSSA
A strong, robust coffee and the leading Italian blend.

LAVAZZA CAFFE ESPRESSO
A smooth flavour and tempting aroma made from 100% carefully selected Arabica beans.

LAVAZZA QUALITÀ ORO
A truly refined premium blend, for the discerning consumer who enjoys a strong but well-balanced flavo
most suitable for Italian mocha pots.

LAVAZZA'S TIPS FOR MAKING PERFECT COFFEE

The lasting impression of a fine meal served either in your favourite restaurant, or at home is 'The Coffee'. The Lavazza range provides the perfect solution, but to ensure that it is prepared and served perfectly, Lavazza have produced some useful tips to take the element of chance out of the operation.

USING THE FILTER MACHINE METHOD

♦ Pour a little boiling water on to the coffee grounds to dampen the coffee first. Leave for 2 minutes before adding the rest of the boiling water.
♦ Ensure the water does not drip through the filter to the jug at too fast a rate.

USING A TRADITIONAL ITALIAN MOCHA POT (ie: THE LAVAZZA CARMENCITA)

♦ Fill the lower section with water
♦ Never heat the pot on full power setting — use medium heat.

perfect coffee...

GOLDEN RULES

♦ Use one dessert spoon of coffee per person.
♦ Never re-heat coffee.
♦ Once opened, always seal the coffee packet and store in the refrigerator.
♦ Always use Lavazza Coffee!

TO MAKE THE PERFECT LAVAZZA ESPRESSO COFFEE

USING THE CAFETIERE METHOD
♦ Always warm the cafetière
♦ Use water which is just off the boil (never boiling)
♦ Always stir the coffee and water and leave to stand for at least 3 minutes, before plunging the filter.

♦ Once the top pot is filled with coffee — always remove from heat and stir before serving

TO MAKE THE PERFECT CAPPUCCINO

Prepare the espresso coffee using any of the above methods.
♦ For two cappuccinos, pour 1/4 pint of milk (for best results use skimmed or semi-skimmed) into a tall jug and place in a microwave until luke warm — do not boil.
♦ Rapidly agitate heated milk with a swizzle stick or other whisk method until frothy.
♦ Spoon milk froth on to the top of an espresso coffee.
 ♦ Dust with chocolate powder to taste.

For further information on Lavazza coffee, please call 0181 994 6382.

Open
Every day
Hours
Mon–Sat 12.00–
11.00pm, Sun
12.00–10.30pm
Credit cards
AmEx, Mastercard,
Visa, Switch, Delta
Service charge
12.5%
Set-price lunch
£9.95
Nearest tube
stations
High Street
Kensington, Earls
Court
Map 2

The Abingdon   £25

54 Abingdon Road W8 (937 3339)

+ *mine host, chef Brian Baker*
- *customers' voices could engrave glass*

This sprauncy neighbourhood was doubtless pleased to see the back of Henry J. Bean and his friends who call him Hank. Only faint traces remain manifest, in the less-attractive part of the premises furnished with red-leatherette banquettes. Although owned by My Kinda Town, this is chef Brian Baker's operation. Between taking coats if necessary, chatting over coffee and supervising service, Baker — who gained a Michelin star for Hambleton Hall — cooks dishes such as fish stew with saffron and potato aïoli, and grilled breast of chicken with leeks and sun-dried tomatoes. He has an easy intuition for simple combinations of pan-European ingredients, but for the most part the style is rustic French. Vegetable assemblies are interesting, and include combinations such as aubergine terrine with sweet peppers, and roasted vegetables with Roquefort. The two-course £9.95 lunch is simple good value; Sunday lunch is a pleasant, relaxed event.

Open
Every day
Hours
12.30–2.30pm
6.30–11.30pm
Credit cards
Mastercard, Visa
Service charge
12.5%
Set-price lunch
£11.50
Nearest tube
stations
Queensway,
Bayswater,
Notting Hill Gate
Map 6

L'Accento   £26

16 Garway Road W2 (243 2201)

+ *tempting, good-value set menu*
- *noise ricocheting off hard surfaces; cursory list of desserts*

A model of restraint in the pricing policy of an interesting set menu: after three years at £10.50 for two courses, owner Giovanni Tomaselli has raised the price by just £1, and in choosing this option you don't feel that you are drawing the short straw. An enlightened and occasionally ingenious treatment of pasta is often the most alluring first course (say, fresh tagliatelle with an octopus stew), and something homestyle (say, braised rabbit) the inviting main course. Fresh vegetables are included, but may or may not complement what you order. On the à la carte menu, dishes are introduced by their main ingredient: for example, MAIALE (pan-fried fillet of pork with leek and lemon sauce) or BRANZINO (sea bass baked in foil with a julienne of vegetables, plum tomatoes and polenta). L'Accento works well as a neighbourhood restaurant, and is usually thronged with Notting Hill's chattering class.

Adam's Cafe £19

77 Askew Road W12 (0181-743 0572)

+ *wholesome North African food at fair prices*
- *no longer BYO (but corkage is nominal)*

Business is bubbling along nicely at the Boukraa family's friendly neighbourhood restaurant, which serves couscous by night and huge English breakfasts all day. The couscous is Tunisian in style and beautifully made, but there is now also a Moroccan chef producing tagines of chicken, preserved lemons and olives or lamb with almonds and prunes. Perhaps it is time to break away from the familiar order of brik à l'oeuf (a stuffed filo-pastry envelope) and the couscous Imperial divided between two. Certainly the menu now offers more diversions and the presence of north African customers suggests that the range is appreciated.

Open
Dinner every day
Hours
7.00-11.00pm
Credit cards
Mastercard, Switch, Visa
Nearest tube station
Ravenscourt Park
Map 1

Agadir £20

84 Westbourne Grove W2 (792 2207)

+ *a scarce resource*
- *chilly in winter*

Food writers continue enthusiastically to greet the dawning of the new age of Moroccan cooking, but there is still precious little evidence of it in London restaurants. (However, see the entry for Bruno Soho.) Agadir is currently one of the few Moroccan-owned places to specialize in the food of the Maghreb. It is a simple place which, to look at, you might easily mistake for just another Indian restaurant in Westbourne Grove, but the execution of harira and chorba (traditional soups), briouat (savoury pastries), cooked and raw vegetable salads, couscous and tagines is of a fairly high standard – the couscous being rather better than the tagines – and sold at notably reasonable prices. A Moroccan food festival at the rather improbable location of The Berkeley Hotel in early 1996 seemed to galvanize Agadir into laying on belly-dancing displays on certain evenings.

Open
Lunch Fri-Sat, dinner every day
Hours
12.00-4.00pm, 6.00pm-12.00am
Credit cards
AmEx, Mastercard, Switch, Visa, Delta
Set-price dinner
£9.99
Nearest tube station
Bayswater
Map 6

Open
Lunch Mon-Fri,
dinner Mon-Sat
Hours
12.00-3.00pm,
6.00-10.30pm
Credit cards
AmEx, Diner's,
Mastercard, Visa
Set-price lunch
£9
Set-price dinner
£19.50 (£35 for 2)
Nearest tube
station
Convent Garden
Map 4

Ajimura £30

51-3 Shelton Street WC2 (497 2240)

+ *a good place to learn about Japanese food*
- *ski-lodge decor*

When Ajimura opened its doors in 1972, there was little or no competition: it claims to be the longest-established Japanese restaurant in Britain. Now that we can pick up a tray of sushi at a sandwich bar, rarity value is not the issue. There is something slightly do-gooding about the atmosphere here (you cannot help wondering if they opened in the same year as Cranks), but the menu is wide-ranging and easily comprehensible, with nine different set dinners for times when composing a balanced meal proves too great a burden. Ignore the silly titles of the sushi sets, such as Nessy's Delight and Mother Ocean; sushi chef Tora-San is a craftsman. Vegetarians also fare well. Aficionados look to the monthly-changing list of specials, where esoteric and sea vegetables are deployed. The Covent Garden location makes sense of the pre-theatre menu, as does its price. As at most Japanese places, lunch is much cheaper than dinner.

Open
Lunch Mon-Fri,
dinner Mon-Sat
Hours
12.00-3.00pm,
6.00-11.00pm
Credit cards
All major except
Diner's
Set-price lunch
£15 & £25.00
Set-price dinner
£28.00
Nearest tube
stations
Leicester Square,
Tottenham Court
Road
Map 5

Alastair Little £32

49 Frith Sreeet W1 (734 5183)

+ *no rocket salad*
- *paper napkins*

This guide has previously criticised Alastair Little – the byword for intrinsic simplicity at haute-cuisine prices – for having become mired in its former reputation. The casual informality began to irritate, and the eclecticism of the cooking – which once thrilled us with its bracing flavours – lost its conviction and innovatory zeal. A short, straightforward menu and the return of Juliet Peston to the kitchen should signify a recovery to more consistent standards, although a minimum food spend of £28 in the evening still creates expectations that are not always fulfilled. Escoffier's injunction to keep it simple is not followed in dishes such as Caesar salad with avocado; asparagus and Parma ham in a phyllo (sic) crust with mesclun salad; or a wild-mushroom, asparagus and spinach risotto. In each of these dishes, the supernumerary ingredients detract from the overall conception of the dish.

Alastair Little Lancaster Rd £28

136a Lancaster Road W11 (243 2220)

+ *the quintessential W11 neighbourhood caff*
- *waiting staff on a hiding to nothing*

A decade after Alastair Little took the culinary world by storm with his minimalist, eponymous Soho restaurant (q.v.), where menus evolved in a mealtime according to supplies, inspiration and sometimes the latest ethnic meal that Little had eaten, the Godfather of modern British cuisine converted a caff close to his home in Notting Hill Gate. There is no name: only a Prince of Wales check canopy and a lower-case 'a' on the wall near the front window alerts you to its presence. Having suffered a set back by badly breaking the bones of one foot, but also apt to give a little mocking laugh at the notion that customers could be so naïve as to expect a chef to be cooking in a restaurant named after him, Little employed a young chap called Toby Gush to run the kitchen. Gush had flowed quickly through the fashionable kitchens – Kensington Place, The Brackenbury, The River Cafe and, very briefly, the more classic La Tante Claire – and was well-poised to produce modern dishes such as marinated home-salted cod with rocket and butterbean salad; poached ox tongue with carrots and horseradish sauce; roast Hereford duck with cabbage, root vegetables and pancetta; and ginger ice cream with giant brandy snaps. Those dishes, when tried, were exemplary. However, another meal delivered a dull Mantuan-style capon salad; impossibly salty tagliatelle with purple sprouting broccoli; and red flannel hash so overcooked it was more of a loofah. Stephen Fry smiled at this observation when I passed it on to him in the restaurant. The name dropping is deliberate: *le tout* W11 gathers here. The cost of the set-price menus is reasonable – something one had stopped expecting from Alastair – and there is comfort and tablecloths, other appurtenances we did not previously associate with him. Despite some downs as well as ups to the food, this is the dream neighbourhood restaurant.

Open
Mon-Sat
Hours
Mon-Fri 12.30-
2.30pm, 7.00-
11.00pm, Sat
12.30-3.00pm,
7.00-11.00pm
Credit cards
AmEx, Mastercard,
Visa, Switch
Service charge
12.5% (parties of
6 or more)
Set-price dinner
£25
**Nearest tube
station**
Ladbroke Grove
Map 6

Alba £28

107 Whitecross Street EC1 (588 1798)

+ *a corner of Piedmont in the gritty city*
- *the price of white truffles*

The Barbican is beginning to fight back in the skirmish for the theatre- and concert-goer's gastronomic pound (see entry for Searcy's Brasserie), but nearby Alba remains a worthy

Open
Mon-Fri
Hours
12.00-3.00pm,
6.00-11.00pm
Credit cards
AmEx, Mastercard,
Switch, Visa,
Delta, Diner's
Service charge
12.5%

Set-price dinner
£16.90
Nearest tube
stations
Barbican,
Moorgate
Map 1

alternative with its pre-theatre menu at £9.95 for two courses and coffee. In white-truffle season – usually November to January – the restaurant's Piedmontese origins show through in a particularly enticing way. Other items in season, such as porcini or asparagus, are also celebrated in a range of dishes. At any time of year the Piedmontese set-price menu degustazione is worth exploring. City gents flock to Alba at lunchtimes. There are substantial dishes such as stinco di maiale (roasted knuckle of pork in a herb gravy) to sustain them, but a sign of the times is a symbol denoting vegetarian options – most of them pasta. Finish a meal with taleggio, walnuts and celery, followed by one of the well-chosen dessert wines.

Open
Dinner every day
Hours
5.30-11.30pm (hot
food),12.00am
(cold food)
Credit cards
AmEx, Mastercard,
Switch, Visa,
Delta, Diner's
Service charge
15% (parties of 6
or more)
Nearest tube
station
South Kensington
Map 2

Albero & Grana   £25

89 Sloane Avenue SW3 (225 1048)

+ *suckling pig; tapas; Spanish surrealism*
− *occasional baroque approaches to what should be severe food*

Catalan, Andalucian and Basque dishes, some with a modern twist, are the mainstay of Angel Garcia's menu. Rich casseroles and stews, seafood, roasted suckling pig and tripe are all specialities. The bar area offers a wide selection of tapas: pickled anchovies; baby squid in their ink; garlic prawns; paella; lentils with cured pork; and chorizo sausage with chickpeas. Crowded with the South Kensington style-conscious and Eurotrash, the look of the bar is nevertheless ordinary compared to the dramatic restaurant with its brilliant primary colours juxtaposed with details in black and white. It is a late-night place in true Spanish style, so don't even think about dinner before 10pm.

Open
Every day
Hours
Lunch 12.00-
6.00pm, dinner
6.00-11.00pm
Credit cards
AmEx, Diner's,
Mastercard, Visa
Nearest tube
station
Knightsbridge
Map 2

Al Bustan   £30

27 Motcomb Street SW1 (235 1668)

+ *meze in Belgravia; courteous service*
− *chicken in a special sauce*

Lebanese restaurants tend to be serving to the converted who expect – and usually get – a predictable list of dishes cooked to a high standard. The family-run Al Bustan is no exception. The long list of hot and cold hors d'oeuvres is where interest lies. After crunching raw vegetables dipped into a bowl of oil and garlic (accounting for the cover charge), graze on a selection of small dishes predicated on the healthy array of pulses, vegetables, fish roes, pastries, grains, nuts, herbs and wilder ingredients such as raw lamb and offal which are the underpinning of the cuisine. The chargrilled main courses can seem like an anti-climax. Breads, sticky dessert pastries, coffee and the diplomatic service all come in for praise.

Alfred   £26

245 Shaftesbury Avenue WC2 (240 2566)

+ *the drinks list (including beers); defiantly English nursery puds*
- *when sitting outside, food can become sooty*

On a spur of unsalubrious pavement at the northern end of Shaftesbury Avenue perches Alfred, with its modern slant on old British favourites. The stark, refectory feel of the place belies the delicacy of some of the cooking: there are brains (intelligence, not just offal) as well as brawn, along with a recognition of the validity of a traditional style, which lends confidence to such retro dishes as faggots with gravy and toad-in-the-hole. However, it is not just our childhood memories revisited: something new is smoked-quail salad with marinated artichoke, and something borrowed is rabbit in beer and sage sauce. Oh, and something proverbially blue are the walls.

Open
Lunch Mon-Fri,
dinner Mon-Sat
Hours
12.00-3.30pm,
6.00-11.30pm
Credit cards
AmEx, Delta,
Diner's,
Mastercard,
Switch, Visa
Set-price lunches
£12.95 & £15.90
**Nearest tube
station**
Tottenham Court
Road
Map 4

Al Hamra   £30

31-3 Shepherd Market W1 (493 1954)

+ *outdoor tables; the breads*
- *lapses in service*

There are two strategies that you can adopt when eating here. The first - a foolish one - is to pick a single dish as a starter and to follow it with a main course (and those choices could be as mundane as avocado with prawns followed by veal escalope); the second - the sage way forward - is to build your own meze from the 48 authentic small dishes on offer. As well as the familiar Middle Eastern assemblies of tabbouleh, houmus and fattoush, there are Lebanese delicacies such as bastourma (dried, cured fillet of beef); makdoue (aubergines stuffed with walnuts, spices and garlic); batrakh (fish roe with garlic and olive oil); nchaat pane (lamb's brains scrambled with eggs); and arayes (the self-styled Lebanese 'pizza' of flat bread, featuring sliced lamb and olives in the topping). A copious spread makes main-course grills somewhat otiose, but check out the Lebanese dish of the day. The hefty cover charge delivers a basket of raw vegetables. However, most of the customers, apparently engaged in secret deals, seem not to give a fig about cost.

Open
Mon-Sun
Hours
11.30am-11.30pm
(last orders for
lunch at 4.00pm)
Credit cards
AmEx, Mastercard,
Visa, Diner's
Cover charge
£2.50 (includes
salad bowl)
**Nearest tube
station**
Green Park
Map 3

Ali Baba

£14 BYO

Open
Every day
Hours
12.00-11.30pm
Credit cards
None
**Nearest tube
stations**
Marylebone, Baker
Street
Map 1

32 Ivor Place NW1 (723 7474)

+ *family (good) values*
- *the baklava*

Behind the take-away counter in this family-run enterprise is what was presumably once a living-room but is now the restaurant, open all day, every day from noon to midnight. Cable TV will probably be playing; a grandmother may be minding a baby; other family members tend to wander in and out. The basically Middle Eastern menu politely includes what are called 'Continental Dishes', but skip the spaghetti Napolitan (sic) and make inroads into a spread of first courses such as labne salad, falafel, foul (purée of brown beans), mutabel (aubergine dip), tabbouleh and chicken wings, followed by kebabs, couscous, Saudi Arabian capsi (lamb on red rice) or the Ali Baba speciality of lamb with nuts on a bed of rice. Low prices and the high standard of cooking will inspire you to tell all your friends. Arrange a party: a whole lamb will be prepared if ordered one day ahead.

Alounak

£14 BYO

Open
Every day
Hours
12.00-12am
Credit cards
None
**Nearest tube
stations**
Westbourne
Grove/Olympia
Map 6

44 Westbourne Grove W2 (229 4158); 10 Russell Gardens W14 (371 2350)

+ *perfect rice*
- *the secret is out*

Anyone in the know, my dear, knew about the Iranian food being served in the portakabins in the carpark near Olympia. Sadly, it is no more, and that part of the business has moved to premises (which were all too briefly Uma) in nearby Russell Gardens. This is the third venture of Mr Yousef, who was encouraged by his success in the car park to open up in Westbourne Grove, where there is the bonus of a tamour (a clay oven used for bread-baking). Central to the cuisine is the reverential cooking of rice: the 'chelo' in chelo kebab, where butter- and saffron-infused long-grain rice is served with chargrilled meat. Sprinkle on a pinch of sumac and incorporate any fresh herbs left over from a first course, which might be bread served with strained yoghurt plus mint, tarragon and chives. Dishes of the day provide further enlightenment concerning this healthy cuisine. On a Wednesday, it is worth going for ghaimeh bademjoon (lamb with split yellow peas, dried lemon, aubergine, special sauce and rice). The Persian take on lassi is called dogh, and a jug of dogh costs £4.50.

Al San Vincenzo £35

30 Connaught Street W2 (262 9623)

+ *a warm, charming room in an attractive street*
- *the tendency of the owners to grizzle*

Some years ago Vincenzo and Elaine Borgonzolo famously made a restaurant swap, taking over the premises of an Indian restaurant near Marble Arch in exchange for the premises of their Italian venture in Cheam. However, they are now firmly ensconced in the West End, running a relatively small business that may not suit their ambitions but does match their capabilities. Borgonzolo's cooking is singular and rugged, mercifully free of modern Mediterranean fads and often quite homely in style. Pasta tends not to be his forte (he is better at risotto); a mixed antipasto proved drab. Something like an old-fashioned melanzane alla parmigiano, or pan-fried squid with peppers and black olives, could be the best way to start. Game is capitalized upon when in season, and there is always a fish of the day. Desserts are more irresistible than is usual in Italian restaurants. The wine list is well-assembled, with enough halves for experimentation or to suit a clashing choice of dishes.

Open
Lunch Mon-Fri,
dinner Mon-Sat
Hours
12.30-2.00pm,
7.00-10.00pm
Credit cards
Mastercard, Delta,
Visa
Nearest tube
stations
Marble Arch,
Paddington
Map 6

L'Altro £34

210 Kensington Park Road W11 (792 1066)

+ *a sense of munificence*
- *smoke gets in your eyes*

A change of ownership has brought other changes in its wake. The long list of antipasti on which one could graze has been jettisoned, and instead there is a noon–8.30pm set-price deal based on the number of courses chosen. Portions are flamboyantly generous. Colourful plates overflow with food and the spirit of largess seems to infect the clientele, who talk and smoke and eat and drink, more and more and louder and louder. The holiday atmosphere is enhanced by the trompe-l'oeil interior, which resembles a set for the courtyard scene in an Italian operetta. Fish is the main thrust of the menu, but there are a few meat dishes such as homemade gnocchi with a ragu of beef and luganica sausage, or marinated pigeon served on wet polenta. Linguine with lobster in its own sauce is hard to resist, as are the seafood platters. Good fun.

Open
Mon-Sun
Hours
12.00-3.00pm,
7.00-11.30pm
Credit cards
AmEx, Mastercard,
Visa, Switch,
Delta, Diner's
Service charge
12.5% (parties of
5 or more)
Set-price lunch
(& dinner before
8pm)
£7.95, £10.95 &
£13.95
Nearest tube
station
Ladbroke Grove
Map 6

Open
Sunday lunch,
dinner every day,
Hours
Sun 1.00–4.00pm,
7.00–11.30pm
Credit cards
AmEx, Mastercard,
Visa, Switch,
Delta, Diner's
Service charge
10%
Set-price dinner
£9.95
**Nearest tube
stations**
Bayswater,
Queensway,
Notting Hill Gate
Map 6

Amazonas £20

75 Westbourne Grove W2 (243 0090)

+ *Caipirinhas cocktails*
− *rather one-paced menu*

Brazil is the land of samba, carnival and football. The food is not bad either, in a laid-back, all-embracing sort of way. A mandioca frita (deep-fried cassava) may be slow to catch on, but peixe de escabeche (fish 'cooked' in lime juice and chilli) will be familiar – as ceviche – from a host of other restaurants. Main courses have more substance, particularly the Brazilian national dish of feijoada (a casserole of black beans cooked with every kind of porcine extremity), plus sausages and bacon served with farofa, greens and oranges. Filling enough to put a serious crimp in your samba.

Open
Every day
Hours
1.00–3.00pm,
6.00–11.00pm
(Sun 6.00–
10.30pm)
Credit cards
AmEx, Mastercard,
Visa, Switch, Delta
**Nearest tube
stations**
Oxford Circus,
Piccadilly Circus
Map 5

Andrew Edmunds £24

46 Lexington Street W1 (437 5708)

+ *jovially brisk service...*
− *...whisks you in and out in a flash*

From the old-curiosity-shop frontage and spit-and-sawdust interior to the simple, daily-changing menu majoring in hearty soups, imaginative salads and seasonal game, this unpretentious restaurant rejoices in its old-fashioned, clubby image. Booking is essential: both the functional ground-floor restaurant and the low-ceilinged tenebrous basement room fill up very quickly with the West Soho boho media brigade. Low prices make up for the bum-numbing discomfort, and there are some bargains in a quirky wine list demanding to be put out of their misery.

Open
Lunch every day,
dinner every day
Hours
12.30–2.30pm,
7.30–10.30pm
Credit cards
Mastercard, Visa,
Switch, Delta
**Nearest tube
station**
Ravenscourt Park
Map 1

The Anglesea Arms £20

35 Wingate Road W6 (0181-749 1291)

+ *Dan Evans's feverishly fresh food*
− *variable results; longueurs in service*

Prolific press coverage greeted the early-1996 launch of this pub conversion in the area that estate agents, with their inimitable idealism, describe as Brackenbury Village. Having thrilled to the cooking of Dan Evans at various other establishments, including Odette's (q.v.) and The Waterloo Fire Station (q.v.), restaurant journalists – myself included – hurried along to The Anglesea Arms and were not disappointed. However, some *Evening Standard* readers have since been disappointed, as they let me know in their letters. Quality is evidently variable, and tempers on both sides of the divide between the tables and the open kitchen can grow frayed under pressure. Yet, when it is good, the kitchen is very, very good, as was exemplified by steamed sea kale with a blood orange hollandaise; a Middle Eastern flavoured seasonal salad entitled (not exactly accurately) fattoush; chargrilled swordfish with couscous and Moroccan salad of aubergine and carrots; and rhubarb and ginger sorbet with almond tuile. From these dishes you may infer the style of food: inventive, vivacious, reactive to the market. The blackboard menu changes at every meal. The list of wines is short and peculiar, perhaps signifying that people in pubs should drink beer: indeed, in the structural and decorative changes necessary to render it a 'gastro pub', the new landlords have not lost touch with the notion that this is just another local on just another street corner.

Anna's Place £26

90 Mildmay Park N1 (249 9379)

+ *gregarious proprietor Anna Hegarty*
- *intimacy can verge on the cloying*

All you needed to know about gravadlax and were afraid to ask is eloquently elucidated by the eponymous Anna, whose jolly little restaurant puts the lie to myths about Scandinavian moroseness and lumpen food. The only lax thing on this menu is the salmon. There is a strong affinity for fish, cured and au naturel: tuna, sea bream, prawns, turbot and herring. Starters are given stimulating piquancy by careful blending of dill, mustard, caraway, juniper and bay; curing, pickling and marinades being a fundamental part of Swedish cooking alchemy. Biff Strindberg, which sounds as though it might be Bulldog Drummond's Scandinavian alter ego, is in fact beef pan-fried with mustard and heartily delicious, as well as packing the requisite sharp punch. Surroundings are cosy. If you secure a table in the garden you might raise your spirit level with an akvavit (the prize-winning Idyll perhaps) and re-enact Bergman's 'Smiles of a Summer Night'.

Open
Tues-Sat
Hours
12.15-2.15pm,
9.15-10.45pm
Credit cards
None
Service charge
10%
Nearest tube stations
Highbury & Islington, Angel
Map 1

Open
Mon–Fri
Hours
12.00–3.00pm,
6.15–8.30pm
Credit cards
Mastercard,
Switch, Visa
Set-price lunch
£8.50
Nearest tube
stations
London Bridge,
Tower Hill
Map 1

The Apprentice ★ £20

Butlers Wharf Chef School, Cardamom Building,
31 Shad Thames SE1 (234 0254)

+ discover the chefs of tomorrow at prices of yesterday
– is this the cooking of the future?

Restaurants need chefs and front-of-house staff, a knotty problem that The Butlers Wharf Chef School (patron Sir Terence Conran) was opened in 1996 to address. There is a chronic shortage of trained personnel in this town where new, ambitious establishments seem to open almost daily; poaching is a culinary term more often applied nowadays to the luring away of chefs and managers. Central to the Butlers Wharf school is The Apprentice, a restaurant open to the public on weekdays for lunches and early dinners. It quickly becomes apparent from the menus offered that trainees are not spending their time plaiting chives or forcing quenelle mixtures through tammy sieves: these chefs will graduate and go on to sear salmon, pan-fry scallops, chargrill tuna, mix pesto into mashed potatoes, turn onions into marmalade and pretend that wild mushrooms have been foraged for that morning in the depths of the New Forest. Although we all agree that restaurant food has improved immeasurably over the last decade, there is something slightly lowering about seeing the clichés of modern cooking codified in a training programme. Having said this, the cooking is on the whole competent and the prices charged are (quite rightly) lower than at most restaurants comparable in intent. The Apprentice is certainly the cheap cousin of the various outlets – Le Pont de la Tour, Cantina del Ponte and The Butlers Wharf Chop House – in the nearby 'gastrodrome'. The atmosphere is that of a working kitchen, whose activity is on view to many of the tables. The ceiling is low and ventilation is minimal, creating stuffiness in warm weather; the view to the back is of a car park. It is sometimes as well to bear in mind that you are, as they put it, making a 'vital contribution' to the training of the staff. The inept service that this guide experienced must have coincided with the first mealtime on the first day of a new term. There are short courses open to members of the public (details may be obtained from the School): you too could learn artfully to scatter rocket.

Arcadia £25

Kensington Court, 35 Kensington High Street W8 (937 4294)

+ *a canteen for Associated Newspapers*
- *the dogs and parrots*

The departure of chef Steve Taylor is keenly felt by the staff of Associated Newspapers and other regulars. Arcadia's menu is now somewhat tentative in its aim to please, with a variety of Italian, French and modern British dishes. However, the kitchen abilities stretch to competent execution of first courses such as mussels steamed in white wine, garlic and shallots; mozzarella with plum tomatoes and basil oil; and deep-fried Camembert with a relish of figs and gooseberries. Pasta with wild mushrooms and cream has generous slices of fungi; breast of duck is ample, meaty and well matched with a sweet onion marmalade. Warm toffee cake accompanied by pecan ice cream is a delightfully calorific way in which to finish a meal. Portions are large, prices reasonable and service easy-going. Arcadia should be avoided if you are haunted by the fear of psittacosis: there are a couple of screeching parrots, or perhaps they are macaws.

Open
Lunch Mon-Fri, dinner Mon-Sun
Hours
12.00-2.30pm, 6.30-11.00pm
Credit cards
AmEx, Mastercard, Visa, Switch, Delta, Diner's
Service charge
12.5%
Set-price lunch
£13.95
Set-price dinner
£14.95
Nearest tube station
High Street Kensington
Map 2

Arisugawa £40

27 Percy Street W1 (636 8913)

+ *classic Japanese cuisine accessible to Westerners*
- *some specialities written in Japanese you may never decipher*

If the remorseless spread of Japanese fast food has left you feeling that there must be more to the cuisine than packet soup with noodles, fried fish without the chips, dumplings and mass-produced sushi, then Arisugawa just off Tottenham Court Road is the place to find out. Chef Takeuchi, a chap with 43 years' experience, is one of the few chefs with a licence to prepare fugu fish, and this excitingly lethal species is probably where to end your journey of discovery. Start with a set dinner based on sashimi or tempura; on another occasion, move on to choosing from the extensive à la carte menu, which has items as comprehensible as niku-jaga (boiled potatoes with slices of beef) and as strange as konnyaku-kimpira (spicy burdock root and jerry [sic]). From the simmering dishes to share, yosenabe delivers a subtle, aromatic stock and blamelessly fresh fish. Eventually, like some Japanese customers, you may get to leave your own bottle of Chivas Regal on the shelf.

Open
Lunch Mon-Fri, dinner Mon-Sat
Hours
12.30-2.30pm, 6.00-10.00pm
Credit cards
AmEx, Mastercard, Diners, Visa, Switch
Service charge
15%
Set-price lunch
£7
Set-price dinner
£28
Nearest tube stations
Goodge Street, Tottenham Court Road
Map 4

Open
Lunch Mon-Fri,
dinner Mon-Sat
Hours
12.00-3.30pm,
6.00-11.00pm
Credit cards
Mastercard,
Switch, Visa, Delta
Service charge
10%
Set-price
lunch & dinner
£12.50 & £15.00
Nearest tube
stations
Great Portland
Street, Warren
Street
Map 3

L'Arte £30

126 Cleveland Street W1 (813 1011)

+ The Arts Theatre Cafe reborn
- lacks the clubby atmosphere of its predecessor

The Arts Theatre Cafe was enthusiastically reviewed in previous editions of the Guide. Tucked away beneath the Arts Theatre in Great Newport Street, it provided imaginative, healthy, quite rustic, reasonably priced Italian food. The end of a lease or an agreement has meant a move to less quixotic premises, and a probably unavoidable increase in prices. However, the Fitzrovia premises are lean and attractive, and the kitchen keeps its pledge to provide seasonal ingredients parlayed through a short, resourceful, oft-changing list of dishes with a better-than-usual choice of vegetarian options. Following two ingredients — wild rocket and vine tomatoes — through a menu might find them incorporated into a salad of buffalo mozzarella, grilled aubergine and roasted peppers; in a sauce for spaghetti that also contains buffalo ricotta and black olives; making a contribution to the tomato sauce for rolls of organic free-range beef filled with garlic cheese and ham; and popping up in the mixed-leaf and herb salad accompanying jauntily seasoned, grilled, spatchcocked, cornfed baby chicken. Desserts are tempting. Consider peach stuffed with mascarpone and amaretti, with raspberry sauce and chocolate shavings; poached plums with honey and rosemary; chilled zabaione with vin santo, whipped cream and raspberries; and Italian cheese with pears. The exclusively Italian wine list is well-balanced and informatively annotated. It forms a significant part of the pleasure of this enterprise.

Open
Lunch Tues-Sun,
dinner Mon-Sun
Hours
12.00-3.00pm,
7.00pm-12.00am
Credit cards
AmEx,
Mastercard,
Switch, Visa,
Delta, Diner's
Service charge
12.5% optional
Set-price lunch
£12.50 & £15.00
Nearest tube
station
Notting Hill Gate
Map 6

L'Artiste Assoiffé £34

122 Kensington Park Road W11 (727 4714)

+ a pretty house where, at last, a good chef has moved in
- abstracted service

This attractive restaurant, disposed over various rooms of a corner house with a willow weeping outside, opened long before Notting Hill Gate became wall-to-wall restaurants but latterly offered food that pointed up the fact in a negative sort of way. New ownership resulted in Mark Broadbent joining as chef in the autumn of 1996. Broadbent made a name for himself with his own venture, the short-lived Wild World in Hammersmith, and then went on to bring gastronomic respectability to Avenue West Eleven. As you might infer from the name he gave to his own place, his ideas and inspirations know no boundaries. On one menu, marinated bay scallops, Thai spiced noodles and black beans sit above Caesar's (sic) salad, marinated anchovies and soft-boiled eggs, and below Parma ham with wild rocket, ripe pears and pecorino. Roast rump of lamb, braised borlotti beans and crispy (sic) sage share space in a main-course list with croustade of wild mushrooms, velouté of cèpes and garlic confit, and zarzuela of salt cod, mussels, chorizo, chickpeas and saffron. The chef is keen on Spain. The dishes are well-prepared, and once the staff figure out what business they are in – a simple request for a menu was met with a look of total incomprehension – The Thirsty Artist will become a good pal. Sunday brunch offers free papers but, apart from scrambled eggs, salmon caviar and dill, a rather un-brunchy menu. Bleary-eyed at noon, do you want seared wild sea bass and Piedmontese peppers?

Assagi at The Chepstow £32

39 Chepstow Place W2 (792 5501)

+ *authentic Italian food*
- *influx of customers from the titivated pub below*

Open
Lunch Tues-Sun,
dinner Tues-Sat
Hours
12.30-2.30pm
7.30-11.00pm
Credit cards
AmEx, Mastercard,
Visa, Switch, Delta
**Nearest tube
station**
Notting Hill Gate
Map 6

Above a pub is where nowadays you expect to find Thai restaurants or Antipodeans peddling the fusion cooking referred to as Pacific Rim. It is not where you would necessarily look for authentic Italian cooking, and particularly not in Notting Hill Gate. However, Pietro Fraccari and Nino Sassu, manager, chef and joint owners of Assagi, present a menu uncompromising in its adherence to Italian culinary customs and style. It is served in a notably attractive room, made vibrant through the use of colour on walls and canvases, and via flowers. As the restaurant name suggests, the emphasis is on first courses – 11 choices here, against four in the main course – and the temptation is to have more than one or, at least, to split a pasta dish as a midway course. In this fashion you could try one of their intriguing, healthy salads such as fennel, rocket and radicchio with scamorza (a soft curd cheese similar to provolone) and speck (smoked ham), or fresh stone crab with celery in a lemon and oil dressing; and then split a small serving of, say, the pasta loaf (a sheet of pasta dough Swiss-rolled around sautéed vegetables, served with an agreeably spinsterly tomato sauce). Main courses — so often the course that disappoints — are elegantly restrained. Lamb cutlets with an aubergine and raisin salad (based on some of the fixings for caponata) were so neatly trimmed that they resembled five lollipops of meat presented on slender bones. A flavourful suprême of chicken had only bittersweet braised chicory as accompaniment. Desserts are similarly unfussed; ripe figs (in season) and hard cheese is another route to take. Breads are excellent and include the irresistible Sardinian carta da musica, unleavened and twice-baked, polished with oil and pitted with coarse salt. Service is delightful. In my book – which this is – Assagi is the Italian restaurant of 1996.

Les Associés £30

Open
Lunch Wed-Fri,
dinner Tues-Sat

Hours
12.30-2.00pm,
7.30-10.00pm

Credit cards
Mastercard, Visa,
Switch

Set-price lunch
£15.95

Set price dinner
£17.95

**Nearest tube
station**
Finsbury
Park/Highgate

Map 1

172 Park Road N8 (0181-348 8944)

+ *fluent French menu with the correct accents*
- *hard to locate on a busy road*

A little corner of provincial France lives on in Crouch End. Two of the original three musketeers who opened it – Didier Bertran and Dominique Chehère – work the front of house, moving gravely and seriously between tables, establishing the pace of what will be a leisurely meal. Their view is that dinner forms your evening's entertainment. Chef Marc Spindler deviates not a jot from a wholly French menu, with choices such as la charteuse d'escargots à la crème d'ail fine; la salade de raie et sa sauce ravigote; le dos de cabillaud en croûte; and le filet de boeuf en croûte d'échalotte et son jus à l'éstragon. In very scarce supply these days, such a menu is becoming a rare pleasure. Cheeses are well-selected, and the range of desserts a sweet bargain at £3.70. Cream Anaglypta wallpaper featuring ears of wheat is hung with bizarrely bad paintings.

A Tavola £28

Open
Every day

Hours
12.00-3.00pm,
6.00pm-11.00pm

Credit cards
None

Service charge
10%

**Nearest tube
station**
St John's Wood

Map 1

7 St John's Wood High Street NW8 (586 4776)

+ *a misfit in St John's Wood*
- *antipasti a curate's egg*

This expensive neighbourhood is curiously under-endowed with interesting restaurants, and the high-street Italian in the shape of A Tavola seems not to belong. Deliberately distressed in appearance, with its scabrous pink walls made to look as if plaster and paint are crumbling and peeling, and with bare tables and chairs, it would not seem to be the obvious choice for its neatly coiffeured denizens. However, this could be said to be part if not most of its charm. The menu is simple. Antipasti are laid out on a table, from which you help yourself for £5.90 (or for £7.90 as a main course, at time of writing). Most of the pasta dishes – such as linguine alla Genovese with pesto; triangoli al peperone (spinach-and-ricotta-stuffed triangles with a sauce of peppers) – use homemade pasta. Main courses, complete with vegetables, might focus on roast lamb, mixed grill, mussels, cod or king prawns. Tiramisù is about as complex as desserts get; wine is rough and ready.

Atelier £34

41 Beak Street W1 (287 2057)

+ *Carluccio, look to your morels*
- *evenings could use more Soho bohemian rhapsody*

Cooking and art go together like a horse and cart, as may be inferred from the name, a homage not only to Canaletto who once had a studio in the building, but to chef Stephen Bulmer's intricate and painstaking flavour canvasses. Harmonising richness of ingredients with a lightness of touch and a clarity of flavour, successful dishes in a frequently-changing repertoire may include a straightforward herby salad of sweet scallops; pan-fried monkfish with crab and ginger tortellini in a fragrant lemongrass jus; grilled red mullet with saffron potatoes surrounded by a splashy kaleidoscope of vegetable purées (after Van Gogh) and numerous variations on a theme of mushrooms which have received enthusiastic endorsements. As is the occasional wont with ambitious cooking, one flavour brush stroke too many can eclipse the central feature of the dish, producing a colourfully bland result. Atelier seems to appeal to the executive advertising and film studio locals who can afford the high prices, although set menus are something of a lure to those wandering confusedly in this forgotten corner of West Soho.

Open
Lunch Mon-Fri, dinner Mon-Sat
Hours
12.00-2.30pm, 6.00-10.45pm
Credit cards
AmEx, Mastercard, Visa, Switch, Delta, Diner's
Set-price lunch & dinner
£12.50 & £15.50 (before 8pm)
Nearest tube station
Piccadilly Circus
Map 5

Atlantic Bar & Grill £35

20 Glasshouse Street W1 (734 4888)

+ *riot of art deco*
- *an objectionable door policy (although not applicable to diners)*

Its flavour-of-the-month status of last year may have been eclipsed by other openings, but a queue still forms in the late evening for this cavernous bar/restaurant, most of it aiming for the bar. The problem that the kitchen has with this we-keep-late-hours-but-it's-not-a-club establishment is that, at the forefront of the minds of the wannabes, has-beens, beancurd eaters and self-elected bees' knees who populate its tables, is

Open
Lunch Mon-Fri, dinner every day
Hours
12.00-2.00pm, 6.00-11.30pm (bar open until 3.00am)
Credit cards
AmEx, Mastercard, Switch, Visa, Delta
Service charge
12.5% (parties of 8 or more)

Set-price lunch
£14.90
Nearest tube
station
Piccadilly Circus
Map 5

probably not concern with the limpidness of a sauce or the debate over the wisdom of filling tortellini with foie gras – so it must be hard to maintain concentration. Recent reports suggest that cooking standards – originally set high by chef Richard Sawyer – are wavering. However, with last orders at 11.30pm, the Atlantic is a thought for after-theatre eating when dishes such as pan-fried artichoke risotto wrapped in Parma ham; sashimi platter; roasted tiger prawns with cauliflower curry; or free-range chicken with goat's cheese fritters might be just the ticket.

AN OCEANIC LIST covering the four corners of the globe. Kick off with a glass of Louis Roederer NV (£6). Alsace features eloquently with Gassmann, Schoffit and Ostertag; and there are nine white Rhônes for those lovers of honeysuckle-scented Viognier and for addicts of herby Roussanne. Burgundy includes Jean Thevenet's sumptuous Mâcon-Clessé, and Spanish whites get an uncommonly good airing. Plurality also extends to the Californian and Australian contingent. There are 43 clarets from exemplary vintages, topping out at Château Pétrus 1979 (a decent but not earthshattering example) for £355, for which money you could help yourself to a quartet of super seconds (Ducru-Beaucaillou, Léoville-Las-Cases, Pichon-Lalande and Gruaud-Larose) and still have change for four more glasses of house Roederer.

The Atrium £25

4 Millbank SW1 (233 0332)

+ *cheap set lunch*
- *indefatigable championing of champ*

Open
Mon-Fri
Hours
8.00am-10.00pm
(last orders for
lunch 3.00pm)
Credit cards
AmEx, Mastercard,
Visa, Switch,
Delta, Diner's
Service charge
10%
Set-price lunch
£16.95 & £19.95
Nearest tube
station
Westminster
Map 1

Descending the long staircase into a courtyard carved from the interior of a tall, hollow Legoland office block, you half-expect to be greeted by an explosion of pigeons as from an Italian piazza, but here the continental theme bends over to the firm smack of Home Rule Cooking. The Anglo-Irish menu is somewhat gimmicky in its construction, it being one of Antony Worral Thompson's trademarks to invent (and re-invent) menu styles. As well as the usual starters and main courses there is a daily roast (such as spiced pork, colcannon and beetroot), and perhaps a potato, chicken and leek pie: the sort of olde-schoole fayre suited to stout yeomen and chubby chancellors alike. When there is fish pie, you know it must be Friday. Unfortunately, the whole effect is rather reminiscent of school dinners – in the pejorative sense.

Auberge de Provence £40

St James Court Hotel, 41 Buckingham Gate SW1 (821 1899)

+ *privacy at well-spaced tables; efficient, formal service*
- *mock-hacienda decor*

Each year Les Alpilles in Provence, home to L'Oustau de Beaumanière (restaurant of consultant chef Jean-André Charial), seem to recede further into the distance from the restaurant's supposed evocation in a converted Edwardian mansion block that is the Taj-owned hotel. Chef Bernard Briqué does his best in the rather unpromising circumstances to convey Charial's liking for vegetables (unusual in a French Michelin-starred chef), and to give a flavour of Provence. The set menu Provençal is where to find it, whereas the à la carte strays from the region and becomes instantly more hotel-oriented with predictable lists of luxury ingredients: roast fillet of Scotch beef; whole lobster with garlic butter; steamed sea bass. Provençal wines – some produced by the Beaumanière – are the sensible choice. Customers tend to be men in suits rather than holidaymakers in shorts.

Open
Lunch Mon-Fri,
dinner Mon-Sat
Hours
12.30-2.30pm,
7.30-11.00pm
Credit cards
AmEx, Mastercard,
Visa, Switch,
Delta, Diner's
Set-price lunch
£22.50
Set-price dinner
£29.50
Nearest tube
station
St James's Park
Map 3

Aubergine £47

11 Park Walk SW10 (352 3449)

+ *set-price lunch is still a comparative bargain*
- *the self-congratulatory glow of customers who have a table*

A polite voice informing you over the phone that no table is available in the evening for five weeks attests to the popularity of this restaurant, so keep a large number of windows open in your diary. Few restaurants are worth such a wait, but this one is. Chef Gordon Ramsay's food is brilliantly conceived, and executed with a lightness of touch and eye for balance that allows one to explore the seven-course menu prestige and not expire through over-eating. Certain dishes – such as a cappuccino of haricot blancs with sautéed morels; blanquette of turbot with a ravioli of oyster and cucumber; and the 'Assiette de l'Aubergine' (which gives you a piece of all the pudding action) – have acquired a minor classic status. However, pretentious touches spoil some of the creations, as if someone is striving for supreme thaumaturgical effect. The service oils decorously on French castors, and a verbal interpretation of the Franglais-fied menu is solemnly intoned by the Maître d', who seems on the verge of lapsing into self-parody as if recalling the Red Queen's advice to Alice to 'speak in French if you can't remember the English for a thing'. The largely French wine list is

Open
Lunch Mon-Fri,
dinner Mon-Sat
Hours
12.15-2.30pm,
7.00-11.00pm
Credit cards
AmEx, Mastercard,
Visa, Switch,
Diner's
Set-price lunch
£22
Set-price dinner
£40
Nearest tube
stations
South Kensington,
Gloucester Road
Map 2

accomplished, with a line to the best growers, yet it lacks some discernment in the way it is laid out, with too many inconsistencies for a restaurant of this standard.

L'Aventure £32

Open
Lunch Mon-Fri &
Sun, dinner
every day
Hours
12.30-2.30pm,
7.30-11.00pm
Credit cards
AmEx, Mastercard,
Switch, Visa
Set-price lunch
£18.50
Set-price dinner
£25
**Nearest tube
station**
St John's Wood
Map 1

3 Blenheim Terrace NW8 (624 6232)

+ *virtuous neighbourhood restaurant with loyal following, but...*
- *...one longs for Provence*

A sylvan terrace forecourt hung with fairy lights overlooks a tranquil village street, and on balmy evenings in summer the French windows are thrown open to admit the more mature diners of Au Bois de St Jean-en-Provence who appreciate the conservative French experience: le formulaire rather than l'aventure so to speak. To accompany your starter of pan-fried Coquilles St Jacques you will not get a jazzy salsa or a perky pickle: instead, the juices will be incorporated into a light cream sauce. Similarly, a main course of halibut is enhanced not overpowered by a delicate saffron-cream reduction; while pavé de porc pôelé aux morilles (casseroled pork chops basted in a good beef bouillon with thyme) is for those who have time on their hands. Vegetables are treated with Gallic indifference for the season. Complete the artery-hardening with truffe au chocolat. The style: *toujours* 1980s.

The Avenue £35

Open
Lunch Mon-Fri,
dinner every day
Hours
Mon-Fri 12.00-
3.00pm, 5.45pm-
12.00am (Fri-Sat
12.30am);
Sun 6.45-10.00pm
Credit cards
AmEx, Mastercard,
Diner's, Visa,
Switch, Delta
Service charge
12.5%
Set-price lunch
£16.50 & £19.50
**Nearest tube
station**
Green Park
Map 3

7-9 St James's Street SW1 (321 2111)

+ *the design: an illuminated block between St James's and
  Crown Passage*
- *fluctuating food standards; a sea of suits*

P ut together by a consortium of city businessmen backed by a number of investors and consultants, The Avenue opened in December 1995. The ingredients at the outset included a chef, Enda Flanagan, who had worked briefly at Mezzo; a manager from The Neal Street Restaurant who had come by way of Cecconi's; a receptionist from Quaglino's; an architect, Rick Mather, who had set the contemporary style of the Zen restaurants; and a fashion designer, Nicole Farhi, who styled outfits for the staff ('The Avenue's floor managers will be dressed in navy-blue wool-and-cashmere, single-breasted, three-button suits with chambray shirts and gold Jacquard ties.'). If anything were left to chance, it might have been the niggling question of whether an ambitious restaurant can be successfully run without an experienced, passionate, dedicated restaurateur at the helm. The continuing existence of The Avenue suggests that this worry was foolish, and connected to an out-of-date romantic notion, but another way of looking at it would be to see a venture like The Avenue as the up-market face of fast food, in the sense of that now ubiquitous modern British mix of salads, cured fish, risotto, bruschetta, grills, confits, etc. And who needs to put a face to a name behind a fast-food joint? One meal has delivered a first-rate endive tarte Tatin; excellent fillet of beef with salsa verde; and flavoursome chicken with field mushrooms, spinach and lentil bread. Another meal disappointed over and over again with crab spring rolls accompanied by black-bean vinaigrette; Bolognese risotto (a dish more suited to a children's menu); roast cod with mashed potatoes, cabbage and bacon; and chocolate tart with orange cream. The first meal was dinner, the second lunch. Staff can be witless, but the arrival of Marian Scrutton as manager will doubtless sort that out. The restaurant itself is a vast, stunning space, with that play of light and white of which Rick Mather is master. The spacious bar area (in which irritating videos are screened) is supposed to bring New York to mind, but, as you see St James's Palace across the road reflected in your Manhattan, it is a concept to tussle with. Prices are expressed @ whatever they might be. Ashtrays are sold @ £8.50.

Babe Ruth's £23

172-6 The Highway (corner of Wapping Lane) E1 (481 8181)

+ *deep-fried onion rings...*
- *...leave you with calories to burn*

Babe Ruth, the chap, is a legend in American baseball. Babe Ruth's, the bar and restaurant, which opened in the spring of 1996, may never become (as the publicity describes it): 'A Legendary Eating Place'. However, in the ever-expanding domain of themed restaurants, it looks set fair to challenge market leaders such as Planet Hollywood. The restaurant is housed in purpose-built premises which actually bring some distinction to a drab stretch of road. The purposefulness of the architecture means that the interior space is lofty enough to swallow sound, so, if you can keep your head when all about you are losing theirs, you will at least be able to hear yourself – and your companions – speak. There is a no-bookings policy for tables. When you arrive, you are handed a pager that buzzes you in the bar when a table becomes free: this might be in the

Open
Mon-Sun
Hours
Mon-Fri 12-
11.00pm, Sun
12.00-10.30pm
Credit cards
AmEx, Mastercard,
Visa, Switch, Delta
Service charge
12% (parties of 8
or more)
**Nearest tube
station**
Tower Hill
Map 1

area itself, in the large ground-floor restaurant or at mezzanine level. Chefs work in an open kitchen at the far end of the main dining space, underneath a diorama featuring Babe Ruth in action. There are other video screens, monitors, suspended sculptures and assorted memorabilia. Nothing new there, but the owners have had the sense to realize that quality of food and service is ultimately more important than razzle-dazzle effects. The menu is a scaled-down version of the sort that you find at TGI Friday's: the heroes of American fast food are joined by oriental favourites such as spring rolls, chicken and noodle salad and a take on sushi entitled shrimp and vegetable roll. It is likeable food, appealing to the palate of the inner child, but also, when well done (as for the most part it is), not shaming if defined as American cuisine. In the main course, tidier items such as baby back ribs win out over sprawling Tex-Mex assemblies. Desserts — and many of the other items — are of a size for sharing. Waiting staff manage to be friendly and efficient without resorting to glib exhortations gleaned from manuals. Shoot a few baskets in the one-on-one basketball court before leaving.

Babur Brasserie £22

119 Brockley Rise SE23 (0181-291 2400)

+ *regional food festivals*
- *how do you get to SE23?*

Forest Hill may not be your neck of the woods, but this Indian restaurant goes to such lengths to please that it is only fair to make the journey. How could anyone resist the description, in the summer menu, of mausami murgh subzi as: 'A delightful rosary of baby vegetables and chicken morsels, cooked in a Burmese-style sauce based on chicken-bone broth, mustard seed, curry leaf and coconut milk'? (Rosary! — in this context, it must be a first.) There may be a food festival in operation, such as (at time of writing) 'The Bengal Tiger', featuring an interesting river-fish dish and a hollowed-out pumpkin filled with the pulp mixed with garlic, ginger and green chillies before the whole coach and four is roasted. Even the normal à la carte is imaginative, and the vegetable dishes — such as subze tandoori (red pumpkin, green peppers, onion, okra, tomatoes and carrots, marinated in yoghurt and spices and tandoori-baked) — are a delight. For dessert, try the soufflé invented in the Byculla Yacht Club in Bombay, based on four little-known liqueurs.

Open
Lunch Sat-Thurs,
dinner Mon-Sun
Hours
12.00-2.00pm,
6.00-11.15pm
Credit cards
AmEx, Mastercard,
Diner's, Visa,
Switch, Delta
Nearest railway station
Honor Oak
Map 1

Bahn Thai £30

21A Frith Street W1 (437 8504)

+ *neau khen (fried salt beef)*
- *scatty service*

The avowed aim of this restaurant — to present authentic Thai cooking — remains laudable, although the exhaustive proselytizing approach contained within a menu of some 10 pages and descriptions, explanations and heat codes can panic you into playing safe. From the familiar options to more recondite dishes such as stewed pig's trotters, wild boar curry and roasted marinated duck with pickled ginger and soy sauce, there is something for everyone. However, not everything works and some dishes are expensive disappointments, such as thumbnail-sized queenie scallops or fried baby quail that look uncannily like sparrows flattened in a traffic accident (a case where small is definitely not beautiful). The wine list is helpfully annotated, and it also attempts to match style to spice: not an easy task.

Open
Mon-Sun
Hours
Mon-Sat 12.00-2.45pm, 6.00-11.15pm; Sun 12.30-2.30pm, 6.30-10.30pm
Credit cards
AmEx, Mastercard, Visa, Switch, Delta, Diner's
Service charge
12.5% optional
Set-price lunch
£12.50 & £25.00
Nearest tube stations
Leicester Square, Tottenham Court Road
Map 5

Bangkok £18

9 Bute Street SW7 (584 8529)

+ *undemanding exoticism*
- *you must perforce listen to your neighbours' conversation*

Owned by the same family for nearly 30 years, Bangkok has provided many Londoners with their first taste of Thai food. The menu is suitably short and unintimidating, with none of those transliterated Thai names of dishes that trick you into calling your friend Tom a prik. Soup or satay to start, followed by a curry, a beef or chicken stir-fry, perhaps a fish dish such as halibut in curry leaf sauce, and Thai rice-noodle (not to be missed), makes a pleasant meal in simple, almost spartan, surroundings, even if the boundaries of authenticity remain unbroached. A core South Kensington clientele must account for the Laurent Perrier NV Champagne (at £32.50) on the wine list.

Open
Mon-Sat
Hours
12.15pm-2.15pm, 7.00pm-11.00pm
Credit cards
Mastercard, Switch, Visa
Nearest tube station
South Kensington
Map 2

Bank £32

1 Kingsway WC2 (379 9797)

The quest for capacious restaurant sites knows no bounds. This is a converted Nat. West bank on the corner of Kingsway and the Aldwych, where your money will be invested in the cooking of Christian Delteil, once the Michelin-starred

Open
Every day
Hours
Mon-Sat 7.00-10.30am, 12.00-3.00pm, 5.30pm-12.00am, Sun 12.00-3.00pm, 5.30-11.00pm

Service charge
12.5%
Nearest tube
station
Holborn
Map 3

chef of L'Arlequin in Battersea (now The Stepping Stone [q.v.]). His head chef is Tim Hughes, who previously worked at Le Caprice (q.v.). Eric Garnier, who launched Quaglino's (q.v.), is manager. The backers are Cutty Catering, fish suppliers to the trade. Designer is Julyan Wickam, perhaps best known for his restaurant work for Kensington Place (q.v.) and for Harvey Nichol's The Fifth Floor (q.v.). Expect fish dishes, plus much more.

Open
Every day
Hours
12.00-4.00pm,
7.00-11.45am
Credit cards
AmEx, Mastercard,
Visa, Switch, Delta
Service charge
12.5% (parties of
6 or more)
Set-price lunch
£7.50
Nearest tube
stations
Angel, South
Kensington &
Waterloo
Maps 1, 2 & 3

Bar Central £25

3-5 Islington High Street N1 (833 9595); 316 King's Road SW3 (352 0025); 131 Waterloo Road SE1 (928 5086)

+ *the ticket to ride various cuisines*
- *some unnecessary stopovers*

The apotheosis of a thoroughly modern menu: at Bar Central there are Chinese crispy-duck pancakes with cucumber noodles; Italian rigatoni with meatballs and tomato sauce; English deep-fried cod in beer batter with minted pea purée (the mushy peas *de nos jours*?); and even a Cuban-style burger. Chorizo sausage, Dutch eel fillets, Lebanese chicken sandwich and Thai fishcakes continue the globe-trotting approach. Anything goes but, as you might imagine, some do so more successfully than others. Desserts are more stay-at-home and are very good: examples include lemon and clotted-cream tart; pecan pie; and bitter chocolate cake with hazelnuts. A shorter bar menu served from noon until 6pm features interesting sandwiches, such as fontina, rocket and roasted red onions on walnut bread. The interior is clean, bright and well-organized. Staff are young and cheerful – sometimes more cheerful than efficient.

Open
Every day
Hours
12.00-11.30pm
Credit cards
AmEx, Mastercard,
Visa, Switch,
Delta, Diner's
Set-price lunch
& dinner
'Lunch for a fiver';
£6, £12 & £10

Belgo Centraal £26

50 Earlham Street WC2 (813 2232)

+ *subterranean shellshock*
- *chaos and cacophany*

A wire-cage lift grinds slowly down to reveal a massive open kitchen with chefs bawling into microphones attached to headsets. To the left is the restaurant which accepts bookings; to the right a beer hall where you take your chance on a table. As at the original Belgo (see below) mussels are flexed at the heart of the menu, served with chips and mayo and better in pots than platters. Lobsters, spit-roasted chicken, asparagus and Belgian *plats cuisinés* such as waterzooi, carbonnades, steak tartare, gratin of ham-wrapped chicory and wild boar sausages are alternatives. There are over 100 different beers offered. It does not take much imagination to figure out that on occasion spirits get too high and staff stretched beyond endurance. There are various good set-price deals, the most elegant being Beat The Clock: From 6pm-8pm sharp on weekdays you pay the price for your set meal according to the time it is ordered. Thus if you order at 6.05pm half a roasted chicken served with frites and apple purée and a Jupiler lager you pay £6.05 (as against the £11.00 standard price). Clever.

Nearest tube station Covent Garden Map 4

Belgo Noord £20

72 Chalk Farm Road NW1 (267 0718)

+ *the beer list; groovy loos*
– *in-and-out booking policy in the evenings; 15% service charge*

Less strident than its ebullient younger brother, Centraal (q.v.), several years on from its inception the novelty of the post-modern design, surprisingly, still hasn't palled. Approach via an elevated walkway (a clever wheel-and-pulley contraption), glancing downwards at the kitchen with its huge chrome ventilation ducts and mighty steaming cauldrons of moules. The restaurant is as 'Grand Guignol', but less based on the Hieronymus Bosch representation of an infernal meal than Centraal. The dining-room – an up-market canteen with refectory tables – is patrolled by young men clad in monks' habits carrying the inevitable bowls of mussels, but if you are not a shellfish person there is stoemp with bavette steak, witloof au gratin and excellent smoky wild boar sausages to soak up the ale. Beers are a speciality, running the gamut from fruit-fermented brews to barley-wine creations.

Open
Every day
Hours
Mon-Fri 12.00–3.00pm, 6.00–11.30pm; Sat 12.00-11.30pm; Sun 9.00am-10.30pm
Credit cards
AmEx, Mastercard, Visa, Switch, Delta, Diner's
Set prices
See Belgo Centraal
Nearest tube
Chalk Farm
Map 1

The Belvedere £35

Holland House, off Abbotsbury Road, Holland Park W8 (602 1238)

+ *the location*
– *uneven cooking standards*

Johnny Gold, owner of The Belvedere, seems happy to let the site be the restaurant's USP (unique selling point). It is indisputably romantic to eat in the former orangery of Holland House within one of London's nicest parks, particularly on a pretty day or balmy evening (assuming that you succeed in

Open
Lunch every day, dinner Mon-Sat
Hours
12.00-3.00pm, 6.00-11.00pm
Credit cards
AmEx, Mastercard, Visa, Switch, Delta, Diner's
Nearest tube station
Holland Park
Map 6

securing a table on the terrace), but why should that mean putting up with sloppily executed food and tentative service? Summer set menus geared to the open-air opera season are a nice idea, but the actual wild mushroom and saffron paella (for 'Carmen') made the gesture seem exploitative rather than supportive. This is the place where modern British food starts to attract the opprobrium given to ancient British food.

Bengal Clipper £26

31 Shad Thames, Butlers Wharf SE1 (357 9001)

+ *oriental cooking beside an historic spice wharf*
- *more P & O ferry than posh*

It is fitting that an Indian restaurant should be situated in the Cardamom building, close to what was once the main wharf for the importing of spices from the East. Sadly, Bengal Clipper has no river view, but there is a vaguely nautical air to the interior design in its extensive use of wood. 'India's Most Remarkable Dishes' is the heading for the main courses, which take their inspiration from various regions. Despite the restaurant's name, the Bengali influence is not all that marked, although river-caught tiger fish features, as do giant Bay of Bengal prawns. In one of the first courses — golda chingri nizami roll — the prawns are minced, enclosed in a spicy poppadum and deep-fried. Perhaps the Conran 'gastrodrome' having the monopoly of the better sites, or perhaps uneven cooking standards (as have been reported) is the reason, but Bengal Clipper sometimes seems a bit becalmed.

Open
Every day
Hours
12.00-3.00pm,
6.00-11.00pm
Credit cards
AmEx, Mastercard,
Diner's, Visa,
Switch, Delta
Set-price lunch
£9.75
Set price dinner
£28
**Nearest tube
stations**
London Bridge,
Tower Hill
Map 1

Bentley's £35

11-15 Swallow Street W1 (734 4756)

+ *the oyster bar and the old-fashioned, clubby dining-room*
- *its stuffiness may not appeal*

Established at this address in 1916, Bentley's is well-versed in selling oysters and fish to the gentry. Commendable efforts to move with the times have not always had the happiest results on the plate, but the menu this year has divested itself of too many inappropriate exotic flourishes. If you want to stray from the straight and narrow of, say, a dozen oysters followed by a grilled Dover sole, chef Keith Stanley (formerly at The Ritz Restaurant [q.v.]) handles well skate and artichoke terrine with red-pepper pesto, and baked salmon with ginger, garlic and Szechuan vegetables. Fresh marinated anchovies perk up a

Open
Mon-Sat
Hours
11.30am-11.30pm
Credit cards
AmEx, Mastercard,
Visa, Switch,
Diner's, Delta
Service charge
12.5%
**Nearest tube
stations**
Piccadilly Circus,
Oxford Circus
Map 4

Caesar salad, and fillet of cod with a sauce of mussels and spring onions is well-judged. Non-fish dishes are not mere tokenism. Consider maize-fed chicken with black pudding, apples dauphine and onion marmalade; confit of duck leg on creamed potatoes; and pappardelle with roasted aubergine and pesto. There is a noteworthy British cheese selection.

Beotys £26

79 St Martin's Lane WC2 (497 0355)

+ *gruffly avuncular waiters*
- *parties of freemasons*

When Beotys opened in 1945, a 'continental' menu, complete with flambés, was commonplace. Now, with L'Épicure in Soho sadly no more, it is probably true to say that this theatreland fixture is the last place in the West End offering l'entrecôte de boeuf à la Diane prepared over a flame at the table. It makes a welcome change from chargrilled tuna with a chipotle salsa. Indeed, the old-fashioned values of Beotys are all the more to be prized now that so-called 'modern' food, served in huge, noisy rooms by travelling Antipodeans, is becoming the norm. Ordering la bisque d'homard followed by le caneton rôti à l'orange is not essential (although they sound good to me): the Greek/Cypriot ownership makes kalamarikia and stifado another good option, and there is also a vegetarian menu or dishes of the day such as whitebait and poached wild salmon. The ground floor is the better place to sit.

Open
Mon-Sat
Hours
12.00-3.00pm,
5.30pm-11.30pm
Credit cards
AmEx, Mastercard,
Visa, Diner's
Set-price lunch
£14.00 & £16.50
Nearest tube station
Leicester Square
Map 5

Bertorelli's £30

44a Floral Street WC2 (836 3969)

+ *no glutinous lasagne; buzzy atmosphere*
- *'over-egging' the virgin olive oil*

The public may crave three things: novelty, novelty and novelty, and if Maddalena Bonino's cooking is no longer technically in the vanguard it nevertheless cannily embraces modern trends while retaining the comforting classics – not an easy mission in the artichoked heart of tourist land. So your meal might proceed on two lines: the pizza/pasta/veal cutlet Milanese safety route, or, via a plate of antipasti containing a clever assortment of bites (deep-fried mozzarella, roasted peppers, smoked eel), to grilled mackerel with parsley and garlic or perhaps lean pork stuffed with sultanas and pinenuts served with pickled red cabbage. It is appropriate that a restaurant

Open
Mon-Sat
Hours
12.00-3.00pm,
5.30pm-11.30pm
Credit cards
AmEx, Mastercard,
Visa, Switch,
Delta, Diner's
Service charge
12.5%
Cover charge
£1.50 per person
Nearest tube station
Covent Garden
Map 4

situated so close to The Royal Opera House understands about playing to varied audiences, and, despite the occasional invasions of recently disgorged theatre-goers, the service maintains a sunny equanimity.

Bibendum £50

Michelin House, 81 Fulham Road SW3 (581 5817)

+ *chocolate sauce with vanilla ice cream; sun streaming through the stained-glass window (two types of epiphanies)*
- *prevalence of cream in recipes; wine disappearing to distant waiters' stations*

Open
Every day
Hours
12.30-2.30pm,
7.00-11.30pm
Credit cards
AmEx, Mastercard,
Visa, Switch,
Delta, Diner's
Service charge
12.5% optional
Set-price lunch
£28
Nearest tube
station
South Kensington
Map 2

With cooking like this you forgive the prices and allow yourself to be hanged for a truffle as for a mushroom. At lunch the prix fixe enables one to escape relatively financially unscathed (although the food rarely scales great heights, and not much atmosphere is generated by the bored-looking suits), but at dinner you may as well inhale deeply and accept that treats like this are worth the subsequent penitential retrenchment of bread and water. The food is rich in cholesterol: brioche with bone marrow, lobster and beurre rouge thrills the tastebuds while clotting the blood; other dairy-drenched starters are crêpe Parmentier with crème fraîche, and caviar and black risotto with grilled squid and gremolada. In main courses, whether your predilection is for things piscatorial (fillet of sea bass with saffron and tarragon cream); whether you are a resolute organ-grinder (calf's sweetbreads en croûte is a stately pleasure dome of pastry where the show is not just in the dough, but in the melting meats nestling beneath); or whether you are a dedicated game hunter (the smoky-sweet roast grouse is served as high as a kite), the menu caters to all. The room itself is a delight. Since you undoubtedly pays your money, you are entitled to expect some serious mollycoddling from the waiting staff, but there have been reports of supercilious service.

Bibendum Oyster Bar £25

(Address as above)

Open
Every day
Hours
12.00-10.30pm,
Sun 12.00-
10.00pm
Credit cards
All major
Service charge
12.5%
Nearest tube
station
South Kensington
Map 2

Located on the ground floor, just inside the Michelin building, is The Oyster Bar, a cramped, white-tiled art deco loo of a room. As well as the expected prominence given to shellfish (diverse rock oysters in multiples, lobster with excellent mayonnaise, crab salad and the all-embracing plateau de fruits de mer) the menu favours snack-sized appetites: crostini; Caesar salad; egg mayonnaise; terrine with toast; smoked salmon. Main courses include fillet of pork and prosciutto with a red cabbage, apple and mustard dressing, and tuna Niçoise salad. There is also a list of specials derived from the daily-changing upstairs menu. Wines are largely light, zingy, white and sympathetic to the needs of crustacea. Drinking Muscadet is allowed. No bookings are taken and meals tend to be speeded on by the eyes of those in a queue boring into you.

THE WINE LIST at Bibendum is fabulous, although those who don't know their asti spumante from their Elbling will need to seek guidance. Contrary to supposition, the mark-ups are no higher than in many West End establishments, although you are paying a small premium for the massive diversity of wonderful bottles available, and for the knowledge that they are stored and served correctly. That spare £2,000 in your pocket will purchase you a bottle of the celestial Mouton-Rothschild 1945 (you would pay even more for it at auction!), but I would prefer to spend my hard-earned on Jim Clendenen's rich Aligoté for £29.95, or on a bottle of Mas Jullien — a Languedoc red containing 13 grape varieties — for a mere £24.50. All areas are covered, but the Rhône, Italy and Burgundy merit especial investigation, as do the eight dessert wines served by the glass.

Bice £35

13 Albemarle Street W1 (409 1011)

+ *tiramisu*
- *the difference between here and the rest of the world*

Part of an international group with branches in Milan, New York and Buenos Aires, the London operation has failed to make its mark as the chic, cosmopolitan destination it seems to believe it is. Perhaps a basement location was a sad start. However, if you are in this area looking for an Italian meal, the kichen delivers satisfying, varied and healthy antipasti and follows with the pasta, fish and meat dishes you might expect. The tiramisù comes in for extravagant praise but the twig girls who eat here would probably only push it round their plates.

Open
Lunch Mon-Fri, dinner Mon-Sat
Hours
12.00-2.45pm, 7.00-10.45pm
Credit cards
AmEx, Mastercard, Diner's, Visa, Switch
Set-price lunch
£20
Nearest tube stations
Green Park, Piccadilly Circus
Map 3

Bistrot 190 £26

190 Queen's Gate SW7 (581 5666)

+ *if you want to eat well, eat breakfast three times a day*
- *the noise level increasing exponentially throughout the evening*

Trouble at (pepper) mill is indicated by the fact that Mark Emberton, Antony Worral Thompson's troubleshooting chef, is back in the executive saddle at Queen's Gate. The egalitarian

Open
Every day
Hours
Mon-Fri 7.00am-12.30am; Sat 7.30am-12.30am; Sun 7.30am-11.30pm
Credit cards
AmEx, Mastercard, Visa, Switch, Delta, Diner's

Set-price lunch
£15.50
Nearest tube
stations
South Kensington,
Gloucester Road,
High Street
Kensington
Map 2

menu makes no distinction between starters and mains, and the familiar yoking and oft-times yanking together of disparate ingredients so beloved of Wozza has been tempered. Bouillabaisse is chunky with firm fish; chilli squid has an agreeable smoky tang, and is cooked properly al dente; and, while spicy Italian sausage with borlotti beans makes simple rustic fare, an Amarone risotto with pan-fried foie gras embodies the maxims that more is less, and rich is poor. The no-bookings policy creates a pressure on tables, and the presentation of food flags dramatically during service. A clever and comprehensive breakfast menu is still a highlight.

Blakes ★new £22

31 Jamestown Road NW1 (482 2959)

+ *good food in an area where it is thin (or, indeed, often squashed) on the ground*
- *the Stringalongs from Gloucester Crescent find that they cannot hear themselves speak*

Open
Every day
Hours
Mon-Sat 12.00-
3.00pm, 7.00-
11.00pm; Sun
12.00-4.30pm,
7.00-10.30pm
Credit cards
AmEx, Mastercard,
Visa, Switch
Service charge
10% optional
(parties of 6 or
more)
Set-price lunch
£6.95
Nearest tube
station
Camden Town
Map 1

The crowds that Camden Town's shops and street markets attract are not the sort to create a forcing ground for ambitious new restaurants. Snack food is what is required and, for the most part, the cafes and bars in the area provide just that. Blakes — a converted pub a few steps away from the main action, near the Camden recycling centre and Arlington House, where homeless 'men of the road' are recycled — provides in its purple-painted first-floor room a reasonably priced, quite creditable restaurant. The modern European menu, written in a rather uncertain hand and with shaky spelling ('Marrocan chicken' is one example), contains some bright ideas. Among them have been finnan haddock soufflé with a horseradish sauce; various dips for dunking crisp little life-preservers of deep-fried squid; fennel and Parmesan gratin to accompany a marinated tuna loin; and a selection of dishes in the mid-price range to serve as substantial starters, prudent main courses or the basis of a one-dish meal. Energy flags slightly in the dessert list. The clumsily titled banoffi pie never fills me with confidence — just calories. Service is well-meaning. The music is loud but not uninteresting, even to those of us who prefer ragtime to rap or reggae.

Bleeding Heart
Restaurant & Wine Bar £28

Bleeding Heart Yard, off Greville Street, EC1 (242 2056)

+ *50 wines under £15*
- *the mainly business-orientated clientele*

The name and address of this establishment, which is tucked away between Hatton Garden and Smithfield, have an unappetising history concerning Lady Elizabeth Hatton, the toast of 17th-century London, and her jilted lover, a swarthy European ambassador with a vicious temper and a clawed right hand. Tourists are apparently attracted by the story, while perspicacious Londoners seek out the place for chef Alan Bergman's French menus (quite elaborate in the restaurant; bistro-style and so less expensive in the wine bar) and for the long, interesting, ever-evolving wine list. As well as dishes of the day, there are wines of the day and special offers such as a saving of £3 on a bottle during New Zealand wine week. In clement weather the terrace is used and a light menu served, with some nice cold dishes such as lobster and black-pasta salad.

THIS WINE LIST is a compendious document of the liberal persuasion, weighing in at 400+ bins. The Bleeding Heart Burgundy (from the Cave de Buxy) will probably attract the more conservative tendency, and is available in both colours for £14.95, but those seeking more substantial mouthswillers will be enticed by the ever-increasing number of excellent New World wines such as Saintsbury, Qupé and Devil's Lair. New Zealand's offerings are enthusiastically exhibited here: Martinborough, Kumeu River and Morton Estate contribute their quality wares. And one note of personal pleasure: Château Pibarnon, Comte de St Victoire's complex and densely structured Bandol from old Mourvèdre vines, is available from a great vintage.

Open
Mon-Fri
Hours
11.45-3.00pm,
6.00-10.30pm
Credit cards
AmEx, Mastercard,
Visa, Switch,
Diner's
Service charge
12.5% optional
Set-price dinner
£9.95 (bistro only)
Nearest tube station
Farringdon
Map 3

The Blenheim £24

21 Loudoun Road NW8 (625 1222)

+ *al-fresco eating; half-price wine on Monday evenings*
- *'shaved Parmesan', 'shaved fennel', etc.; ozone-unfriendly hairdos*

Having finally nailed its culinary colours — in this case the Italian tricolour — to the mast, the Blenheim is achieving the high standards of consistency to satisfy the fussiest of an admittedly fastidious clientele. The structure of the menu allows

Open
Lunch Tues-Sun,
dinner every day
Hours
12.00-3.00pm,
7.00-11.00pm
(Sun 7.00-
10.30pm)
Credit cards
AmEx, Mastercard,
Visa, Switch
Service charge
12.5% (parties of
6 or more)

both light grazing and more gustatory gravitas. There are invariably three or four types of pasta, which may be ordered in starter or main-course portions; salads on a mozzarella, tomato and basil theme; risottos; and a tasty carpaccio of some fish or other. Robust main courses may include roast shoulder of lamb with wet polenta, or grilled calf's liver with Parmesan, spinach and Serrano ham. A more unusual proposition is the idea of seared scallops with champ and pea-and-mint purée, a shotgun marriage of ingredients that is a candidate for instant divorce. On the other hand, chef Harry Greenhalgh's penchant for unusual relationships succeeds in a savoury chicken-liver, dill and chilli risotto. A beacon in the culinary darkness of St John's Wood. Try also Blenheim bis at 37 Kensington Park Road W11 (243 0666).

The Blue Elephant £36

4–6 Fulham Broadway SW6 (385 6595)

+ *Royal Thai Cuisine*
- *theme-park decor*

Open
Every day
Hours
12.00-2.30pm,
5.00pm-12.30am
(Sun 10.30pm)
Credit cards
AmEx, Mastercard,
Visa, Diner's
Service charge
£1.50 per person
Set-price lunch
£29 & £34
Nearest tube
station
Fulham Broadway
Map 2

If the staff were less gracious one might cringe at the various elements of service and decor that make The Blue Elephant what it is: a Thai stage set without a script. However, many are seduced by the babbling brooks, the horticultural abundance, the staff dressed as if for the chorus of 'The King and I', the colourful descriptions on the menu ('jungle salad', 'bags of gold', 'floating market', 'emerald chicken'), and the carved vegetable and fruit plate decorations. If the food didn't match the theatre of the setting there would be no applause, but cooking standards are consistently sound. Most dishes are not emphatically spiced, but they are flavourful enough and attractive; the number of elephants adjacent to the descriptions indicate the power of the spicing. All the senses have a workout. Fish and seafood are delicately handled, and the soups are particularly good. There is also a lengthy vegetarian menu. 'Royal Siam Parade', the set-price menu at £29, saves decision-making – and a bit of money too.

Blue Print Cafe £32

The Design Museum, Shad Thames SE1 (378 7031)

+ *the view of the river and Tower Bridge*
- *the service*

Open
Lunch every day,
dinner Mon-Sat
Hours
12.00-3.00pm,
6.00-11.00pm
Credit cards
AmEx, Mastercard,
Visa, Switch,
Diner's

Its lofty position compared to the other restaurants in Conran's gastrodrome gives this restaurant within The Design Museum a distinct advantage in terms of outlook. Sitting on the terrace on a fine day or Mediterranean evening is pure pleasure. The short menu fits the mood with dishes such as chilled lovage and yogurt soup; baby beetroot salad with a soft-boiled egg; morcilla with a sautéd potato salad (nice one); risi e bisi; zarzuela of hake; slow-cooked rabbit leg with girolles and garlic; pepper chicken with a couscous salad. Desserts always get a mention in talk of this place. Marsala parfait with chocolate sauce; lemon posset with blueberry muffins; caramelized apple with mascarpone and crisp wafers will help you to understand why. Complaints are about service. One customer was finally so irate that she said she couldn't remember a thing she had eaten.

Service charge
12.5%
Nearest tube stations
Tower Hill, London Bridge
Map 1

Blues Bar & Bistro £26

42–3 Dean Street W1 (494 1966)

+ *first-class girth-threatening desserts*
- *not enough American accent to make it a little SoHo within Soho*

Some restaurants are born with concepts, some achieve conceptual status, and some have concepts thrust upon them. Blues falls into the first category with the brilliantly nebulous tag-line: 'It's not a colour, it's a concept', whereby you are conspiratorially enjoined to deconstruct the Blues eating experience. You might be perplexed at a vision that involves eating in a modern-art gallery: here a glass cabinet filled with Venetian glass, there a couple of original Picasso plates, and hung all around the strikingly colourful paintings of Nick Moore. As if confirmation were required of the looking-glass world that PR agencies inhabit, an A-board on the pavement advertises the presence of the restaurant in mirror image. Back indoors, a modish American menu printed the right way round sets clam chowder next to zucchini and saffron risotto, while Maryland crabcakes with lime mayonnaise and sauce vièrge rub shoulders with pan-fried fillet of rabbit with celeriac fondant and a grain-mustard sauce – all in more than competent renditions. Calorific Key lime pie and New York cheesecake will tempt even the most confirmed Caesar-salad pushers. And have the blueberry pie – it's a dessert, not a concept.

Open
Lunch Mon-Fri, dinner Mon-Sat
Hours
Mon-Thurs 12.00-11.00pm, Fri-Sat 12.00pm-12.00am
Credit cards
AmEx, Mastercard, Visa, Switch, Diner's, Delta
Service charge
12.5% (parties of 5 or more)
Set-price lunch
Mon & Tues £10 (set menus for parties available)
Nearest tube stations
Leicester Square, Piccadilly Circus, Tottenham Court Road
Map 5

Bombay Brasserie £35

Courtfield Road, Courtfield Close SW7 (370 4040)

+ *the grand sweep of the interior – aim for the conservatory*
- *your table never seems 'ready', necessitating a drink in the bar*

Bombay Brasserie, when it opened about 14 years ago, did sterling work in emphasizing the regional differences in Indian food to an audience who, for the most part, just thought

Open
Every day
Hours
12.30-3.00pm, 7.30-11.30pm
Credit cards
Mastercard, Visa, Switch, Diner's

of it as hot curry. Now an awareness of creamy Kashmiri cooking, subtle Keralan coconutty approaches, Gujarati vegetarian dishes, fiery Goan spicing, Parsee customs and much more is widespread, thanks also to other restaurants, TV programmes and cookery books. However, the menu here still offers a rewarding guided tour – including Bombay street snacks such as sev batata puri and samosa chaat served as first courses – in palatial surroundings that, with generous spirit, hark back to the glory days of the Raj. This restaurant is ideal for times when meat eaters dine with vegetarians. Breads are excellent; the chutneys could be improved. Sunday lunch buffet is a nice event.

Boyd's £32

135 Kensington Church Street W8 (727 5452)

+ *light and bright but not airy-fairy (cooking and decor)*
- *this Boyd's song will not move you to lyrical wonder*

Restaurants, like proverbial buses, arrive in threes, as a saunter up Kensington Church Street will reveal. That this creditable neighbour to Clarke's (q.v.) and Kensington Place (q.v.) does not suffer in comparison has been achieved by conceiving a cross-section of pared-down Anglo-French dishes, imbuing them with delicate oil and herb infusions, and serving the same in calm, congenial surroundings. Chicken livers are sautéed on homemade toasted brioche. Another time, the ante may be upped with pan-fried fresh foie gras. A simply dressed garden salad with fresh herbs, or asparagus risotto, ushers in meaty main courses such as lamb, duck or pigeon, roasted or braised, and perhaps served with a balsamic- infused reduction. There is always a fish of the day from the chargrill: sea bass with baby vegetables and tomato-chive butter, for example. Ice-creams are evidently a speciality, insinuating themselves into four of the six desserts on one visit. There is a restful viridian theme to the decor, evoking Marvell's line about green thoughts in a green shade.

IF YOU HAD to preserve a small but global sample of wines from extinction, you could do worse than take the contents of this restaurant's well-chosen collection. The names read like a cast list of the great and the good: Sauzet in Puligny, Lafon in Meursault, and Colombo and Beaucastel in the Rhône; while Au Bon Climat, Thelema and Hamilton Russell serve as worthy ambassadors from the New World. We will forgive the owner's whim in listing five vintages of the underperforming cru-class Château Boyd-Cantenac (the well-known restaurant across the street doesn't list Château Clarke, for example), since he redeems

Set-price lunch £14.95
Nearest tube station Gloucester Road
Map 2

Open Mon-Sat
Hours 12.30-2.30pm, 7.00-11.00pm
Credit cards AmEx, Mastercard, Diner's, Visa
Set-price lunch £12.50, £15
Nearest tube station Notting Hill Gate
Map 6

himself with three German Rieslings – the vinous equivalent of hen's teeth – and a superb selection of half-bottles and dessert wines. Prices duck under the West End average.

The Brackenbury £22

129–31 Brackenbury Road W6 (0181-748 0107)

+ *the sweet agony of choosing from the many things you want*
- *your table is needed for those customers waiting*

It is tempting just to print an entire Brackenbury menu – a list that changes, at least in part, at each and every meal – so intelligent, imaginative, well-balanced and plugged-in to the seasons and sensibilities are the dishes. Consider, for instance, warm salad of salted pork, chorizo and fried potatoes; shaved foie gras and watercress salad with walnut oil; roast salt cod with sardine purée and a mussel and fennel salad; slow-roasted shoulder of lamb with Greek salad and grilled flat bread; Scotch woodcock; apple fritters with ginger ice cream; and rhubarb knickerbocker glory – just some of the choices at dinner on Monday 3 June 1996. Energy has not flagged since Adam and Kate Robinson opened The Brackenbury, nor has its popularity inflated the prices. Run like a canny household, smart shopping makes the most of a modest budget. The nous – there is no substitute – also extends to the wine list, on which mark-ups are reasonable and the number of wines served by the glass greater than is usual.

The Brackenbury is this year's 21st Eros – the Reader's Eros.

Open
Lunch Tues–Fri & Sun, dinner Mon–Sat
Hours
12.30–2.45pm, 7.00–10.45pm
Credit cards
AmEx, Mastercard, Switch, Visa, Delta
Nearest tube stations
Hammersmith, Goldhawk Road
Map 1

Brady's £15

695 Fulham Road SW5 (736 3938); 513 Old York Road SW18 (0181-877 9599)

+ *apple crumble and treacle tart with a jug of cream*
- *queues (although tables are turned around fast)*

There is a jolly bucket-and-spade, shrimping-net, beach-hut atmosphere at these attractive family-run fish-and-chip restaurants (not chippies: the frying takes place out of sight). They offer straightforward English food at its best. The blackboard menus list first courses such as smoked salmon, smoked cod's roe, a pint of prawns, salmon fishcake and superior (homemade) potted shrimps. Fish – battered or grilled, and served with chips – depend on the market and the season, but might include cod, haddock, plaice, skate, lemon sole, tuna,

Open
Lunch Tues–Sat, dinner Mon–Sat (dinner only on York Road)
Hours
12.00–2.30pm, 7.00–10.45pm
Credit cards
AmEx, Visa
Service charge
10 % optional
Nearest tube station
Parsons Green
Nearest railway station
York Road
Map 1

swordfish and tiger prawns. Mushy peas are 65p extra. Owners Luke and Amelia Brady have had the good sense to define their terms precisely and to stick to them, and not to compromise on quality.

Brasserie du Marché aux Puces £24

349 Portobello Road W10 (0181-968 5828)

+ *a French bistro that is not part of a chain; Sunday lunch*
- *hard seats; tentative service*

Open
Lunch Mon-Sun,
dinner Mon-Sat
Hours
Mon-Sat
10.00am-3.00pm
7.30-11.00pm;
Sun 10.00am-
3.00pm
Credit cards
Mastercard, Visa,
Switch, Delta
Service charge
12% optional
Set-price lunch
£8.50
**Nearest tube
station**
Ladbroke Grove
Map 6

Achange of ownership, but not of the restaurant's rather cumbersome name, sees young French restaurateur Laurent Viguié in charge. His chef is Lionel Lemaître, whose sous-chef Fred Flamme is an example of a rare and seldom-seen species, the French vegetarian. In that most despotic of regions, the restaurant kitchen, claims are made here for a policy of democratic rule. Evidence of this is a palpably pleasant, friendly atmosphere in the L-shaped dining-room; in chefs willing, if necessary, to serve tables; and in the better linguists springing to help new recruits whose French is limited to a smile. Flamme — if it were he — has achieved the near-impossible: making something decent out of baby sweetcorn. Chargrilled, these play best supporting actors in a salad of asparagus, green leaves and Parmesan shavings. Salade de la Brasserie du Marché has at its heart a particularly fine example of melting goat's cheese; homemade marinated salmon served in a lemon and olive-oil dressing with leaves of poussé spinach is another good starter. Although filo pastry and oven-dried tomatoes can infiltrate the vegetarian main courses, the rest of the choices are refreshingly one-nation — in this case, France. Chicken breathes garlic fumes and comes with homestyle sautéed potatoes; sea bream is accompanied by a spring-vegetable ragoût; lamb is garnished Provençal style; and pears poached in cinnamon-spiced red wine — a dessert so staid that it must now be hip — are served with crème fraîche. Viguié's other passion is African music, which is gently played in the background. His recent production of the reggae band The Herb's new album seems neatly to encapsulate the two interests. Note the good-value weekday lunch.

Brilliant Restaurant £18

72-4 Western Road, Southall, Middlesex (0181-574 1928)

+ *the butter chicken*
- *no more dropping in — booking is essential*

No room for false modesty with a name like this: K.K. and D.K. Anand are only too happy to list the celebrities they have fed (the most prized scalp being the Prince of Wales). What they will not tell you, or even hint at, is the recipe for Brilliant's signature dish: butter chicken. No wonder; Southall is not lacking in competition. It really is very good indeed, and in some strange way (a ghee factor?) manages to taste more buttery than butter itself. Also good are the jeera chicken (be prepared for your hand to smell of jeera [cumin] for days) and the chilli chicken (be prepared to suffer). Go with at least three others or, preferably, with your extended family.

Open
Lunch Tues-Fri,
dinner Tues-Sun
Hours
12.00pm-3.00pm,
6.00-11.30pm
Credit cards
AmEx, Mastercard,
Visa, Switch,
Delta, Diner's
Service charge
10%
Set-price lunch
£10
Set-price dinner
£12.50
**Nearest railway
station**
Southall

Browns Restaurant & Bar £26

47 Maddox Street W1 (491 4565); 114 Draycott Avenue SW3 (584 5359); and 82-4 St Martin's Lane WC2 (497 5050)

+ *friendly staff serving unintimidating food*
- *drinkers drowning out diners*

Browns will be a familiar restaurant name to anyone who has eaten in one of Jeremy Mogford's establishments in the university towns of Oxford, Brighton, Cambridge or Bristol. The 'Browning' of London — a process whereby architecturally notable premises (as a rule) are converted into havens of familiar, unthreatening food — began in South Kensington, and moved to the West End and then to Covent Garden. Other districts will also no doubt be infiltrated. The impressive aspect of what is quite shamelessly a formula is that, within an almost wine-bar context, attention is paid to detail in the dishes and, despite chaotic crowds, service achieves a balance of friendliness and efficiency. Toasted olive bread with sun-dried tomatoes is offered, but hot garlic bread is what is usually ordered: the Browns' customer knows that no fashionable sourdough or cornbread can beat the pungent, buttery, soft embrace of that dinner-party standby of the '60s. Other friendly old faces of a culinary persuasion are on offer, including chicken-liver pâté; pasta with a traditional meat sauce (spag. Bol.); avocado, bacon and spinach salad; kidneys turbigo; stroganoff (even if applied to mushrooms); and profiteroles with chocolate sauce. More fashion-conscious palates are catered for with items such as roasted red peppers; chargrilled-tuna salad; venison steak;

Open
Mon-Sat
Hours
12.00-10.30pm
Credit cards
AmEx, Mastercard,
Visa, Switch
Set-price lunch
£15
**Nearest tube
station**
W1: Oxford
Circus, Bond
Street;
SW3: South
Kensington;
WC2: Leicester
Square
Maps 2 & 3

vegetarian club sandwich; and natural yoghurt with fruit and honey. Most dishes are well-enough executed, although the 'classic Browns recipe' of steak, mushroom and Guinness pie was a vinegary disappointment. The wine list is unedifying, but thus fits in with the rather agreeable time-warp feel of the place. The Maddox Street branch, situated in ornate premises that for nearly a century and a half housed the Mayfair tailors Cooling and Wells, serves an area not well-endowed with restaurants. Breakfasts and afternoon teas are also available.

Bruno Soho £24

63 Frith Street W1 (734 4545)

As the Guide goes to press Bistrot Bruno and Cafe Bruno next door are being converted into one restaurant, Bruno Soho. The inspiration for the menu is the Maghreb and the Levant — in other words, north Africa and the eastern Mediterranean. Chef Bruno Loubet (see entry for L'Odéon) brings his own interpretation to the dishes, for which his head chef Pierre Khodja — who is French-Algerian — has an innate understanding. The stated aim is for very reasonable prices. At last, a fusion of unexploited cuisines — which other chefs such as Antony Worral Thompson and Alastair Little have been taking little rushes at — should come into full flowering.

Open
Lunch Mon–Fri,
dinner Mon–Sat
Hours
12.00–2.30pm
6.00–11.30pm
Credit cards
AmEx, Mastercard,
Visa, Switch,
Delta, Diner's
Set-price lunch
£15.50
Set-price dinner
£18.50
**Nearest tube
stations**
Tottenham Court
Road, Leicester
Square
Map 5

B Square £25

8 Battersea Square SW11 (924 2288)

NOW SWX1

The fact that this restaurant isn't busier than it is may be testimony either to the fact that the inhabitants of Battersea are indeed equilateral rectangles, or to do with the lack of easy parking in the vicinity. You cannot blame the food, which showcases the talents of Sebastian Snow with its clever Mediterranean tripartite coalitions (such as marinated sardines, vine-tomato salad and parsley pesto; or baked cod, Lyonnaise potatoes and green garlic sauce) nor the breezy, professional service overseen by manager Carolyn Finn. Careful thought has gone into the enterprise, from the construction of well-balanced, daily-changing short menus down to the use of very good-quality wine glasses. Of the three rooms off the central horseshoe-shaped bar, the elevated conservatory is the most picturesque and desirable, although the greenhouse effect operates on hot summer days. With occasional special offers —

Open
Every day
Hours
12.00–11.00pm,
Sun 12.00–
10.00pm
Credit cards
AmEx, Mastercard,
Visa, Switch,
Delta, Diner's
Service charge
12.5% optional
Set-price lunch
£9.50, £13.50 &
£17.50
**Nearest railway
station**
Clapham Junction
Map 2

such as half-price food between 6pm and 8pm, a happy hour for drinks and various other tempting promotions – this neighbourhood restaurant should appeal to people of all shapes.

MEDITERRANEAN FOOD DEMANDS bold, fruity wines – hence the predominance of Aussie throat charmers on this list. Among the whites, the apricot-rich Marsanne from Château Tahbilk and the sumptuously aromatic, elderflower-perfumed Palliser Estate Sauvignon from New Zealand lead the way, while in the red corner you can weigh the merits of Syrah/Shiraz with Graillot's roasted-coffeebean-scented Crozes-Hermitage against the silkily spicy Mount Langi. Attention to detail extends to the house wines, which are particularly good.

Bu-San £30

43 Holloway Road N7 (607 8264)

+ *casual, jolly surroundings for Korean food*
- *the bill quickly mounts up*

The port of Bu-San on the south-eastern tip of Korea looks across to Japan, and a few Japanese dishes are incorporated into Mr Lee's long Korean menu at this friendly, family-run restaurant. Introducing, say, sunomono (seafood seasoned with rice vinegar) or the salmon-based sashimi into your order is a good way of creating balance in what might otherwise be too relentless a barrage of deeply savoury sauces and sweet marinades. It would take more than BSE to deflect Koreans away from their favoured main ingredient, and a Korean meal should have a beef dish as its centrepiece – the best-known being bulgogi (slices of beef marinated in chilli and sesame oil). The side dish of kim chi (pickled, chilli-infused cabbage) is another essential. Well-stocked fish soups are good. By persevering with your menu reading to dish number 65, you will find pajeon (Korean omelette with shrimps, oysters and spring onions), and, even further on, the delicious dolsot bi bim bap (rice with egg, seaweed and vegetables in a stone bowl). Service is helpful but can be slow.

Open
Every day
Hours
12.00-2.30pm,
6.00-11.00pm
Credit cards
Mastercard, Visa,
Switch
Service charge
10%
Set-price lunch
£4.20 & £6.60
Set-price dinner
£16.30
Nearest tube station
Highbury &
Islington
Map 1

Butlers Wharf Chop House £34

36e Shad Thames SE1 (403 3403)

+ *the proximity of Tower Bridge; jugs of claret*
- *awkwardly designed interior*

This, the most felicitously sited of the restaurants in Conran's 'gastrodrome', should answer the question of where to find the British in modern British cooking. So much of what is

Open
Lunch Sun-Fri,
dinner Mon-Sat
Hours
12.00-3.00pm,
6.00-11.00pm
(Sun 12.00-
6.00pm)

Credit cards
AmEx,
Mastercard,
Switch, Visa,
Diner's
Service charge
12.5%
Set-price lunch
£18.75
Nearest tube
stations
Tower Hill,
London Bridge
Map 1

available in London under the heading 'English Restaurant' is overlaid with creaky tradition, anachronistic historical achievements, the snobbery of gentlemen's club habits (where it is considered vulgar to pay too much attention to what you put in your mouth), or attempts to give tourists what they think they want, that the field was wide open for a showcase of fine indigenous produce treated with British restraint and good manners. If this is not always achieved to a high standard, an explanation might be the polyglot community that we have become — head chef here is currently Henrik Iversen. However, palpable effort has been made to source regional ingredients and not to muck them about. The emphasis is on traditional grills and roasts, from simple plaice to veal chop with anchovy butter to roast rib of beef with Yorkshire pudding. Pot-roast rabbit leg with chestnuts and button onions in white wine (from Kent) was succulent. Lighter dishes include a salad of smoked trout with horseradish dressing; and mussel, cockle and spinach pie. Peach sorbet, lime curd ice cream and rhubarb crumble are typical seasonal desserts. Afternoon teas and weekend brunches at the bar are another thought for when you want to wave the flag.

A QUIRKY LIST that encompasses all manner of things, from Burgess Hill (Chapel Down) to Hermitage hill (Chapoutier's 'La Sizeranne'). Wines from Aquitaine — that's Bordeaux to you and me — commence the Old World section, which continues with 28 superbly chosen burgundies, then Alsace (including a Tokay Pinot Gris Grand Cru, described as having 'incredible complexity and magnitude'), Loire, Rhône, etc. The remainder of the wines on the list are all defined with sprightly tasting notes brimming with charming verbal infelicities. We are informed that a Rioja crianza from Viña Amezola is a real rustuc (sic) Rioja, but with a 'blueberry backbone to maintain its freshness'. *Que?* Of the pudding wines, Anselmi's oak-aged Recioto di Soave, with its gorgeous apricot crème-brûlée tones, is still a steal at £3.95 a glass.

Open
Mon-Fri & Sun
Hours
Mon-Fri 9.30-
5.00pm, Sun
12.00-4.00pm
Credit cards
AmEx, Mastercard,
Switch, Delta, Visa
Nearest tube
stations
Green Park,
Oxford Circus,
Bond Street
Map 3

The Cafe at Sotheby's ⭐ new £25

Sotheby's, New Bond Street W1 (408 5077)

+ *the fun of marching confidently into a Bond Street auction house*
- *small portions: going, going...oh! it's all gone*

B ores do it. Stores do it. Even churches — behind doors — do it. So why should an auction house not open a restaurant to the public? Sotheby's has not allocated a great deal of space to its first catering venture, but it is stylishly designed. Dark, glossy wood panelling is broken up by mirrors: all the better to facilitate watching who is lunching with whom, and what treasure is being carried past in the corridor outside. The cafe has access to the in-house art, which provides a changing display. Open for breakfast, lunch and tea, the emphasis is on light dishes using well-sourced produce (British where possible). The daily-changing lunch menu starts with a soup (usually based on vegetables) and composed salads such as asparagus, quails' egg, spinach and cherry tomato, and moves on to a choice of four main courses, one of which is a constant: Alfred Taubman, chairman of Sotheby's, decreed that there should always be a lobster club sandwich. This is made with toasted brioche and is not over-priced at £8.50 (at time of writing). Other main courses are often salads in essence, although reports of more robust cooking have come in. Desserts feature staunchly British ideas such as rhubarb fool, steamed ginger pudding and fruit crumble. A British cheese is served with homemade oatcakes. Serena Sutcliffe has advised on the short wine list. As part of that 'in for a penny, in for a pound' mood that auctions engender, you might order the 1992 Sassicaia, Tenuta San Guido, Marchesi Incisa della Rochetta at £48, tax and service included.

Cafe dell'Ugo £26

56–8 Tooley Street SE1 (407 6001)

+ *a set menu for retaining custody of the quids*
- *decor reminiscent of the London Dungeon; the drizzle, drizzle, drizzle of olive oil*

One of the better of Antony Worral Thompson's Club Med outlets (or units, as they are referred to in the business) is located at the edge of the empire, built into a converted railway arch by London Bridge. At the time of writing, head chef Matthew Fanthorpe has decamped to take over the reins at Dell'Ugo (q.v.). As usual, it is difficult to pin down the cooking to one particular region or style: expect apparently incongruous elements to fuse under the broad umbrella of 'Mediterranean'. Chilled panzanella salad is studded with myriad-hued peppers and makes a refreshing start to a meal; you might follow on from this with roast chump of lamb, or braised veal shank with borlotti beans. For indigent Lloyd's investors there is a brilliant value 'Ten Quid Cuisine'.

Open
Lunch Mon-Fri, dinner Mon-Sat
Hours
12.00-3.00pm, 6.00-11.00pm
Credit cards
AmEx, Mastercard, Visa, Switch, Delta, Diner's
Set-price dinner
£12 & £15
Nearest tube station
London Bridge
Map 1

Open
Every day
Hours
12.00pm-3.00pm,
5.30pm-12.00am
Credit cards
AmEx, Mastercard,
Visa, Switch,
Delta, Diner's
Service charge
15% optional
Set-price lunch
£9.95 & £13.50
Nearest tube
station
Covent Garden
Map 4

Cafe du Jardin £30

28 Wellington Street, Covent Garden WC2 (836 8769)

+ *more adventurous cooking than the name suggests*
- *more expensive than the name suggests*

This site would always do well, placed as it is on the main drag of Covent Garden. However, chef and co-owner Tony Howorth, who has worked at Le Caprice (q.v.), The Ivy (q.v.) and Soho Soho (q.v.), aims to do more than just take money off tourists and theatre-goers. Sometimes descriptions of dishes on his pan-European menu and even the menu vocabulary are more exciting than what arrives on the plate, but there are definite successes: scallops with Pernod-flavoured risotto; and warm Sicilian ratatouille on toasted olive bread topped with a soft poached egg were two. Pastas are inventive: namely, pappardelle with anchovies, shredded spinach and mushrooms; and linguini with roasted peppers, smoked chicken, sun-dried tomatoes and pinenuts. Recent refurbishment has created an attractive bar area downstairs. Summer pavement tables are popular.

Open
Lunch Mon-Fri,
dinner Mon-Sat
Hours
12.00-2.30pm,
6.00-10.00pm
Credit cards
Mastercard, Visa,
Switch, Delta
Service charge
15% optional
Set-price lunch
£21.50
Nearest tube
station
Barbican
Map 3

Le Cafe du Marché £30

22 Charterhouse Square, Charterhouse Mews, EC1 (608 1609)

+ *the romantic location*
- *City lads being laddish*

In a converted Smithfield warehouse off one of London's more hidden gems in terms of architectural assembly, is this restaurant poised to fulfil in almost every detail an English person's expectations of a French bistro. The set-price menus at £19.95 for three courses, which differ only slightly in content depending on whether they are served in the ground floor Cafe or the upstairs Grenier, have dropped their little excursions into franglais – as in le fishcake de crabe or le bagel, gravad lax, crème fraîche – and become wholeheartedly Gallic. Although you could have soupe du jour followed by Châteaubriand rôti, sauce Béarnaise (for two) and crème caramel, there are more original options such as salade tiède d'asperges et choufleur au speck; coquelet sauté aux morilles; bavarois du jour. It is a hugely successful formula, so booking well ahead is necessary. Waiting for a table can be done in the newly built bar.

Cafe Fish £28

39 Panton Street SW1 (930 3999)

+ *covers the angles*
- *the sea is a long way away*

The idea of swamping fish in a rich, buttery sauce or battering it to death is thankfully confined to a few select establishments that wear the epithet 'old-fashioned' as a proud accolade. Here you can have your hake and eat it in any fashion you choose: chargrilled, steamed, meunière or fried. As with the other restaurants in the Chez Gerard group, there is an attempt to reconstruct Parisian brasserie standards with an occasional innovation or frill, especially in the plats du jour, where a skittish flirtation with more modish ingredients such as lemongrass may be revealed. Great for a swift bite pre- or post-theatre; or, if you enjoy kitsch 'n' chips, you can linger and listen to the pianist. As you might expect, the wine list majors in the crisp aromatic whites.

Open
Lunch Mon–Fri,
dinner Mon–Sat
Hours
12.00–3.00pm,
5.45–11.30pm
(wine bar
11.30am–11.00pm
Mon–Sat)
Credit cards
AmEx, Mastercard,
Visa, Switch,
Diner's, JCB
Service charge
12.5%
Cover charge
£1.50 per person
**Nearest tube
stations**
Leicester Square,
Piccadilly Circus
Map 4

Cafe Med £26

184a Kensington Park Road W11 (221 1150)

+ *good grilled meat*
- *it is the prototype for a chain*

Simon Binder, proprietor of this establishment located within a clutch of Notting Hill Gate restaurants, has secured venture capital funding to open 10 further restaurants in London over the next two years. So if you don't want to go West for a chargrilled steak (cut from first-rate Scottish beef), sit tight and maybe soon enough a Cafe Med will open near you. To justify the Med in the title there are dishes such as merguez sausages with white beans on rocket salad, mixed crostini, grilled tuna Niçoise, and fish brochette; but burgers, steak and bootlace chips are the popular order. To precede them, votes go to Caesar salad; for dessert it is New York-style cheesecake. At Sunday brunch, independent and observant customers choose scrambled eggs with smoked salmon. When the weather in the streets is appropriate to the name, the lower-ground-floor dining-room can become rather stifling.

Open
Every day
Hours
12.00–11.30pm
(Sun 12.00–
10.30pm)
Credit cards
AmEx, Mastercard,
Switch, Visa,
Delta, Diner's
Service charge
12.5% optional
Set-price lunch
£10.00 & £12.50
**Nearest tube
stations**
Lancaster Gate,
Notting Hill Gate
Map 6

Cafe O   £25

Open
Lunch Mon-Sat,
dinner every day
Hours
Mon-Fri 11.00am-
3.00pm, 6.00-
11.30pm, Sat
11.00am-4.00pm,
6.00pm-12.00am,
Sun 6.00pm-
10.30pm
Credit cards
AmEx, Mastercard,
Visa, Switch,
Delta,
Service charge
12.5%
Set-price lunch
£8.50 & £10.00
Nearest tube
station
South Kensington
Map 2

163 Draycott Avenue SW3 (584 5950)

+ *Greek food that discards the package-holiday image*
– *uncomfortable chairs*

Both the upgrading of surroundings and the care taken in preparing Greek food were long overdue when Cafe O opened in the summer of 1995. The room is attractive: in its seaside blue and chalky white it is reminiscent of the tasteful architectural images in the generic postcards now sold all over Greece. Modern Hellenic cuisine is how the cooking is described, and it is palpably different from the usual Greek/Cypriot formula on offer in London. Kakavia (fisherman's soup) is stylishly made, while grilled Mediterranean vegetables with balsamic vinegar could hold their heads high in any fashionable restaurant – such as Daphne's opposite (q.v.). In the main course, apart from grills the list includes chicken stuffed with spinach and feta; baked sea bass with halloumi cheese; leg of duck roasted with Greek thyme honey and grapes; and some interesting vegetarian options. Reflecting the huge improvements being made in viniculture in Greece, Cafe O has been holding wine tastings. The Greek restaurant is growing up.

Cafe Royal Grill Room   £60

Open
Lunch Mon-Fri,
dinner Mon-Sat
Hours
12.00-2.30pm,
6.00pm-10.30pm
Credit cards
AmEx, Mastercard,
Visa, Diner's
Set-price lunch
£24
Set-price dinner
Pre-theatre £25
Nearest tube
station
Piccadilly Circus
Maps 4 & 5

68 Regent Street W1 (437 9090)

+ *the historic, romantic, rococo interior*
– *the out-of-town clientele*

It is in the heart of London, but modern London, sadly, has not taken the Cafe Royal Grill Room – once frequented by Wilde, Beardsley and Beerbohm – to its heart. The overblown decor, which should provoke and endorse excess of all kinds, seems to act as a magnet mainly to tourists. Staff, ably led by the smooth-as-silk David Arcusi, are perhaps too formal, and chef Herbert Berger's food perhaps too fancy, although the execution is often faultless. Combinations of luxurious ingredients are well-matched, and each presentation is artful. Classics are much in evidence: tournedos of Angus beef, roast rack of lamb, seared fillet of sea bass. Berger's inventive culinary talent emerges in dishes such as carpaccio of tuna and scallops with roasted sesame seeds; galette of pig's trotter, sweetbreads and foie gras; and cream of cèpes with poached egg, pancetta and white-truffle oil. Having its own entrance would benefit the Grill Room, obviating the need to walk past announcements of corporate dinners and masonic meetings taking place elsewhere in the building.

Cafe Spice Namaste £23

16 Prescot Street E1 (488 9242)

+ *wildly unconventional Indian dishes*
- *aimless service; occasional bathos in the cooking*

Open
Lunch Mon-Fri, dinner Mon-Sat
Hours
12.00-3.00pm, 6.15-10.30pm (Sat 6.30-10.00pm)
Credit cards
AmEx, Delta, Diner's, Mastercard, Switch, Visa
Set-price lunch
£20
Nearest tube stations
Aldgate, Aldgate East, Tower Hill
Map 1

A definite feeling of being 'in the know' about Indian food used to attach to visiting Namaste in Alie Street E1, where drab, small premises and practically mute service gave no clues to the invention, spirit and daring of the kitchen run by Cyrus Todiwala, a Parsee whose cooking has been strongly influenced by working in Goa. The nearby Prescot Street premises, a handsome, Italianate building that has done time as a courthouse, contains Cyrus Todiwala's new venture in partnership with his wife Pervin and Michael Gottlieb of Smollensky's Balloon. Interior design by Steve Thomas has transformed two large, interconnecting spaces into a riot of colour, pattern and texture. His pink may not be the navy blue of India, but the overall look reinforces the idea that this is an Indian restaurant with a difference. In the long standard menu, plus the weekly-changing list of specialities, Todiwala is able to give full rein to his creativity, underpinned by his knowledge of Indian regional traditions. At least one Goan speciality should be part of any order. Xit (the X is pronounced 'sh') ani suncta chi kodi is a terrific Goan prawn dish using stridently spiced large prawns mellowed in a coconut-based sauce. The pungency of palm vinegar as a grinding medium for spices is apparent in the tandoori-chicken dish frango no espeto piri piri. The effect of the tandoor on venison should also be experienced. However, there is sometimes an element of straining for effect, with ingredients such as crocodile, ostrich, wild rabbit, wild boar, kangaroo and shark featuring as specials. Just as interesting – if not more so – are authentic regional dishes such as Kashmiri quail, Mogul lamb, Gujarati vegetarian snacks and sorpotel (the Goan wedding dish of long-simmered pork); as well as the vegetable assemblies that use ingredients such as porcini mushrooms, bamboo shoots, yam and lotus seeds (deep-fried). With so much attempted, including – for no sound reason that I can think of – Malaysian and Middle Eastern dishes, disappointments can happen. Todiwala has not cracked the presentation problem where curries are concerned, and this can render a lyrical description a sullen stew. Note the delicious homemade pickles and chutneys; these are also for sale.

Open
Tues–Sat
Hours
6.30pm–12.00am
Credit cards
Visa, Mastercard,
Switch, Delta
Service charge
10%
Nearest railway
station
Westcombe Park

Caffe Italia £17

107 Humber Road SE3 (0181–858 7577)

+ *a genuine passion for good food*
- *the necessity for togetherness*

Just up the hill from Westcombe Park station, this restaurant has twin driving forces in Domenico Lo Vecchio, the surprisingly loud 'front of house', and his wife Sarah, the surprisingly good cook. The pretty dining-room on two levels is generally jam-packed, and tables are crowded tightly together. Homestyle dishes are both homely and stylish, and include simple pastas with superb sauces; game in season; grilled peppers salmoriglia; and hot focaccia with fresh rosemary and sea salt. Start with one of Domenico's obscure Italian 'aperitivas', and finish with a damned fine cup of coffee.

Open
Lunch Mon–Fri,
dinner Mon–Sat
Hours
12.30–3.00pm,
6.00–11.30pm
Credit cards
AmEx, Mastercard,
Visa, Diner's, Delta
Service charge
10%
Cover charge
25p per person
Nearest tube
station
Covent Garden
Map 4

Calabash £18

38 King Street WC2 (836 1976)

+ *Abyssinian coffee poured through a piece of pot scourer*
- *plastic plants and institutional serving dishes*

In the basement of the Africa centre the menu of the restaurant Calabash lets you roam the Continent, taking in couscous from north Africa; egusi (a soup/stew of meat or fish cooked in palm oil with ground melon seeds and spinach) from Nigeria; yassa (grilled chicken in lemon sauce) from Senegal; dioumbre (lamb stew cooked in palm oil with okra) from the Ivory Coast; and more. It is interesting food as much for the accompaniments — which include injera (a bread cunningly designed to resemble a face flannel), pounded yam, plantain, black-eyed beans, fried sweet potatoes and sadza (pounded maize) — as for the mainly spicy casseroles. The atmosphere of a slightly despondent canteen (as opposed to a sad cafe) may not be to everyone's taste, but it makes a soulful change from the tourist-baiting tricksiness of most of Covent Garden's eating establishments.

Open
Every day
Hours
12.00–2.30pm,
7.00–11.30pm
Credit cards
AmEx, Mastercard,
Visa, Switch, Delta
Nearest tube
station
Gloucester Road
Map 2

Cambio de Tercio £24

163 Old Brompton Road SW5 (244 8970)

+ *serious, sympathetic young waiters; a great Spanish wine list*
- *too few tables to meet demand*

Abel Lusa and David Rivero, owners of this Iberian bar and restaurant in South Kensington, first met when studying catering and wine-making in the Rioja region of

Spain. They made contact again working at Albero & Grana (q.v.) in Chelsea. Like Albero & Grana, the name and decorative theme of their venture take inspiration from the bullring. Colours used in the decoration echo the sand of the ring and the crimson of the matador's cape, and reinforcing the atmosphere are banderillas, toreros' hats and a deep-pink cape hung on the wall. Yet this is by no means a themed establishment. Chef Elixabete Segurado has worked in San Sebastian, home of many of Spain's most acclaimed restaurants, while the wine list is among the best Spanish assemblies in London. Staff take the subjects of food and drink beguilingly seriously, to the extent of wearing a version of seminarians' garb. While studying the menu, order a plate of Iberian ham and a glass or two of sherry. There is a choice of six, and the pleasure of a good, chilled manzanilla is one worth renewing. First courses can and really should be ordered as a spread — a table-service version of tapas. Good options to try are Galician octopus; clams in their own juices spiked with garlic; crab salad; scrambled eggs with prawns; hokey, crumbed croquettes filled with ham in a creamy mixture; and griddled squid. Some of the main courses are priced more or less in line with starters. In true Spanish style, these are fiercely proud of their own identity and come with scant garnish. Paella mixta of seafood and chicken has a great smoky flavour from charred prawn shells. Home-salted cod and suckling pig Segovian-style are also recommended. Desserts confirm the Spanish love of crème caramel; alternatively, a selection of Spanish cheeses with quince marmalade is a good tack to take. A final glass of zoco pacharan, with its slightly medicinal flavour, ends an evening on what seems like a sensible note.

The Canteen £33

Harbour Yard, Chelsea Harbour SW10 (351 7330)

+ *marina views; desserts from patissier Alain Ronez*
- *certain tables are self-evidently social Siberia*

When Christina Rossetti wrote: 'Will the day's journey take a whole long day?' she might have been contemplating the prospect of a trip by public transport to Chelsea Wharf (nearest tube: nowhere near). Nor if you approach by car is the signposting clear, although checkpoints might indicate that you are entering a restricted gastronomic zone. The interior of the apartment and leisure complex is like an echoing shopping mall, where you follow the travel-weary to the front desk and in exchange for your coat and belongings you are given a playing

Open
Lunch Mon-Fri &
Sun, dinner Mon-
Sat
Hours
12.00-3.00pm,
6.30-11.00pm
Credit cards
AmEx, Mastercard,
Visa, Delta
Service charge
12.5% (except 7
or more)
Cover charge
£1 per person

card. Trumps were starters. One player was dealt a plate of pappardelle with field mushrooms and truffle oil, an ingredient which – like vermouth in dry martini – must only be hinted at. His partner finessed this with a ravioli of veal sweetbreads poached in a light bouillon of cèpes. Main courses were more prosaic but no less accomplished: roasted cod with Asian greens came in a gingery broth; other dishes of lamb, calf's liver, sole and salmon were simply rendered and plated with their own vegetables. The fact that Marco Pierre White is no longer around means that the staff, although not of the swiftest, do not look as though they are treading fearfully on exploding eggshells.

THE LIST WITH the playing-card motif has burgundies in spades – a few rough diamonds from the former colonies – but its heart is most definitely in Bordeaux, on which you can gamble to be reliable. As with so many lists, it seems to have been thrown together with little regard for the subtleties of the cuisine, being top heavy in heavy wines when more delicate and aromatic flavours should have been sought, with more examples such as Zind-Humbrecht's Turckheim Riesling or the white Roussanne-dominated Châteauneuf-du-Pape from Domaine Chante Cigale. Prices are more expensive than is warranted either by the cost of the food or by the surroundings.

Set-price lunch £19.50
Set-price dinner £23.85
Nearest tube stations Fulham Broadway, Sloane Square
Map 2

Cantina del Ponte £30

36c Shad Thames SE1 (403 5403)

+ *the most affordable on the Conran map of Europe*
– *sullen staff; loud customers*

Unforgiving surfaces, with nothing but a mural and an antique model of Tower Bridge beached on sand to soften impact, make for an extremely noisy atmosphere when the Cantina is crowded, but in the right mood this can be construed as fun. First courses include Serrano ham with grilled figs; bresaola with sweet mustard dressing; and chilled roast aubergine and sweet pepper soup with yoghurt and tapenade crostini. In other words, all fashionable bases are covered. Pizzas from the wood-fired oven are more Cal-Ital than Neopolitan: smoked salmon with goat's cheese and basil; and prosciutto with avocado, pousse and pine kernels. Grills run from fresh sardines with lemon and parsley to leg of lamb with pan-fried peppers and potatoes. Desserts are traditional: peach melba, pavlova, raspberry trifle and an unimpressive chocolate cheesecake. If after your meal you can't wait to have it again, most of the ingredients are on sale at the door.

Open Lunch every day, dinner Mon-Sat
Hours 12.00-3.00pm, 6.00-11.00pm
Credit cards AmEx, Mastercard, Switch, Visa, Diner's
Service charge 12.5% optional
Nearest tube station Tower Hill
Map 1

La Capannina   £30

24 Romilly Street W1 (437 2473)

+ *family-owned, venerable Soho trattoria*
- *cover charge and separately priced vegetables*

Open
Lunch Mon-Fri,
dinner Mon-Sat
Hours
12.00-2.30pm,
6.00-11.15pm
Credit cards
AmEx, Mastercard,
Visa, Diner's
Cover charge
£1 per person
**Nearest tube
stations**
Leicester Square &
Piccadilly Circus
Map 5

Owned and run by Linda and Gianni Frattini for over 35 years, this Italian restaurant with its hokey hunting-lodge interior harks back to a Soho of more innocent — but also less innocent — days. Lunch is the meal to take here, when the dining-rooms are full of local media folk. Regulars ignore the long printed list, looking instead at the typewritten page of dishes of the day, or at the ingredients displayed on trolleys driven by waiters of the old school. Pasta dishes tend to be somewhat overbearing for today's fairy appetites: a first course of stuffed vegetables, marinated fresh anchovies or a chicory salad with tuna fish is more suitable. You can look the fish — say, halibut or bream — in its gleaming eye before it is taken away to be grilled or served with a white-wine and butter sauce. Fresh (Dutch) calf's kidneys, beef in Barolo, roast shoulder (the best roasting joint) of lamb and rabbit stew are all satisfactory. Wild mushrooms are hunted in season.

Capital Hotel   £70

Basil Street SW3 (589 5171)

+ *the seven- and nine-course set menus...*
- *...unfortunately titled 'Temptation and Seduction'*

Open
Every day
Hours
7.30-10.15am,
12.30-2.15pm,
7.00-11.15pm
Credit cards
AmEx, Mastercard,
Switch, Visa,
Delta, Diner's
Set-price lunch
£25, £55 & £75
**Nearest tube
station**
Knightsbridge
Map 2

Many chefs can cook 'in the style of'; few have the patience, perseverance and, indeed, talent to develop to the point where they have a touch that you might recognize when coming across a dish — just as you can recognize a painting done by a particular artist. The somewhat self-effacing Philip Britten has achieved his own way of looking at things, and this is best experienced in what sound like dauntingly long set-price menus but which are deliciously manageable. Relatively, they are not expensive when compared with the same dishes à la carte; the meal is knowledgeably balanced; everyone eating the same food improves wine ordering; there is the feeling of a special event; and you can always return another time to eat more of what you liked best. Dishes that seem fundamentally Brittenish are vegetable purées overlaying jellied consommés; contrasting treatments of foie gras; lobster and morel soup souffléd and glazed, and served with a dill risotto; sea bass in black bean sauce with coriander, ginger and a saffron cream; and pot-roasted squab pigeon with forest mushrooms, their cooking juices and oils. The Capital's patissier Camille Jauffret has the ability to end these menus on a high note: I would bet that you will even finish the petits fours. The dining-room nowadays almost manages not to seem like part of an hotel. Service is polished, and the sommelier a chap you can trust your meal with.

CHÂTEAU LÉOVILLE-BARTON 1982 at £85 seems not unreasonable until you discover that downstairs at Le Metro (q.v.) it is only £50. Long on Burgundy, longer still on Bordeaux, the list begins to unravel until it collapses with a gentle, indifferent sigh around Italy and Spain (four and two respectively) before reviving with an energetic New World contingent. Best buys are the brooding giant of Berthoumieu's Madiran (£19.50) and a terrifically earthy white Santenay 'Le Bievaux' from Domaine Olivier. Claret is the strength, with a good smattering of glorious '82s and '78s, and, more oddly, '71s and even a pair of lesser-spotted 1929s. Specializing in renowned vintages is meritorious, but when they are of necessity exorbitantly priced, their use as quotidian restaurant wines is severely curtailed. You will be relieved to know, however, that you will save £65 by drinking Léoville-Las-Cases '83 here rather than at The Dorchester (q.v.). By the way, having vin de Levin rouge as your only red Loire is a spankable offence.

Le Caprice   £32

Arlington House, Arlington Street SW1 (629 2239)

+ *the restaurant with 'it': the indefinable sex appeal*
- *the cover charge*

Open
Every day
Hours
12.00pm-3.00pm,
5.30pm-12.00am
Credit cards
AmEx, Mastercard,
Visa, Switch,
Delta, Diner's
Cover charge
£1 per person
**Nearest tube
station**
Green Park
Map 3

What is it that puts Le Caprice on to so many people's list of top 10 London restaurants? The simple answer is consistency: Christopher Corbin's and Jeremy King's institutional restaurant is run with the effortless precision of a well-rehearsed military manoeuvre. From the moment you walk in the door, an alert receptionist – who appears to have been expecting you – takes you under her wing so that, although celebrities haunt every table, there is also a democratic feel. The menu is ur-Modern Brit: the Caesar salad and salmon fishcakes are benchmarks, as are the eggs Benedict and Lincolnshire sausage with bubble and squeak. Scribbled in the margins of the page are daily specials, such as Catalan roast hake with clams and chorizo. Were the food not very good in its own right, it would be the vicarious glamour of eating such simple fare among the firmament of stars that adds aplomb to the experience.

PARTITIONED INTO THREE categories: France, New World, and Italy and Spain, this is the perfect example of a well-chosen, conservative wine list. All the names that you might expect are there: Marqués de Murrieta in Rioja, Leeuwin Estate in Australia and Anselmi in Soave, but there is a marked lack of choice at under £15. Some compensation is provided by 25 half-bottles, 12 wines by the glass and nine dessert wines, although it is surely a sign of complacency when a list of this size totally ignores South America, South Africa, Languedoc and Gascony, from whose vineyards so many interesting new wines are now emanating.

The Captain £19

131 Stroud Green Road N4 (263 0378)

+ *waterworld without Kevin Costner*
- *sudden eruptions of the fountains can be tiring*

This Greek/Cypriot family-owned Finsbury Park fish-and-chip shop has a thriving take-away section and a fanciful restaurant. Each tabletop — handmade by one of the owners, Chris Neophytou — is a water-filled glass box from which a fountain spurts into a glass centrepiece of varying design (some of these are rather suggestive). The table-aquariums are furnished with pebbles, shells, little plastic seahorses and the like. Waiters and waitresses are decked out in sailor suits, an effect slightly impaired by the accompanying baseball caps. However, Hallo Sailor! staff and ejaculating tables are not enough on their own to merit inclusion in a good-restaurant guide: the standard of the fish and also the chips is high. The left-hand side of the menu relays 'Captain's Specialist Dishes', which feature the more expensive species such as sea bass and rely to some extent on exotic, unfathomable sauces. These items are relatively expensive. The right-hand side of the menu is standard chippie fare, but fish can be grilled rather than battered if you prefer. Raw material is obviously bought with discrimination. The wine list includes Greek wines, some of which demonstrate the improvements in viniculture which have been taking place in that country.

Open
Lunch Tues-Sat,
dinner Mon-Sat
Hours
12.00-2.30pm,
4.30-10.30pm
(Fri & Sat 4.30-
11.30pm)
Credit cards
AmEx, Mastercard,
Visa, Switch
Set-price lunch
£9.95 & £7.95
**Nearest tube
station**
Finsbury Park

Caraffini £28

Open
Mon-Sat
Hours
12.15-2.30pm,
6.30-11.30pm
Credit cards
AmEx, Mastercard,
Visa, Switch, Delta
Cover charge
£1 per person
**Nearest tube
station**
Sloane Square
Map 2

61–3 Lower Sloane Street SW1 (259 0235)

+ *almost no larking around with the pepper mill*
– *the fantasia di carne e crostaceo*

On the site of the original Le Gavroche, this Italian restaurant – one of many fairly similar in the Chelsea/ Knightsbridge/South Kensington axis – attracts a grown-up clientele. Paolo Caraffini, previously manager of Como Lario, works the room less egregiously than some of his compatriots. Within the menu – a long list – a certain amount of fashionableness has been grafted on to traditional roots. For example, in the first course there are chargrilled vegetables, but also on offer is an assembly of avocado with mozzarella, smoked salmon, fresh crab and prawns; while in the main course chargrilled monkfish with herbs sits near veal scaloppine in lemon sauce. The section of seasonal dishes has some nice ideas such as, in summer, marechiaro (clams and monkfish in spicy sauce) and vitello tonnato (cold veal in tuna mayonnaise). Prices have crept up in the past year, but remain comparatively restrained. The Italian wine list has some interesting content.

Caviar House £35

Open
Mon-Sat
Hours
12.00-3.00pm,
7.00-10.00pm
Credit cards
AmEx, Mastercard,
Diner's, Visa,
Switch
Set-price lunch
£17.50 & £21.50
**Nearest tube
station**
Green Park
Map 3

161 Piccadilly W1 (409 0445)

+ *caviar in a fairly casual atmosphere*
– *30g of Beluga costs £70*

It would be foolish to enter, dine and not sample the raison d'être, but the kitchen's (to my mind, correct) stance would seem to be that caviar should be eaten plain and in quantity. As an ingredient in the dishes of the short menu, it barely gets a look-in. The menu style is typified by ballotine of foie gras served with fig mousse and Sauternes jelly; millefeuille of langoustine with spinach and a light curry sauce; and lamb fillet with aubergine gâteau, ginger and shallot cream sauce. Sevruga caviar does make a guest appearance in fillet of sea bass with confit of leeks. The caviar list has six options, all of which are served with blinis and Jersey potatoes. A sampler may be the best bet: a trio of Sevruga, Oscietre and Royal Black is on offer for £32.75, or a more modest option is a mini-blini with pressed caviar and soured cream (a mere £12.50). A tempting caviar shop (under the same ownership as those at Heathrow airport terminals) is at the entrance to the restaurant.

Cento 50 £25

150 Notting Hill Gate W11 (221 3113)

+ *occupying a middle ground between chain and classy*
- *the canteen-like feel to the ground-floor dining-room*

The copious advertising and PR bumph that heralded the launch of this restaurant in the summer of '96 might have led punters to expect some sort of breakthrough — in catering in general, in Italian food in particular. However, in this guide's experience, the reality was something of an anti-climax: the architect has made uninspiring use of a double-storey site with history (it was the plate-smashing Cleopatra's) and potential, rendering it a faint, drab imitation of nearby Kensington Place (q.v.); a pizza chef with a CV that includes stints at Pizzeria Castello and Casale Franco had one looking longingly at Pizza Express across the road; and, by straining for a sort of arcane authenticity, chef Enrico Sartor — formerly of The Peasant (q.v.) — managed to include one ingredient too many or one process too odd in almost every dish. Unfamiliar vocabulary, such as trofie (a pasta speciality of Genoa); spelt (dictionary definition: an old-fashioned species of wheat); salmoriglio (a Calabrese or Sicilian sauce for fish, traditionally enhanced by a spoonful of seawater); and gianduja (a hazelnut and chocolate confection) sets up expectations of something special about to arrive, which tend to go unfulfilled. However, an attempt to push out the boundaries of what is a well-trodden field should not be discouraged. In addition, three refreshing elements are (a) an absence of that anomalous Italian habit — making a cover charge — even though bread, olives and olive oil are on the tables; (b) many of the wines supplied by Enotria Winecellars are offered in 250- or 500-ml carafes; and (c) a clientele who by dress, physique or phizzog you would not automatically associate with W11. Open all day, Cento 50 is not the vaunted 'capital's most chic Italian', but — ironically — is rather restfully dull.

Open
Every day
Hours
12.00pm-11.30pm
Credit cards
AmEx, Mastercard,
Visa, Switch
**Nearest tube
station**
Notting Hill Gate
Map 6

Chada Thai £25

208–210 Battersea Park Road SW11 (622 2209)

+ *the stately dining-room*
- *ice cream is the best dessert*

Small and rather formal, Chada Thai is run by a husband-and-wife team who are unstintingly gracious. Their (necessary) assistance is offered in trawling through the long but well-organized menu. The Chada combination starter is the best introduction: a once-through the appetizers with spicy fishcakes,

Open
Lunch Sun-Fri,
dinner every day
Hours
12.00-2.30pm,
6.30-11.00pm
(Fri-Sat 6.30-
11.30pm, Sun
7.00-10.30pm)
Credit cards
AmEx, Mastercard,
Visa, Switch,
Diner's

satay, spring rolls, seafood in pancake and stuffed chicken wings. Steamed fish and charcoal-grilled beef and pork are specialities, and chilli is used enthusiastically. While not wildly adventurous, the menu does contain a few real gems: green curry with prawns; tum sai roong (a salad of pork, prawns and transparent noodles); steamed cod with flavourings of preserved plum, celery and ginger; and khao obb mod din (a dish of juicy rice baked with sausage and peas and threaded with fine filaments of fried chicken). Call this last dish rice pudding and the dessert problem is overcome.

Service charge
10%
Cover charge
70p per person
Nearest tube
station
Sloane Square
Map 1

Open
Every day
Hours
12.00-2.30pm,
7.00-10.00pm
Credit cards
AmEx, Mastercard,
Visa, Switch
Nearest tube
station
Edgware Road
Map 6

The Chapel £18

48 Chapel Street NW1 (402 9220)

+ *the pear tarte Tatin*
- *overwhelming quantities*

This is one of the new breed of converted pubs serving excellent food at reasonable prices. Daily specials are chalked up on a board: you order from this and pay at the bar. The style may be termed 'modern eclectic' (in other words, the chef cooks what he feels like), and menus change daily to reflect what is fresh in the market. Chargrilled, chopped lamb steak is bristling with garlic, fresh mint, rosemary and lemon, and is accompanied by a pot of delicious ratatouille; a monumental heap of spaghetti comes with massive coarse meatballs and a fragrant showerdust of fresh herbs. Tables are large, but demand is great — you may have to share at lunchtime. The owner is a wine enthusiast and a genial host.

Open
Lunch Mon-Fri &
Sun, dinner every
day
Hours
12.00-2.30pm,
6.00-11.00pm
(10.00-11.00pm
supper)
Credit cards
AmEx, Mastercard,
Visa, Switch,
Delta, Diner's
Set-price lunch
£8.50 & £ 10.50
Set-price dinner
£12.50 & £15.50
Nearest tube
station
Green Park
Map 3

The Chesterfield Restaurant £34

Chesterfield Hotel, 35 Charles Street W1 (514 5700)

+ *a discreet Mayfair address*
- *the repertoire of the pianist in the bar*

The inventive and reasonably priced menu comes as something of a surprise in this traditionally decorated hotel, with its chintz and Persian carpets stretching as far as the eye can see. It also seems quite a well-kept secret, making the dining-room ideal for a discreet rendezvous. Chefs David Needes and Stephen Henderson offer a set-price, seasonally-changing menu. In summer, the dishes included smoked gazpacho; salad of rabbit and spiced pear with Stilton crème fraîche; chicken breast poached with ginger, lemongrass and basil, with egg noodles and bok choy; seared sea bass on a cassoulet of white beans and pancetta; and mango summer pudding. Meat is obtained from Allen's, the estimable butcher's shop in Mount Street, making a tournedos Rossini something you can feel confident about. Wines do not snatch back the financial advantage that the menu holds out.

Chez Bruce £30

2 Bellevue Road SW17 (0181-672 0114)

+ *praline parfait with chocolate and almond pudding; the unflagging Gallic charm of manager Maurice Bernard*
- *the wine list does not reflect the regional bias of the cuisine*

Bruce Poole is cooking up a storm in this beautifully situated restaurant on Wandsworth Common. The style of the place wavers between the down-to-earth – with no-frills cooking, friendly staff and subfusc. decor – and the stately, as the well-heeled denizens of Cla'am clamour to pay homage to their local chefmeister. Emanating from the kitchen is as near-faultless a rendition of Anglo-French cuisine as can be found in London. Pack an appetite when you go to Chez Bruce, because portions are generous. Confit of guinea fowl is a Vesuvian salad erupting with shredded lettuce and chunky lardons, topped with a poached egg. Magret de canard is fanned-out duck breast, properly pink and moist, on a bed of spinach and Pithivier; while calf's liver comes pan-fried with a reduced sauce of startling intensity. Other favourites have been calf's brains with sauce gribiche, and, still on a bovine theme, a côte de boeuf (for two), which elicits a positive moo of approval. What the cooking lacks in finesse at times it provides in gusto and in the devil of detail. As a finale, you can opt either for the multi-tiered cheese board (which looks as though it has been hijacked from a grand hotel), or sample one of the superb desserts (pastry is evidently a strong suit in Bruce's kitchen) – or have some of each. Refined rusticity, as Wordsworth might say.

Open
Lunch every day, dinner Mon-Sat
Hours
12.00-2.00pm (Sun 12.00-3.00pm), 7.00-10.30pm
Credit cards
AmEx, Mastercard, Visa, Switch, Delta, Diner's
Service charge
12.5% optional
Set-price lunch
£17.50
Set-price dinner
£24.50
Nearest tube stations
Clapham South, Balham
Map 1

Chez Gerard £29

8 Charlotte Street W1 (636 4975)

+ *what is there to beef about? You'd be mad to eat anything else*
- *runs the entire French gamut from côte de boeuf to Georges Duboeuf*

Chez Gerard is as institutional as 'The Mousetrap' in its way. You know the story: a definitive tourist French menu, cut off for years from contemporary cooking trends, brimming with all the stock suspects of chicken liver pâté, moules marinières,

Open
Every day
Hours
12.00-3.00pm, 6.00-11.30pm (Sun 10.30pm)
Credit cards
AmEx, Mastercard, Visa, Switch, Delta, Diner's
Service charge
12.5%

Set-price dinner
£15
Nearest tube station
Goodge Street
Map 4

paillarde de veau. The hors d'oeuvres are a sinister prelude; while the sweaty, oily French onion soup, or the grandly named brioche de champignons (more of a floury bun really, stuffed with flavourless button mushrooms which out of self-respect would not dream of calling themselves champignons), are murdered in Act One. The main action comes under the heading of 'Les Grillades', with the claim to serve 'the best steak frites this side of Paris': a case of mistaken identity when a test meal revealed unexceptional chips and Béarnaise of cheese-custard consistency. The filet mignon was good and steak tartare was benchmark, kicking with spiciness. Finish with cheeses from the well-kept cheeseboard – an excuse to continue drinking red wine, of which there is plentiful choice on the list. Chez Gerard needs a new script: it is not enough to peddle steak frites to an undemanding clientele and to neglect the finer points of French bourgeois cuisine. Otherwise it will continue to function merely as an Angers Steak House for those people who fondly believe that Paris teems with accordion-playing French onion sellers who subsist purely on frogs' legs and snails in garlic butter.

Chez Moi £34

1 Addison Avenue W11 (603 8267)

+ *a romantic restaurant haven with appeal for all generations*
- local resident Michael Winner is often seen here

Open
lunch Mon-Fri, dinner Mon-Sat
Hours
12.30–2.00pm, 7.00–11.00pm
Credit cards
AmEx, Mastercard, Visa, Switch, Delta, Diner's
Set-price lunch
£15
Nearest tube station
Holland Park
Map 6

If only as an outward symbol of the energy and dedication that never let up, we must welcome the change of interior decoration at this restaurant, owned and run by Richard Walton and Colin Smith (chef and manager respectively) since 1967. Rather sweetly, it has left behind its pink and green romanticism for only quite a contemporary look – maybe still a decade in arrears. However, the cooking has always been ahead of its time, and only recently have young chefs caught up with Walton's venerable menu in which chicken and prawn dhosa, scallops served with a futo-maki roll, bortsch, grilled smoked haddock on vermicelli vegetables, rack of lamb with rosemary (classically good); and Moroccan tagine of lamb share the same page. In this context, 'Something Different', as the right-hand page of the menu is entitled, turns out to be salad paysanne, and salmon and asparagus gratin. Chocolate-flavoured orange pot has been a favourite dessert for 30 years, but try also final d'or, a liqueur-flavoured cream-cheese-stuffed hot pancake. New ideas are often rehearsed at the set-price lunch, a bargain at £15 for three courses. Service, led by Philippe Bruyer, is formal in style but unfailingly charming. Plenty of half-bottles are included on the mainly French wine list.

Chez Nico at Ninety Park Lane £80

90 Park Lane W1 (409 1290)

+ *dependability*
- *hotel atmosphere*

When three Michelin stars are awarded — as they have been here — one of the most important criteria is consistency. Dependability is another way of putting it. The serious, dogged, obsessive nature of Nico Ladenis himself has been a means to reliably delicious and diverting gastronomic ends. The flavours that come from his kitchen are direct and uncompromising but can also beguile with balletic delicacy. You know a meal is off to a good start when something like a small cup of chilled vichysoisse inter-leaved with petals of cucumber is presented on a summer's day, or a profoundly intense, creamy langoustine soup with truffle sabayon kicks off the 10-course gastronomic menu. This well-balanced, well-paced extravaganza opens windows on to Nico's style and underlines his versatility in, for example, the soya and sesame seed-sealed scallops served with a chive velouté and shredded leeks and the ravioli of langoustine where, unusually for this dish, textures work together in perfect harmony. The lemon tart is famed in story and fable, but other desserts such as apple tart with toffee sauce and ice cream cradled in a brandy snap should be tried. To get the best from Chez Nico you go knowing what to expect; the results of unwavering dedication to the notion of cooking as a perfectable art; flavours stripped down to their essence; skilled formal service; expensive wines; a substantial bill and probably a proportion of the staid clientele there for the wrong reasons. Although not having been given the separate kitchen he was promised, Ladenis is overseeing the next door Cafe Nico where his style of cooking can be tried for the not exactly bargain price of £24.50 for two courses, £29.50 for three, considering that the air of hotel coffee shop (formerly The Pavilion) is impossible to eradicate.

Open
Lunch Mon-Fri, dinner Mon-Sat
Hours
12.00pm-2.00pm, 7.00pm-11.00pm
Credit cards
AmEx, Mastercard, Visa
Set-price lunch
£31
Set-price dinner
£63; Gastronomic Menu £70
Nearest tube stations
Hyde Park Corner, Marble Arch
Map 3

Chiaroscuro £28

24 Coptic Street WC1 (636 2731)

+ *an enlightened attitude towards children; the antipasto (a picnic on a plate)*
- *nuclear garlic attack to certain dishes may impede romantic plans ('Poore Suters have strong breaths' — Shakespeare)*

The staid interior of this restaurant, an Elgin marble's throw from the British Museum, belies the zestful assembly of earthy taste sensations taking place in the kitchen. A menu

Open
Lunch Mon-Fri, dinner Mon-Sat
Hours
12.00-3.00pm, 7.00-12.00pm
Credit cards
AmEx, Delta, Mastercard, Switch, Visa
Set-price lunch
£12.50

Set price dinner
£8 & £20-30
Nearest tube
stations
Holborn, Tottenham
Court Road
Map 4

containing the adjectives chargrilled, seared, blackened, wokked, minced and shredded indicates a predilection to detonate flavours in every dish, as chef Sally James gives a contemporary British spin to Mediterranean classics, juxtaposing intense components with panache. Although certain elements tend to be recycled in different dishes (roasted peppers or parsley pesto guested severally in one lunch), necessitating forensic planning of the meal, this is the kind of cuisine heureuse about which Roger Vergé waxes lyrical: a light-hearted, natural, healthy way of cooking. The smiling enthusiasm of the staff makes this one of those 'neighbourhood' restaurants that you serendipitously discover in the heart of town and keep to yourself. A wine list of byzantine complexity and great quirkiness – the first items you encounter are an Amarone and a Brunello – is studded with little gems. Fine bottles are given a small, straight mark-up, and the chatty notes ask you to recommend your own suggestions for regions that you would like to see better represented.

Open
Every day
Hours
Mon-Sat 12.00-
11.45pm, Sun
11.30am-11.15pm
Credit cards
AmEx, Mastercard,
Visa, Switch, Delta
Service charge
10%
Set-price lunch
£8
Nearest tube
station
Leicester Square
Maps 4 & 5

China City £20

White Bear Yard, 25a Lisle Street WC2 (734 3388)

+ *laid-back, unfrenetic atmosphere*
- *the composition of set-price meals*

The attractive three-storey building, set back behind a courtyard in Chinatown, has enough space to offer karaoke rooms without letting the dismal sound of merrymakers impersonating Buddy Holly impinge on the keen diners in the ground-floor brasserie, who prefer to hum dim-sum. The dim-sum menu – served before 5pm – has some relatively unusual specials in addition to the standard run of dumplings; the regular menu – served all day – is a comprehensive Cantonese list of over 150 items. Look to the hot-pot section, eel dishes, braised-duck dishes, yee-mian noodle assemblies, barbecues and beancurd for interest, and to the set-price deals for banality. Staff are unusually obliging. The Cantonese food may not be the very best in the area, but China City is one of the most pleasant places to eat.

Open
Every day
Hours
7.00-10.30pm
Credit cards
AmEx, Mastercard,
Visa, Switch, Delta
Service charge
12.5% optional

Chinon £40

23 Richmond Way W14 (602 4082)

+ *original cooking*
- *slightly lugubrious welcome*

Chef Jonathan Hayes, who was a musician before he turned to cooking, sings his own tune in this Shepherd's Bush restaurant. His delight in wrapping parcels and turning out dariole moulds is a feature of many of the assemblies, but flavours and effects emerge intact and vibrant: when the music stops you are left with a jewel of a dish. One of the healthiest and most delectable first courses in London is a salad of leaves and vegetables with hazelnut-oil dressing, in which well-matched leaves, herbs and sprouted pulses are surrounded by individual, dressed root vegetables – it is exactly the sort of trouble you want a restaurant kitchen to go to. Co-owner Barbara Deane's loopy writing and equally loopy spelling (pot of shellfish mannier; a fellute of vegetables) suggests dishes such as tempura of fresh prawns with curry oil; roast stuffed squid with tagatelli (sic); raviolli (sic) of sea scallops with ginger cream; roast boneless quial (sic) with black pudding; fillet of beef with wild mushrooms; and a trio of chocolate desserts (wonderful). The choice of music and art, and the levels of light, colour and noise are all very well-judged. Chinon is a favourite of those in the know.

The Chiswick £24

131 Chiswick High Road W4 (0181-994 6887)

+ *all-round value for money, including £8.50 early-evening menu*
- *lilac-blue walls*

Adam and Kate Robinson's The Brackenbury (q.v.) has spawned many imitators: some good, some bad. The Chiswick, turned out from the original mould so to speak, is a paragon of that type of modern British restaurant. It has struck a popular chord with the local community. Ian Bates, who did a stint at Bibendum (q.v.), improvises deceptively uncomplicated dishes around the primary ingredients of the week. Skate, pan-fried with lentils, fennel and salsa verde on Monday may appear on Friday in salad form accompanied by rocket and cucumber sauce. A lamb salad with summer vegetables and aïoli becomes rump of lamb, haricot beans and rosemary. Crab, squid, chicken, asparagus and cod likewise migrate inventively, in permutations of salads, risottos and tarts. Bates seems to have learned from his mentor Simon Hopkinson the importance of intensifying the impact of ingredients, rather than embroidering casual assemblies.

CLIVE GREENHALGH'S MODEL wine list deserves applause for compressing as much variety and quality as possible into its 40 or so bins, as well as for the enticingly low mark-ups. Intelligent and stimulating, it shows the value of a good wine buyer. Surprises abound: those of a singular disposition will wish to assay the Floc de Gascogne, Armagnac's answer to Pineau de Charentes.

Open
Lunch Mon-Fri & Sun, dinner Mon-Sat
Hours
12.30-2.45pm, 7.00-11.30pm
Credit cards
AmEx, Mastercard, Visa, Switch, Delta
Set-price lunch
£9.50
Set-price dinner
£9.50 (early evening)
Nearest tube station
Turnham Green

Christopher's American Grill £36

Open
Lunch every day
dinner Mon-Sat
Hours
12.00-3.00pm
(Sat-Sun 12.00-
4.00pm), 6.00-
11.30pm
Credit cards
AmEx, Mastercard,
Visa, Switch,
Delta, Diner's
Service charge
12.5%
Set-price dinner
Pre- & post-
theatre £15
**Nearest tube
stations**
Waterloo, Charing
Cross, Covent
Garden
Map 4

18 Wellington Street WC2 (240 4222)

+ *opera winding up the stone staircase*
- *too many un-American activities in the kitchen*

Those who lament the cost of dinner at this Covent Garden restaurant can take refuge in the pre-and post-theatre menu at £15 for three courses which features as one of the main courses what might be considered Christopher's raison d'être, steak (10oz) served with fried or new potatoes and French beans. But bear in mind the pompous note which states that the restaurant regrets that 'we are not responsible for steaks ordered medium, well-done or over'. On the main list the left-hand page encapsulates the inspiration – Christopher Gilmour's conversion at Palm Steak House in Chicago – for the venture, and it is to my mind the page on which to concentrate. Maryland crab cake with red pepper mayo; sweetcorn and crab chowder; fried oysters with olive oil mash; Maine lobster; blackened rib-eye steak; baked New York cheesecake; these are the dishes that fill gaps including the one in the market for adult all-American food. Offering warm tomato and parmesan galette with black olives and crisp basil and magret of duck with carpaccio of pineapple and green peppercorn sauce serves only to demonstrate a lack of conviction. There is a lively bar scene on the ground floor, an area which fills with families for the reasonably priced weekend brunch.

Christoph's   £32

Open
Mon-Sat
Hours
12.30-2.30pm,
7.30-11.00pm
Credit cards
AmEx, Mastercard,
Visa, Switch,
Delta, Diner's
Set-price lunch
£12.50 & £14.50
**Nearest tube
station**
South Kensington
Map 2

7 Park Walk SW10 (349 8866)

+ *the charcuterie plate*
- *drab interior*

This restaurant, which opened in the early summer of 1996 daringly near the much-revered Aubergine (q.v.), is owned by manager Christopher Brooke (a veteran of Foxtrot Oscar) and self-taught chef Graham Garrett. It is a medium sort of restaurant – medium ambition, medium price, medium formality – an observation that is not meant as a criticism. It is an ideal venue for the South Kensington/Fulham set, who like to conduct their dinner parties in public. Not everything on Garrett's menu is good, but, when it is good, it is very good. In this category belongs the first course of hot-smoked mackerel, sweet mustard, pickled onion, French beans, toasted almonds and cucumber. The fish, prepared in-house, is delicious and the whole a thoughtful, well-balanced yet diverting assembly. Garrett's enthusiasm for making his own pickles and chutneys is also evident in 'The Charcuterie Plate', a mid-course of terrines, rillettes, duck-liver pâté and other cooked meats attended by several sharp-sweet condiments. Little jokes like miniature fish and chips served on a pea purée as a first course can fall flat if the chips are limp, as they were on one occasion. Main courses take no great risks – one summer menu listed as starting points fishcakes, salmon, lamb, veal cutlet, fish stew, smoked duck breast plus a vegetarian option of celeriac and potato lasagne – but dishes like the roast rump of lamb with tomato and shallot tarte Tatin and rosemary pesto, and details like the exquisite marjoram noodles with the chargrilled veal, can be remarkably fine. British cheeses are bought from Neal's Yard Dairy. The choice of mainly fruity desserts is typified by mango and almond cream tart; nougat glacé with strawberry coulis; and peach and mascarpone cheesecake. The eponymous owner works the rooms with charm.

Chutney Mary   £30

535 King's Road SW10 (351 3113)

+ *the effort made to obtain fresh spices and authentic*
  ingredients
- *not getting a table in the conservatory*

The food festivals researched and organized by co-owner Namita Panjabi (look out for the Parsee festival) reveal the serious gastronomic intent behind what, in terms of decor and presentation of the menu, might strike some as a somewhat themed restaurant. In fact, the chefs brought directly from India are capable of some of the most impressive, authentic regional Indian cooking in town. Anglo-Indian dishes and recipes that evolved in the Christian communities of India also feature. Favourite assemblies are calamari chilli fry; moong bhel salad; Goan green chicken curry; Hyderabadi white chicken curry; Punjabi lamb with spinach; and Anglo-Indian 'Country Captain'. Crisply fried okra or cashews in Keralan spices makes a terrific side dish. The arrival of Eddie Khoo as manager has galvanized service, and his advice on wines – his special subject – is well worth taking.

Open
Every day
Hours
12.30-2.30pm, 7.00-11.30pm (Sun 12.30-3.00pm, 7.00-10.30pm)
Credit cards
AmEx, Mastercard, Visa, Switch, Diner's
Cover charge
£1.50 per person
Set-price lunch
£10
Nearest tube station
Fulham Broadway
Map 2

Chutneys £16

Open
Every day
Hours
12.00-2.30pm,
6.00-11.30pm
(Sun 12.00-
10.30pm)
Credit cards
Mastercard, Visa
Service charge
10%
Set-price lunch
£4.95
Set-price dinner
£6.95
Nearest tube
stations
Euston,
Euston Square,
Warren Street
Map 3

124 Drummond Street NW1 (388 0604)

+ *the Santa Fe colour scheme*
− *waiters indifferent to your needs*

The all-you-can-eat-for-£4.95 (the price has risen by £1 since last year) lunchtime buffet is popular with those seeking a cheap fill, but an evening meal à la carte reveals more alluringly the intricacy and beguiling differentiation of Indian vegetarian food. Bombay Chowpatty Beach snacks and Gujerati thalis — specialities of north-west India — and vegetable curries provide the basis for the composition of a meal. Don't miss out on special pooris (hollow wholewheat crisp spheres filled with potatoes and sev, flavoured with yoghurt, chutneys and spices); dhosa (dramatic pancakes made from fermented batters); idli (steamed rice cakes with a savoury sauce); and the smoky tarka dhal. Surroundings are surprisingly groovy. With absolutely no appeal to logic, organic wines are offered as being 'suitable for vegetarians and vegans'.

Cibo £30

Open
Lunch Sun-Fri,
dinner Mon-Sat
Hours
12.00-2.30pm
7.00-11.00pm
Credit cards
AmEx, Mastercard,
Visa, Switch,
Delta, Diner's, JCB
Set-price lunch
£12.50, £17.95
Set-price dinner
£14.95
Nearest tube
station
Olympia
Map 1

3 Russell Gardens W14 (371 6271)

+ *the two-course, set-price lunch for £12.50*
− *breadcrumbs on scallops are like sand in shellfish*

Strong-coloured, oversized pottery plates on which the food is served emphasize the Mediterranean paintbox of flavours in Cibo's Italian food, which in turn emphasizes seafood. A meal starts with unbidden crostini: slender stalks of asparagus bedded down on country bread with skeins of melted cheese is one example. Vegetables appeal in the first course, including the eat-me edibility of whole baby artichokes or the brain-shaped wrinkles of broad beans served with melted goat's cheese and toasted bread. Filled pastas are interesting: namely, ravioli of duck in a mushroom sauce, and agnolotti with leeks and ricotta in a walnut sauce. Lobster with spaghetti in a lobster sauce, and baked whole sea bass with herbs, are two piscine stars of the main course. Petits fours, including pastry puffs hiding a custardy cream, bring what should be a languorous meal in the slightly decadent surroundings to an end. Interesting Italian wines appear on the list.

Claridge's – The Causerie £40

Brook Street W1 (629 8860)

+ *Miss Scarlet dining with Colonel Mustard*
- *the cost of more than one drink*

Here is a period piece. The curious pricing policy of the cost of the first drink including the self-service buffet dates from the last war, when it was introduced to get around the price limit imposed on meals. Having chosen to eat in this small, genteel, drawing-room-like dining-room, sitting side by side on a diminutive sofa, opt for the buffet (or smorgasbord, as it is called). There are excellent fish and seafood dishes: smoked eel with warm scrambled eggs; a selection of marinated herrings; a gratin of lobster with dill mustard; and buckwheat blinis to accompany lumpfish roe and smoked fish. The impeccably well-behaved staff never bat an eyelid however many times you circle the display. At the time of going to press, there are good reports of the food in the main restaurant. Executive chef John King has been joined by Adam Newell, who made something of a name for himself at The Heights restaurant of St George's Hotel. However, prices remain stratospheric.

THOSE WHO ARE fascinated by these things will be interested to hear that there is a new candidate for the annual Cloudy Bay Sauvignon rip-off – £42 – eclipsing all previous known records. Otherwise this is the usual depressing digest of untouchables: a lot of negociant Burgundy, a few mediocre Italians and heaps of commercial dross.

Open
Mon-Fri
Hours
12.00-3.00pm,
5.30-11.00pm
Credit cards
AmEx, Mastercard,
Switch, Visa,
Delta, Diner's
Nearest tube
Bond Street
Map 3

Clarke's £45

124 Kensington Church Street W8 (221 9225)

+ *the deliciousness is in the details; the wine list*
- *no-choice dinner menus*

No choice at dinner is in many ways blissfully restful, but it narrows the gap between dinner-party and restaurant eating rather too dramatically. Thou need not covet thy neighbour's oxtail nor his asparagus – you shall have it too. Of course, everyone eating the same things is helpful when it comes to selecting wines – an important element in this meticulously well-run restaurant. Of the various attempts to bring Californian cooking to London, Sally Clarke's has been the most successful. She and Alice Waters of Chez Panisse are, as it were, coming from the same place. In order to please all of the people all of the time, dishes play safe with their essential identity, but

Open
Mon-Fri
Hours
12.30-2.00pm,
7.00-10.00pm
Credit cards
AmEx, Mastercard,
Visa, Switch
Nearest tube station
Notting Hill Gate
Map 6

impress with the precision in preparation and with the liveliness and appropriateness of herbs, oils, juices, leaves, berries, vegetables, breads, and biscuits. Delectable desserts are the reward Auntie Sally delivers to those who eat up nicely. The ground floor is the more attractive space, but in the basement you can watch the chefs at work.

SUPER CALIFORNIANS ON the list – expedite all your dosh please! A trio of white Rhône rangers, Chalone's Pinot Blanc (it's Pinot Blanc, Jim, but not as we know it) and humdinger Chardonnays from Au Bon Climat, Morgan and Acacia are complemented across the grape divide by Bonny Doon madness with southern French varieties and topnotch Pinot Noir and Cabernet Sauvignon. Add to the blend some Ostertags from Alsace, Yves Cuilleron's Condrieu from the Rhône (as raved about by Andrew Jefford), an ace crop of burgundies and some Italian fashion models (Antinori's Ornellaia at £35). There is a superb selection of eaux de vie from the ubiquitous Bonny Doon, apple brandy from Clear Creek in Oregon, cognacs, grappas and a weird sherry-style Tokaji, dry Szamorodni that is supposedly best 'enjoyed' with soup.

Coast £40

26b Albemarle Street W1 (495 5999)

+ *the charm of owner Oliver Peyton*
- *memories of the Volvo garage it once was linger on*

Chef Stephen Terry has shoplifted ingredients and concepts from his international travels, and the result is a complicated menu that ranges from poetically inspired dishes to downright clangers. The former includes pan-fried calf's liver with creamed polenta, dolcelatte and pancetta; the latter a disastrous salad of lobster with Chinese radish and a sweet-and-sour sauce. Terry's innate talent – honed for some time in the employ of Marco Pierre White – is in evidence when he cooks with European ingredients; it is when he ventures East that he seems to run into trouble. Sunday brunch is a menu at ease with itself. While the plates are busy, the room is as spare as a works canteen, and bad lighting seems somehow to exacerbate the problem of hearing (the fashionable Coast, it has to be said, is usually packed out). Staff, especially at reception, can be rather off-hand.

A SHORTER VERSION of the successful list at Atlantic (q.v.), a coast-to-coast trawl of the trendiest wine fashions fingering the Rhône is the best place to relish a medley of taste sensations. Elsewhere there is everything you would hope to find in the modern repertoire. You can afford to splash out on the Roederer Cristal

Open
Every day
Hours
12.00-3.00pm,
6.00-12.00pm
(Sun 12.00-
4.00pm, 6.00-
11.00pm)
Credit cards
AmEx, Mastercard,
Visa, Switch, Delta
Service charge
12.5% (6 or more)
**Nearest tube
station**
Green Park
Map 3

here, buying two bottles for every one you can't afford at Le Gavroche (q.v.). Offering 10 wines by the glass seems to obviate the need to stock half-bottles. If you've won the Lottery, or are simply feeling nostalgic, there is a bottle of La Tâche 1942 (£295). Worth a punt for history's sake?

The Collection £35

Open
Mon-Sat
Hours
Ground floor
12.00-11.30pm;
mezzanine level
12.00-3.00pm,
7.00-11.30pm
Credit cards
AmEx, Mastercard,
Diner's, Visa,
Switch
Service charge
Ground floor
12.5%, mezzanine
level 15%
**Nearest tube
station**
South Kensington
Map 2

264 Brompton Road SW3 (225 1212)

+ *decorative clientele; food to do more than toy with*
- *a receptionist who studies bookings as if trying to decode Linear B*

Many restaurateurs have yearned for the hangar-like space in Brompton Cross that once housed the Katherine Hamnett collection; Mogens Tholstrup, the owner of Daphne's (q.v.), located a bread-roll's throw away, got it. Mogens (pronounced Moans) made some statement to the effect that The Collection was designed to be Daphne's for the masses. What has in fact transpired is that masses of the same sort of expensively dressed and/or well-preserved customers are happy to trip down the illuminated, glazed catwalk that appropriately forms part of the discreetly signed entrance. The stark ground floor is a long bar area with tables (unbookable), where light dishes are served. Here, savoury items − such as chicken and ginger won tons with soy; guacamole, houmus and tzatziki with pitta; and bruschetta with aubergine, tomato and basil − are all priced at £5.50. Sweet dishes − such as pear tarte Tatin with cinnamon ice cream, and chocolate pot with almonds − are £3.50. On the mezzanine level there is a more elaborate menu in the same style, as if − in fashion terms − a Yoji Yamamoto top were combined with a Jean-Paul Gaultier skirt. Chris Benians, head chef of Daphne's, devised the menu, and it is executed with impressive confidence where orientally inspired dishes are concerned. The size 8 part of the clientele appreciates the vivid salads of seared beef with shiitake musrooms; of crab with sprouted seeds and the very latest leaves; and of chilli-spiked squid with lime and basil. Main courses are more substantial, and include griddled calf's liver with broad beans, chorizo, tomato and sage; marinated duck and crispy noodles with plum sauce; and breast of chicken with tabbouleh and slow-roasted vegetables. I dare say that the dismal cry of 'I think I'll just have two starters' often rings out. Cooking standards overall are quite high (if one was to be cynical, probably higher than they need be), and Mogens, despite his playboy appearance, is actually a very conscientious restaurateur. The wine list is divided by style.

The descriptions of the whites could almost be a picture of a typical Collection couple dining: lighter, elegant, more aromatic (her); and richer, fuller, heavier (him).

The Connaught Restaurant & Grill Room £60

Carlos Place W1 (499 7070)

+ *the centre holds*
- *expectations, inflamed by the prices, may not always be met*

Open
Every day
Hours
12.30-2.30pm
(grill room closed
Sat lunch), 6.30-
10.30pm
Credit cards
AmEx, Mastercard,
Visa, Diner's
Service charge
15%
Set-price lunch
£25, £30, £35
Set-price dinner
£55
**Nearest tube
stations**
Green Park,
Bond Street
Map 3

Anxious to stress that there is only one kitchen, under the supervision of one chef (Michel Bourdin), The Connaught seems to be saying that it is not like other hotels. It is not. It preserves — although not in aspic — the grandeur of Edwardian dining, offering a long menu subdivided by nine headings, on which French and English language and dishes sit side by side in a perfect entente cordiale. There are, in addition, regular luncheon options such as Irish stew or oxtail. Bold type signifies specialities of the moment, which might be salade caprice 'Connaught' au choix (années folles, Aphrodite ou aux crustaces); homard d'Écosse grillé 'My Way'; bécasse rôtie vrai jus; mixed grill; sherry trifle 'Wally Ladd'; and champignons sur 'toast'. It is an approach all but abandoned elsewhere, and to enjoy it you must be ready to abandon yourself to what it costs. Impeccable, courteous service adds another 15%. The choice between the Restaurant and Grill Room is between institution and intimacy.

La Copita £15

63 Askew Road W12 (0181-743 1289)

+ *Balearic ice creams*
- *the sense of an unfulfilled life that all tapas induce*

Open
Lunch Wed-Fri,
dinner Mon-Sat
Hours
12.30-1.45pm,
6.00pm-12.00am
Credit cards
AmEx, Mastercard,
Visa, Switch, Delta
**Set-price lunch
& dinner**
Tapas £7.90
**Nearest tube
station**
Goldhawk Road,
Shepherd's Bush
Map 1

Mike and Rosa Paine have kept this amiable Shepherd's Bush tapas bar going for a reassuring amount of time: it is not — like so many of those little snacks that are still traduced all over town — a flash in the pan. The longer lists on the menu are for seafood and vegetarian tapas. Hake, prawns, mussels and squid are cooked together into a delicate soup. Fresh sardines are fried and served with endive, a popular ingredient that pops up repeatedly: as part of the ensalada de chef and the warm smoked chorizo salad, next to the fried manchego cheese served with quince paste, under the warm parsnip and carrot salad with mustard seed dressing, and alongside roasted vegetables served with a gazpacho coulis. Each day there are different specials. All tapas are priced at under £3, and there is a set-price deal of £7.90 for bread, tapenade, aïoli and olives or garlic bread plus a choice of any three tapas.

Cork & Bottle Wine Bar   £19

44–6 Cranbourn Street WC2 (734 7807)

+ *you are bound to learn something about wine*
- *anecdotal tasting notes reach their anecdotage by page 13*

Open
Every day
Hours
11.00am-11.30pm
Credit cards
AmEx, Mastercard,
Visa, Diner's
**Nearest tube
station**
Leicester Square
Map 5

Difficult as it is to imagine quality existing among the wall-to-wall fast-food emporia of Leicester Square, a trip down the stairs of the Cork & Bottle Wine Bar produces a rare gem and a welcome refuge from the ripe perfumes of the street above. The bar fills up rapidly, however, so grabbing a table is paramount. Food divides into hot dishes of the day (for example, open toasted baguettes filled with steak, mustard and herbes de Provence; or warm salads with grilled sausages or giant Mediterranean prawns); a fish of the day (such as pan-fried monkfish with pineapple salsa and stir-fried vegetables); and a dish of the day (perhaps braised lamb shanks with a zinfandel sauce). The buffet supplies shellfish, pâtés, salads and terrines. The house speciality, a raised ham-and-cheese pie, harks back to the period when characters from Dickens novels in taverns despatched huge pasties at a glance and sighed 'that was wery mellering to the organ'.

ON THE WINE side, Don Hewitson writes the sort of chatty tasting notes that brook no argument. His list is more of a short tome (not surprising, as he has written several books on wine), beginning with seasonal recommendations and enthusiastically promoting bargains culled from around the world. Good producers in France include Willm from Alsace, and François Pacquet's Gamay glut of Cru Beaujolais. It is, however, the New World wines of Australia, California and New Zealand that dominate, from the commercial styles of Mondavi's Woodbridge, Wolf Blass and Montana to a host of smaller boutique wineries. By purchasing direct, particularly from France, Hewitson is able to offer fine wines at remarkably low prices. Château Talbot 1988 is a mere £29.50; the fabulous Lynch-Bages from the same vintage £95 a magnum. Buying champagne should put you in a bubbly mood: Perrier Jouët 'Belle Époque' is £37.50 cheaper here than at Quaglino's (q.v.).

Open
Dinner Mon–Sat,
lunch Sun
Hours
7.00–11.30pm, Sun
12.30–4.00pm
Credit cards
Mastercard, Visa,
Switch, Delta,
Diner's
Service charge
12.5%
**Nearest tube
stations**
Westbourne Park,
Notting Hill Gate
Map 6

The Cow Dining Room £26

89 Westbourne Park Road W2 (221 0021)

+ *charming dining-room*
− *Notting Hillbillies at the next table*

After going dark for a while, the dining-room above Tom Conran's pub The Cow was opened at end of August 1996 by Francesca Melman, who has worked at The River Cafe (q.v.) and at Alastair Little Lancaster Road (q.v.). She has inherited a small but perfectly formed restaurant. Well-designed (as you might expect), laid-back, almost countrified, it is, I would imagine, a budding chef's dream. And apparently the kitchen upstairs is equipped to a very high standard. Melman has introduced a daily-changing menu, served in the evenings only from Monday to Saturday and at lunchtime on Sunday. Basing this evaluation on one meal – there was only time before press date for one meal – the list is Italian-ish. In the first course there was ribollita (twice-cooked Tuscan bean soup); verdura mista with bruschetta; and baked goat's cheese with tapenade toasts; but also Caesar salad and a (light and delectable) onion and Parmesan tart. In the main course, skate wing came poached in minestrone; lemon and fennel flavoured a risotto; and rib-eye steak was served with couscous salad. Some fried aubergines served with monkfish had, like pieces of sponge, absorbed far too much fat. Lamb's sweetbreads with pancetta, thyme and cream were fine. That best of all ice creams, caramel, came with a friable, sand-coloured biscuit. The wine list suits the set-up well. Service is friendly and caring. A nice re-invented addition to the area.

Open
Every day
Hours
Mon–Sat 10.00am–
11.30pm, Sun
10.00am–10.00pm
Credit cards
AmEx, Mastercard,
Visa, Switch, Delta
Service charge
10%
**Nearest tube
station**
South Kensington
Map 2

The Crescent £18

99 Fulham Road SW3 (225 2244)

+ *Good-quality wine glasses in which to appreciate good-quality
wine; excellent coffee*
− *eating in the basement at lunchtime; no air-conditioning*

Affording the opportunity for some serious wine therapy, this bar-cum-brasserie also serves an extensive range of snacks from open sandwiches and burgers to spring rolls and chargrilled Mediterranean veg. Most dishes come liberally salsa-ed and turfed with mixed leaves, where a lighter hand with fresh herbs is called for: in one meal tiger prawns were buried in a jungle of coriander, and crabcakes were all but killed by dill.

THE CROWNING GLORY is Matthew Jukes's studiously compiled wine list of 150 bins, with accompanying user-friendly tasting notes. What you would munch to soak up a bottle of Echezeaux '86 from Romanée Conti for £115 is open to debate: how about ordering a BLT with your DRC? Elsewhere Jukes has his finger firmly on the pulse of wine fashion, and to that end has located some terrific gear from Languedoc and the Rhône. The wines of Domaine Gauby, Domaine de l'Hortus and a Collioure from Château de Jau offer subtle shades of spicy flavour lurking behind their surface robustness. It is quite possible to witness serried ranks of confirmed cappuccino drinkers happily ignoring the treasurable bottles under their noses, but then the concept of The Crescent is to be all things to all people. In the evening the downstairs comes into play, and there is more committed noshing and sloshing.

The Criterion – Marco Pierre White £35

224 Piccadilly W1 (930 0488)

+ *shimmering neo-Byzantine interior*
- *pressure to eat up and go; finding a cab late at night*

This extraordinary site resembling a Byzantine station concourse, originally opened in the 1870s and bought by Forte plc in 1949, has seen some odd incumbents. It seems meet and right that the glittering talent of Marco Pierre White should be the one to restore gastronomic glory; in visual terms he has been helped by David Collins, who has added seraglio lighting and exotic paintings. Here is found White's diffusion line of cooking, executed by former Canteen chefs Tim Payne and Peter Reffell, and some dishes will be familiar to those who have followed White's career. Fortunately for his customers, he only knows one way of doing things: uncompromisingly. The menu offers not the grills and salads and exotica of the modern brasserie, but meticulously made dishes such as beignets of oysters with celeriac remoulade; smoked salmon soup with fromage blanc; Savoy cabbage ancienne; saffron risotto; smoked haddock with poached egg and beurre blanc; pot-roast pork with spices and ginger; and soufflé of blackberries. Pressure for tables means that all is not always perfect: complaints are made about service and about time limits being imposed for dining. Lunch is more relaxed – and significantly cheaper.

Open
Lunch every day, dinner Mon-Sat
Hours
12.00-2.30pm (Sun 4.00pm), 6.00pm-12.00am
Credit cards
AmEx, Mastercard, Visa, Switch, Diner's
Service charge
12.5%
Set-price lunch
£14 & £17.95
Nearest tube station
Piccadilly Circus
Map 3

Cucina £25

Open
Lunch every day,
dinner Mon-Sat
Hours
12.00-2.30pm
(Sun 3.00pm),
7.00pm-10.30pm
(Fri-Sat 11.00pm)
Credit cards
AmEx, Mastercard,
Visa, Switch, Delta
Set-price lunch
£10 & £14.95
**Nearest railway
station**
Hampstead Heath
Map 1

45a South End Road NW3 (435 7814)

+ *heaven-sent in Hampstead*
- *estate-agent frontage*

Cucina continues to be the good deed (*pace* ZenW3) in the naughty world of Hampstead restaurants. The trio who own it also being chefs and manager is a sound basis for continuity of standards. The cooking style is Cal-Ital: expect items such as chargrilled spiced squid with chilli dressing, wilted bok choy and mizuna; baked ricotta and nutmeg terrine with butternut squash, pinenuts and frisée; roast cod with a lime and tortilla crust and gazpacho sauce; corn-fed chicken breast with pecorino mash, black pudding and truffle jus; and balsamic baked figs with lemon, poppy-seed shortbread and mascarpone. Most of the time the ideas come off well – sometimes brilliantly well – but there can be the odd dud, often in the dessert course. An absence of natural light in the main dining-room is countered by tormented modern design.

Daphne's £40

Open
Every day
Hours
Mon-Sat 12.00-
3.00pm, 7.00-
11.30pm
Sun 12.00-4.00pm,
7.00-10.30pm
Credit cards
AmEx, Mastercard,
Visa, Switch, Delta,
Diner's
Service charge
15%
**Nearest tube
station**
South Kensington
Map 2

112 Draycott Avenue SW3 (589 4257)

+ *the back room on a sunny day with the roof open*
- *the waiters' command of English – or anything else*

There was a suspicion that by opening The Collection (q.v.) nearby, owner Mogens Tholstrup would be taking the gloss out of Daphne's, and this was compounded by the departure of manager, Annie Foster Firth. As it turns out, however, there seem to be enough Chanel suits to go around. Chef Chris Benians, who took over from Eddie Baines (now at Randall & Aubin [q.v.]), has found his feet: the risottos are glorious, the grills done to perfection and the salads – particularly chargrilled chicken with red pesto, and Caesar – are notable. Crisp zucchini fritters should be a side order to everything. But there is no getting away from the fact that, if you are a celebrity, you will have an easier ride in getting a table – and a table that you want.

De Cecco £25

189 New King's Road SW6 (736 1145)

+ *good for fish, or, more accurately, for fish eaters*
- *the '70s-style decor*

W hat will the great Wozza Thompson do with this lively outpost of the Chelsea trattoria — one that has its fish sent up from a South Coast boat it part-owns, and has a core clientele nervous about the new proprietor's intentions? Very little, is the official reply, for Wozza's latest wheeze seems to be buying solvent businesses and leaving them be (c.f., The Lexington, q.v.). He could do something here to improve the pasta sauces and the pastry-making, and meat eaters might like an alternative to petto di pollo this and scaloppine that, but the simple and fairly priced antipasti and fish list should be left to continue. Ditto the lovely old plates, medium-priced wines and friendly staff.

Open
Mon-Sat
Hours
12.30-3.00pm,
7.00-11.00pm
Credit cards
AmEx, Mastercard,
Visa, Switch,
Delta, Diner's
**Nearest tube
station**
Parsons Green
Map 1

Del Buongustaio £30

283 Putney Bridge Road SW15 (0181 780 9361)

+ *Italian/Australian ownership reflected in the wine list*
- *often too crowded for comfort*

F resh ideas combine with seasonality to produce monthly-changing menus plus a daily-changing reasonably priced lunch deal (£9.50 for two courses). This is not Italian cooking which skates across the familiar and fashionable, but the result of knowledgeably researched combinations and processes. Baked goat with prosciutto, roasted vegetables, rosemary and marjoram; salad of warm guinea fowl dressed with fennel seeds, radicchio, chicory and peppers; torta of ricotta, oyster and porcini mushrooms with a truffle cream sauce; ribbon pasta with rabbit, olives and mushrooms may be a bit too close to nature, red in tooth and claw, for some of the Putney punters but there are lighter lines such as fresh figs with prosciutto and a gorgonzola dressing. It is a more interesting Italian menu than most and ends on a indulgent note with desserts such as home-made amaretto ice cream with amaretti biscuits and tiramisù with a jug of hot chocolate sauce on the side.

ITALY, OR ENOTRIA, the land of vines meets a brand of boisterous strines. in the one corner you have Banfi's Brunello di Montalcino, a deep crimson red with ground-coffee aromas and a sharp twist of bitter cherry on the palate; in the other, the muscular vanillin softness of Wolf Blass — a total contrast of

Open
Lunch Mon-Fri &
Sun, dinner every
day (not open Sat
& Sun lunch
June-September)
Hours
12.00-3.00pm,
6.30-11.30pm
Credit cards
AmEx, Mastercard,
Visa
Set-price lunch
£9.50, £22.50
**Nearest tube/
railway station**
Putney Bridge/
Putney
Map1

styles and wine-making techniques. It is a pity that the categorization of the list along intuitive and emotional lines has been dispensed with in favour of a more conventional regional approach, and that there also seems to have been a greater commercial imperative in the wine-buying.

Dell'Ugo £26

Open
Mon-Sat
Hours
12.00–3.00pm,
5.30pm– midnight
Credit cards
AmEx, Mastercard,
Visa, Switch,
Delta, Diner's
Set price lunch
£5 (cafe only)
**Nearest tube
station**
Tottenham Court
Road
Map 5

56 Frith Street W1 (734 8300)

+ *lunch for a fiver*
− *zygosis of ingredients becomes psychosis*

A mis-match of mish-mashery: Antony Worral Thompson's menus in this three-tiered restaurant/bistro/bar are a disunited nations of influences. While one applauds the diversity of combinations and cooking styles, it seems that the kitchen can scarcely cope with the logistics of delivering so many meals, the dell boys being compelled to shovel food indiscriminately on to plates that often arrive lukewarm at the table. The menu has its phantasmagoric moments, as if several recipes had been accidentally centrifuged into each other. Complaints about service have been legion, and the air of a run-down operation is further accentuated by cigarette butts on the stairs, rubbish spilling out of bags on Frith Street (which should be renamed Filth Street), and for being the shoe-in candidate for the grottiest loos in London. The captain needs to return to the flagship.

Detroit ⭐new £27

Open
Dinner Mon-Sat
Hours
5.00pm–12.00am
Credit cards
AmEx, Mastercard,
Visa, Switch,
Delta, Diner's
Cover charge
Optional £1 per
person for bread
and olives
**Nearest tube
station**
Covent Garden
Map 5

35 Earlham Street WC2 (240 2662)

+ *cocktails, cocktails and more cocktails from your smooth-talking bar steward*
− *uninspiring wine list*

T he previous restaurant in this basement location, Jones (q.v.), evidently had difficulty in keeping up with its boisterous neighbour Belgo Centraal and, despite good reviews, closed. In its place sprang up Detroit, which has preserved the labyrinthine layout of grottoes and passages carved from prehistoric rock. The primary feature may be the bar — managed by Dick Bradsell, self-styled bartender-guru — but the food is no mere fashion accessory. With the name of the joint being Detroit you would be forgiven for imagining that you would be eating burgers fried in engine oil to the sound of Tamla Motown; instead the cooking is Mediterranean Rim. One summery menu featured chilled gazpacho with soured cream; crispy red snapper with a celery and mango salsa; marinated, chargrilled leg of lamb with a rosemary jus; and – defiantly – steamed mussels with cream, wine and garlic for those who prefer to mull over their moules. Desserts are perfunctory, but you can have a chocolate martini (vodka, cacao and menthe, in case your mind was boggling) if your tooth is in a saccharine mood.

The Dorchester Bar £35

The Dorchester Hotel, Park Lane W1 (629 8888)

+ *the mirrored ceiling; jazz in the evenings*
- *high wine prices*

The bar of this gilded hotel is a world of its own. The mirrored ceiling, Delft tiles, mustard-leather bucket chairs and what looks like Liberace's piano create the sort of look that seems accidentally accrued. Rather surprisingly, an interesting northern Italian menu is offered, featuring excellent pasta dishes. A range of Italian wines by the glass are well-chosen, but a few glasses can lead to a big bill. The bar is host to some interesting food promotions from luxurious hotels abroad. I sometimes come here in order to feel like a tourist in my own city.

Open
Mon–Sat
Hours
11.00–2.30pm,
7.00–11.00pm
Credit cards
AmEx, Mastercard,
Visa, Switch,
Delta, Diner's
**Nearest tube
stations**
Marble Arch,
Hyde Park Corner
Map 3

The Dorchester Grill £45

(Address as above)

+ *Spanish baronial decor*
- *you can't take the hotel out of the chef*

What culinary experimentation there is here takes place on the daily menus, but the heart of the restaurant is in the classics: smoked salmon; steak and kidney pie; roast Aylesbury duck; braised oxtail; and roasts from the stately galleons that are the Grill Room's silver trolleys. The dessert vehicle carries trifle, deep fruit pies and sticky pear pudding, but peppered peaches can be flamed at the table. The Grill is gratifyingly traditional, not ossified, thanks in part to cheerful, unpompous, enthusiastic waiters.

THERE IS A dreadful commercial cynicism about this list. Hence your mark-up on vintage claret is identical to house wines, which exacerbates differentials in the medium and upper price brackets. No Pauillac is to be found under £50, therefore, while £78 only buys you a Château La Lagune (which produced a distinctly average wine in 1979). Jean Durup's Chablis (£31) may be drunk for a tenner less at Quaglino's (q.v.). Under £20, you do

Open
Mon–Sun
Hours
Mon–Sat
11.00am–11.30pm,
Sun 12.00–
10.30pm
Credit Cards
AmEx, Mastercard,
Diner's, Visa,
Switch, Delta
**Nearest tube
stations**
Marble Arch,
Hyde Park Corner
Map 3

have the dubious choice of drinking a non-vintage Chinese wine, Great Wall, a Rosé d'Anjou and a handful of others that you could probably pick up at your local offie for under a fiver. Incidentally, the 1979 Pétrus here is a rock-solid £700, nearly £350 more than at Atlantic (q.v.) and a gruesome £415 more than at Coast (q.v.).

The Dorchester – The Oriental Restaurant £60

(Address as above)

+ *high-falutin' Cantonese cooking; interesting set menus*
– *the cost*

Hong Kong prices are a deterrent, but the Cantonese cooking stands comparison with some of the best in that city. The dining-room is agreeably chaste and the service measured and formal, removing any possibility of the riotous but slightly vulgar mish-mash of flavours often associated with Chinese meals. This is a place to come if you are really interested in the genre and are using a business-account credit card. A cheaper way in is the dim-sum menu at lunchtime.

Open
Mon-Sun
Hours
Breakfast 7.00am–11.00am, lunch 12.30-2.30pm, dinner 6.30-11.00pm
Credit cards
AmEx, Mastercard Visa, Switch, Delta, Diner's
Set-price lunch
£25.50
Set-price dinner
£34
Nearest tube stations
Marble Arch, Hyde Park Corner
Map 3

La Dordogne £34

5 Devonshire Road W4 (0181-747 1836)

+ *forget those breakdowns on Eurostar — take the tube to Turnham Green*
– *overheard reminiscences of* gîte *holidays*

La Dordogne is unusually and restfully immutable. When a craving for things French steals over you, this longstanding Chiswick restaurant will reliably deliver. Salade gourmande (mixed leaves with foie gras, quails' eggs and smoked duck) is a substantial and delectable first course. To follow, quail with pistachio and port stuffing in a foie gras sauce is a delight and, given the quality ingredients, reasonable at £10.80. The full French repertoire is on show, including creditable terrines, soupe de poissons and magret de canard. The waiters' Gallic charm almost overcomes annoyance at a cover charge, and at vegetables priced at £2 per item. The small dining-room can become smoky and hectic, but that, too, is part of the French connection.

Open
Lunch Mon-Fri, dinner every day
Hours
12.00-2.30pm, 7.00-11.00pm
Credit cards
AmEx, Mastercard, Visa, Switch, Diner's
Service charge
10%
Cover charge
£1 per person
Set-price lunch
£15 & £25
Nearest tube station
Tunham Green
Map 1

Downstairs at 190 £33

190 Queen's Gate SW7 (581 5666)

+ *fishily competent*
- *room where the darkness is visible*

It needn't cost you an arm and a leg, proclaims a gruesome Ralph Steadman cartoon by the reception desk, but your eyes might pop out of their sockets when you see that two courses will set you back £22.50. Relegating a fish restaurant to a faded basement room that still hasn't shrugged off its previous incarnation as a club restaurant has a damping effect on the ambience – it might benefit from being renamed 190 Leagues under Queen's Gate. Scallop and saffron tart with cardamom and orange fennel proved to be a suicidal clash of strong flavours, whereas an intense risotto nero with seared baby squid was perfectly executed and classically simple. The best bet in the main course is to share a shellfish platter or to enquire about the 'Catch of the Day' (served with a simple accompaniment of spinach, new potatoes and Hollandaise) which is then cooked to order. Meat eaters are well catered for with suckling pig and calf's liver, but vegetarians are short-changed with an indigestible croustade of artichoke, wild mushrooms and salsify, consisting of the cooked (the veg.) and the virtually raw (the pastry).

Open
Dinner Mon-Sat
Hours
7.00pm-11.00pm
Credit cards
AmEx, Mastercard, Visa, Switch, Delta, Diner's
Service charge
12.5%
Set-price dinner
£22.50 & £27.50
Nearest tube stations
South Kensington, High Street Kensington, Gloucester Road
Map 2

Drones of Pont Street £35

1 Pont Street SW1 (259 6166)

+ *good cheeseburgers; flexible menu; stylish shop*
- *awkwardly designed, uncomfortable premises*

David Niven Jr and Dave Gilmour from Pink Floyd were backers of the original Drones, whose heyday was the '70s. When he was an *Evening Standard* restaurant critic, Quentin Crewe recounted a story about dining at Drones. His guest, who had ordered a hamburger, was partial to having a fried egg on top of it. There was a great deal of to-ing and fro-ing about this, and an insistence on the manager's part that the apparently modest request was quite out of the question. It eventually transpired that there was no egg on the premises. Now that Drones has been re-opened by Antony Worral Thompson (in December 1995) there is probably no ingredient, homely or exotic, that cannot be found in the kitchen or store rooms, or in the shop – The Grocer – that is part of the many-layered premises. When it comes to composite parts of a dish, Wozza

Open
Every day
Hours
12.00-3.15pm, 7.00-11.30pm (Sun 10.30pm)
Credit cards
AmEx, Mastercard, Visa, Switch, Diner's, Delta
Service charge
12.5%
Set-price lunch
£9.95
Set-price dinner
£12.95
Nearest tube stations
Sloane Square, Knightsbridge
Map 2

likes to pile it high and sell it not particularly cheaply. In his statement of intent for this corner of his empire, he declared that he was offering grown-up food. The implication was that new-found maturity would bring in its wake sober culinary restraint, but the results are variable. Some of the best dishes are the crustacea and charcuterie assemblies with appropriate salsas, pestos, chutneys and pickles put together for the restaurant by The Grocer. Some main courses which typify the cooking style are roasted Devon hen, lemon summer savoury and crispy hazelnut potatoes; chargrilled wild salmon, parmesan courgettes, baby chickpea salad; roast breast of veal, la mique dumplings and minted summer peas. Oddly enough, the most enthusiastic report of eating at Drones concerned a cheeseburger served in the cafe section in the front of the premises, and cheeseburgers were what the original Drones was known for. Within clumsily, uncomfortably designed premises, which overall invoke a villa on the Costa del Crime, there is (in addition to the shop and cafe) a restaurant and, in the basement, a blues bar — each with a menu to match.

The Eagle £20

159 Farringdon Road EC1 (837 1353)

+ *earwigging the gossip of* The Guardian *hacks*
– *see above*

Open
Mon-Sat
Hours
12.30-2.30pm
(Sat 4.00pm),
6.30-10.30pm
Credit cards
None
Nearest tube
station
Farringdon
Map 3

The Eagle opened in 1991, and its instant success sparked young entrepreneurs to move into down-at-heel pubs and transform them into pine-and-terracotta joints serving wholesome nosh, real ale and even offering some decent wines. The Eagle still feels like a pub. It may be stripped down but it is not spruced up, and equal weight is given to those who just wish for a drink (which may account for the difficulty in obtaining a table). Should you manage this, the food is usually worth waiting for. A smoking chargrill despatches swordfish or tuna fillets with a minimal dressing of oil and herbs, and with a simple accompaniment of spinach and new potatoes. Pastas, stews, casseroles and salads all feature on a menu that changes twice daily, the accent being on Iberian-influenced specialities such as bacalhoada (baked salt cod and potatoes with green peppers, garlic and bay), or fabada (an Asturian butterbean and pork stew). Good beers and a few earthy wines — including a Portuguese white — are on offer.

East One £22

175–9 St John Street EC1 (566 0088)

+ *sweet staff; pleasing modern design*
- *every bowlful a biff to the tastebuds*

Open
Lunch Mon-Fri,
dinner Mon-Sat
Hours
12.00–3.00pm,
5.00–11.00pm
Credit cards
AmEx, Mastercard,
Visa, Switch, Delta
Service charge
12.5%
Set-price lunch
Unlimited £10
Set price dinner
Unlimited £12.50
**Nearest tube
station**
Farringdon
Map 3

Rodney Kinsman, designer, is owner of the OMK furniture company, his Chinese wife Lisa has worked in catering and food styling, their son trained at the TGI Friday group and their daughter is a graphic designer. East One is a whole-family enterprise, inspired (as the menu tells us in lower-case style, as if e e cummings has been employed as typesetter) by the street kitchens of the Far East. Anyone who has encountered street kitchens in, say, Singapore or Hong Kong, might be more inclined to compare East One to the principle behind the Mongolian Barbecue chain: a system of choosing raw ingredients and having them fried in a large wok by a chef. As at Mongolian Barbecues, a set price entitles you to help yourself as often as you wish – an invitation that has definite self-limiting properties. A stylish white bowl sitting in a small wooden tray is brought to the table. You, the customer, walk to the cold cabinets and make your selection, instilling more than the usual resistance to the idea of an imposed 12.5% service charge. Strips of meat, fish and that creepy species crabsticks, as well as chopped vegetables, a variety of noodles, fresh herbs and omelette strips are the palette from which you create your own masterpiece, daubing it with one of the sauces (the soy-based varieties tend to swamp all other flavours). Whooshed around a wok, the assembly ends up something like a wilted, intimidated salad bar, and bears scant resemblance to South-East Asian street food in which soups, hauntingly flavoured broths and exotic (to us) ingredients are a substantial part of the equation. A certain amount of grim determination is required to plod to the woks often enough – with a fresh bowl each time – to achieve what might seem like good value. However, the room design is pleasing, and a certain amount of trench-warfare camaraderie can grow up among fellow diners.

Ebla £20

262–4 King Street W6 (0181-741 1177)

+ *a welcome addition to the area*
- *not a buzzy lunchtime location*

Open
Mon-Sun
Hours
Lunch 12.00pm–
3.00pm, dinner
6.00pm-11.30pm
Credit cards
AmEx, Mastercard,
Diner's, Visa,
Switch, Delta
Set-price lunch
£13.50

We've seen Thai restaurants on every High Street, but it may be hoping for too much to take the arrival of Ebla in W6 as evidence that there will soon be as many Lebanese establishments. Ebla (which describes itself as Middle Eastern, as one of the owners is Syrian) has adapted to its status as a neighbourhood restaurant with two sensible compromises. The meze — which in a West End Lebanese restaurant might run on for pages — have been narrowed down, and the decor brightened up from the usual beige to shades of blue. Selections from the meze brought some inspired cooking — an attribute less apparent in the main course, although this is a report from the earliest days of this new restaurant.

Ebury Wine Bar £24

Open
Every day
Hours
11.00am-10.30pm
Credit cards
AmEx, Mastercard,
Visa, Switch,
Delta, Diner's
Service charge
12.5%
Nearest tube
station
Victoria
Map 2

139 Ebury Street SW1 (730 5447)

+ *the advance from prim to Pacific Rim*
- *standards slip when Hampton's away*

You can imagine the conversation. Whatever has happened to the Ebury? Whither '80s catering-college grub prepared by fresh-faced country girls? The familiar faces and braying voices now hail each other over a Caesar salad or chilli-flecked crabcakes with cucumber relish and aïoli, chosen from a menu revamped by Josh Hampton, previously chef at Kartouche (q.v.). Certain restrictions are implied by the fact that this is Pimlico, not Notting Hill or Chelsea: hence warm pigeon salad with red-onion relish, and chargrilled onglet with chips and peppercorn sauce, remain among such infiltrators as seared scallops with Thai rice noodles and squid, and mussel and roasted-pepper bruschetta. Expect the consumption of thirst-quenching aromatic and spicy white wines to soar.

Elena's L'Etoile £32

Open
Lunch Mon-Fri,
dinner Mon-Sat
Hours
12.00-2.30pm,
6.00-11.00pm
Credit cards
AmEx,
Mastercard,
Switch, Visa,
Delta, Diner's
Service charge
12.5%
Set-price dinner
£15.50 (6.00-
7.30pm)
Nearest tube
station
Goodge Street
Map 4

30 Charlotte Street W1 (636 1496)

+ *newcomers quickly become regulars*
- *the £1.50 charge for bland bread and over-refined crudités*

Not before time, Elena Salvoni has received a Catey: the Oscar equivalent for the catering industry. Now in her 70s, but a lot more spry than probably you or me, Elena has worked in restaurants since the age of 14. The historic Fitzrovia restaurant L'Étoile, established in 1904, suits her well, and in the photographs of the famous that line the walls she is surrounded by friends. Chef Kevin Hopgood keeps the menu short (well, short-ish), and French (well, French-ish). A few Italian dishes, such as gnocchi 'Elena' and pappardelle L'Étoile, are also included. Salad of roasted sea scallops or of warm duck is a good way to start, and foie de veau grillé (au lard or au lapin braisé) a good way to continue. The wine list could use an injection of verve: the choice by the glass of Georges Duboeuf or Georges Duboeuf is drab.

Emporio Armani Express £25

191 Brompton Road SW3 (823 8818)

+ *designer food wears well*
- *not the place for a bad-hair day*

Open
Mon-Sat
Hours
10.00am-6.00pm
Credit cards
AmEx, Mastercard,
Switch, Visa,
Delta, Diner's
Nearest tube
stations
South Kensington,
Knightsbridge
Map 2

As you pass the ordered displays of mushroom and black outfits, the skinny staff and the perfectly co-ordinated top-to-toe combinations, it is hard for that majority of the population who wear size 14 and upwards not to feel out of place. However, in the restaurant the waiters are smiling, welcoming and quite as stylish as their sales clerk compatriots. The menu allows for picking at small portions, so a plate of antipasto, or small order of pasta or risotto, is permitted. Nothing is heavy or over-rich: roasted mackerel with potato and herb salad; suprême of chicken with aubergine melanzane; and grilled quail with polenta and sage mash are modestly portioned and expertly executed. Morning (great) coffee and afternoon tea are served with biscotti, grilled focaccia with prosciutto, and crostata di mele (apple tart). The booths are much nicer than the little mushroom-shaped stools in the bar area.

Enoteca Turi £25

28 Putney High Street SW15 (0181-785 4449)

+ *specialities from Apulia; the wines*
- *not enough wines served by the glass or in half-bottles*

Open
Lunch Mon-Fri,
dinner Mon-Sat
Hours
12.30-2.30pm,
7.00-11.00pm
Credit cards
AmEx, Delta,
Diner's,
Mastercard,
Switch, Visa
Nearest tube
stations
East Putney,
Putney Bridge
Map 1

Giuseppe and Pamela Turi (who have this year confidently added their name to what was previously simply 'Enoteca': loosely translated as 'wine place' or 'wine library') aim to present traditional Italian dishes − some from Apulia, from where Giuseppe hails − and to encourage exploration among the wines. To this end wine suggestions are made beside the dishes, a system which really only works if everyone eats the same thing (or drinks a bottle of wine each). Artichokes, broad beans fresh and dried (a staple in Apulia), turnip tops, meat-sauced pastas, shellfish stews, smoked fish and vegetables, stuffed fillet of pork and polenta cake are all ingredients and dishes to home in on. The surroundings are rustic, leaning towards grotto.

THIS IS A LIST that satisfies every customer criterion. The format is simple: wines are classified according to style; each entry is accorded a pithy tasting note that not only briskly informs, but also gives you more background info. if required; and, joy oh joy, there are 25 wines under £15.00. To pull out a few random plums: Fiano di Avellino from Campania in southern Italy; Altaserre, made from the unusual Erbaluce; Aglianico del Vulture with its gorgeous chocolate-cherry fruit; and Bricco Manzoni, a traditional blend of Nebbiolo and Barbera. The last four pages are devoted to other fine wines from across the world, and are equally well-chosen. A meditation list.

Esarn Kheaw £20

Open
Lunch Mon-Fri,
dinner every day
Hours
12.00-3.00pm,
6.00-11.00pm
Credit cards
AmEx, Mastercard,
Visa, Delta, Diner's
**Nearest tube
station**
Shepherd's Bush
Map 1

314 Uxbridge Road W12 (0181-743 8930)

+ *cooking from north-east Thailand*
− *son-in-law's eggs*

The list of ox-tripe soup, own-make sausages, catfish and mud fish, sweet liver and green papaya salad, makes this one of the more interesting Thai restaurants, so it is a shame if staff cannot or will not encourage the curious and adventurous. Quite long waits can occur before the woman chef/proprietor sends out the dishes, but this is more than justified as her cooking is generally very good. Illogically, but so often true of restaurants, Esarn Kheaw seems to work best at the busiest time: towards the end of the week when, significantly, there is a preponderance of Thais among the clientele.

L'Escargot £32

Open
Lunch Mon-Fri,
dinner Mon-Sat
Hours
12.15-2.15pm,
6.00-11.30pm
Credit cards
AmEx, Mastercard,
Visa, Switch,
Diner's, Delta
Service charge
12.5% for ground
floor restaurant &
15% 1st floor
**Nearest tube
stations**
Tottenham Court
Road, Leicester
Square
Map 5

48 Greek Street W1 (437 2679)

There are changes in the kitchens at L'Escargot taking place too late to be reviewed in this edition. However, here are the facts. Coming in as executive chef with particular responsibility for the ground floor restaurant is William (Billy) Reid who has worked at a variety of restaurants including The Ritz Hotel, the Waterside Inn, The Box Tree at Ilkley, Northcote Manor and The Stafford Hotel. His menu, priced as has become the system here with one price for first courses (£6.50), another for main courses (£11.95), plus annoying supplements, features dishes such as box of lentils, duck and foie gras, sherry vinaigrette and tarragon (supplement £2); black pudding, poached egg, shallot soubise; roasted cod on grain mustard, pomme purée, red wine thyme jus; seabass, pasta, oysters, rocket and sea scallops, vermouth cream (supplement £5); chump of lamb, rosemary and tomato jus, fresh pulses. Sounds promising. Head chef, Canadian David Hawksworth, has worked with Raymond Blanc and Marco Pierre White in this country and at Le Crocodile in Strasbourg and Bouley in New York. The set-price lunch menu has a feature which I can imagine being popular in Soho; the price of £21.50 for two courses, £25 for three, includes aperitif, wine and mineral water. Incidentally, Garry Hollihead who was one of the pair of Michelin-starred chefs recently employed by L'Escargot has gone to his own thing – Hollihead's – at the premises which were previously Baboon just off Wigmore Street.

L'Estaminet £28

14 Garrick Street WC2 (379 1432)

+ *chariot de fromages*
- *chariot de rest of the desserts*

Sometimes you just want to go back to basics, and French bourgeois food stirs the appropriate atavistic tastebuds: it exists to satisfy a craving, one that can be assuaged in this small tavern. The usual kitsch touches are present to whisk you into the mood: polished copper pans hanging from the bare brick walls, and cheerfully demonstrative service. Escargots en cassolette are suitably dripping with garlic and butter. Other familiar hors d'oeuvres include salade de harengs, crêpe aux fruits de mer and saucisson chaud Lyonnais. The making of palatable French onion soup eludes this restaurant as it does so many others, *hélas*. In the main course, choose from the categories 'Poissons', 'Viandes' or 'Grillades': notably Châteaubriand accompanied by good frites, herby Provençal tomatoes and al dente green beans, or canon d'agneau au thym.

Open
Mon-Sat
Hours
12.00-3.00pm,
5.45-11.15pm
Credit cards
AmEx, Mastercard,
Visa, Switch
Cover Charge
£1.50/person
Service charge
12.5%
Set-price lunch
£9.99 & £14.50
Nearest tube station
Leicester Square
Map 4

Euphorium £28

203 Upper Street N1 (704 6909)

+ *fine art meets cookery craft*
- *nonsensical name*

The horizontal buy-out – acquiring the premises next door for expansion – is a sign of success. Euphorium spread sideways in the early autumn of 1996, adding on a bar, a brasserie and a conservatory and freeing up the first floor of the original restaurant for private parties. Chef Paul Tweedie has succeeded in bringing back the anticipatory frisson of inventive contemporary cooking that disappeared with the departure of

Open
Lunch every day,
dinner Mon-Sat
Hours
12.30-2.30pm,
6.00-10.30pm
Credit cards
AmEx, Mastercard,
Visa, Switch, Delta
Service charge
Optional service
charge of 12.5%
Set-price lunch
£10

the original chef, Jeremy Lee. The menu changes monthly, but August dishes – chillied polenta and nut fritters served with a soy- and sesame-dressed salad; roast sea bass with black beans and lightly pickled fennel and leeks; neck fillet of lamb, cannellini beans, roast shallots and rosemary; and lemon and almond cake with blueberries and mascarpone – give a flavour of the approach. The original art on the walls is interesting, and there is no music to dilute its impact. Islington has to put up with a lot of Tory flack – but it has Euphorium.

Euten's £26

Open
Lunch Tues-Sat,
dinner Mon-Sat
Hours
12.00-3.30pm,
5.30-11.30pm
Credit cards
AmEx, Mastercard,
Visa, Switch,
Delta, Diner's
Set-price lunch
£10.50
Nearest tube
station
Covent Garden
Maps 4 & 5

4–5 Neal's Yard WC2 (379 6377)

+ *West Indian food as one definition of modern British*
- *soul-less interior*

Euten Lindsay, born in Jamaica but raised in Britain, makes the valid point that a West Indian influence on cooking should be part of what gets referred to as modern British cuisine. Euten has worked at The Ivy, Joe Allen, P.J.'s and Peg's Club, but in this incarnation as the Alliance of Black Chefs Ltd he is serving West Indian food and drinks in purpose-built premises near Seven Dials that have seen various restaurants come and go. His menu changes daily, but typical dishes are pan-fried chilli prawns in a spicy tomato sauce; plantain and okra tartlet; grilled red snapper with green-pepper relish; jerk rump steak with cinnamon, mango and taro chips; and sweet-potato meringue pie. It is good to find such dishes in the area; Euten should be supported in his Black British Cuisine.

Fables Restaurant new £32

Open
Every day
Hours
12.00-3.00pm,
7.00-11.00pm
Credit cards
AmEx, Mastercard,
Visa, Switch,
Diner's, Delta
Service charge
12.5%
Set-price lunch
£12
Set-price dinner
£22
Nearest tube
station
Fulham Broadway,
Parsons Green
Map 1

839 Fulham Road SW6 (371 5445)

+ *Neat food at neat prices*
- *the decoration*

The name of this restaurant is explained to some extent by the decor. Walls are papered with a depiction of the La Fontaine fable of 'The Wolf and the Dog', copied, apparently, from a piece of Pierre Frey fabric. Anthropomorphized animals complete with suits and ties make an unsettling sort of mural as you address aspects of their humanity and idly wonder whether it is their friends or relations who will end up in the pot. However, someone thought it was a good idea. Much better ideas in my view are executive chef Richard Neat – who will stay at Fables until January 1997 and then pay flying visits – and his head chef James Kirby. Soon after being awarded two Michelin stars at the restaurant Pied à Terre (q.v.), Neat made the surprising decision to leave, citing reasons that are the culinary equivalent of wanting to spend more time with the family. His creativity and expertise have been brought to bear on the menu here, with the restraining factor of cheaper prices eliminating some of the intricacy and fiddle. Kirby has worked for Neat before, and also for Simon Hopkinson at Bibendum. The luxury in Neat's style of cooking lies not within conventional grand ingredients, but in infinite pains being taken over what might be considered humdrum starting points. Dishes to illustrate this include ballotine of braised oxtail, with roasted aubergine and onion purée; rillette of home-smoked whiting, poached egg and chive sauce; terrine of skate with potatoes and parsley purée; and braised saddle and shoulder of rabbit (a favourite Neat meat), broad beans and anchovy jus. An ingredient's essence — for instance, the rich saltiness of sardines flavouring a vinaigrette for a salad of duck breast and gesiers (giblets) — is capitalized upon. In case this is not whetting your appetite (which it should do), consider the more 'conventional' dishes such as crab with roasted tomato and shellfish jelly; tortellini of basil, peppers and tapenade purée; breast of guinea fowl and confit légumes with cabbage and potato sauce; grilled calf's liver, cannelloni of bacon and crushed peas; and pavé of chocolate fondant and pistachio. Fables has added gastronomic dignity to a stretch of road more familiar with pizza parlours and 'oriental tapas' bars. The rule that a table on the ground floor must be more desirable than one in the basement doesn't hold here: the downstairs area of what was formerly the restaurant Singapura is a better shape. Waiting staff try hard but are sometimes apt to fluster.

La Famiglia £35

7 Langton Street SW10 (351 0761)

+ *the back garden*
- *overpricing*

Family has various connotations in Italy, and various of them may spring to mind during a meal here. An innocent interpretation is the sight of a (necessarily prosperous) family enjoying a meal in the garden on a sunny day. Alvaro Maccioni, is, in the nicest way, the godfather of many a London trattoria, and wrinkling Chelsea roués with their ever-younger consorts come to pay tribute here. Alvaro was serving crostini and panzanella long before young British chefs started jumping into the toaster or using up stale bread, and the region of Tuscany

Open
Mon-Sun
Hours
12.00-2.45pm,
7.00-11.45pm
Credit cards
AmEx, Mastercard,
Diner's, Visa
Cover charge
£1.75 per person
**Nearest tube
station**
Sloane Square
Map 2

still emphatically informs the menu. The staple, white beans, are offered 'al fiasco', i.e., traditionally cooked in a flask. Pastas are generously served and often richly sauced. Plainly grilled fish is a popular main course. Desserts know their place – on the trolley.

The Fat Duck £35

Open
Lunch Tues-Sun,
dinner Tues-Sat
Hours
12.00-2.00pm
(Sun 2.30pm)
7.00-9.30pm (Sat-
Sun 10.30pm)
Credit cards
AmEx, Mastercard,
Visa, Switch, Delta
Service charge
10 %
discretionary
(except for parties
of 8 and over)
Set-price lunch
£14.50 & £19.50
**Nearest railway
station**
Maidenhead

1 The High Street, Bray, Berkshire (01628-580333)

+ *a perfect gastronomic destination for a drive*
– *it isn't in London*

Heston Blumenthal, chef/patron of The Fat Duck – previously a pub called The Bell Ringers – has chutzpah, it must be said, in taking on the culinary vicar of Bray, Michel Roux at The Waterside Inn. All the more so since – except for a short stint in the kitchen of Marco Pierre White – Blumenthal is self-taught. Inspiration, he says, comes from reading and eating when travelling in France, and he cites Alain Chapel and Michel Bras as particular mentors. The dishes on the relatively short menu, although traceable to certain influences (including Roux), are singular. Like a scientist balancing an equation or a novelist polishing a sentence, Blumenthal seems to have worked and reworked his ideas until something approaching perfection is achieved. In the first course, a dish such as gelée of mackerel with Gewürztraminer shows the chef dealing with a not essentially alluring fish, curing and marinating it rather than cooking it, then suspending it in a limpid, flowery jelly dressed with herbs and a slightly acidic froth of tomato. A version of vichyssoise – quite dilute but strengthened by seaweed – conceals in its pale depths a poached oyster. What is presumably the signature dish, petit salé of duck, is a duck leg brined before being slowly cooked with spices (a pronounced flavour of cloves underlines a certain hamminess in the result); the smoothest imaginable potato purée (quite Joel Robuchon) forms the accompaniment. Breaking down potatoes with olives and herbs in the cooking juice for a chicken dish is a nice domestic yet sophisticated touch. Energy and invention are sustained in the dessert course with ideas such as salted-butter caramel with cacao sorbet, and with experimentation such as the use of jasmine tea and orange flower water to flavour a crème brûlée. The pub has been stylishly, quirkily rendered a restaurant, and the sophisticated management and service give it a pleasingly foreign feel. There is no view of the river, but in pretty weather a courtyard at the back is brought into play.

Feng Shang £32

Cumberland Basin, Prince Albert Road NW1 (485 8137/0126)

+ *fulfils canal desires (without making waves)*
- *frenzied applications of blisteringly hot steamed towels*

Open
Every day
Hours
12.00–2.00pm,
6.00–11.00pm
Credit cards
AmEx, Mastercard,
Visa
Service charge
10%
Set-price lunch
£20
Set price dinner
£25
**Nearest tube
station**
Camden Town
Map 1

A pagoda solidly moored in the Regent's Canal turns out to be an up-market double-decker Chinese restaurant, with modern pine furnishings and large round tables occupied mainly by affluent tourists and business people, since opportunities for passing trade are severely limited. Your clacking approach over the metal bridge is monitored by beady eyes, and zealous service is a feature of the meal. As Brer Duck paddles outside the window you can empathize while munching his roasted Szechuan cousin in a purse of bread, or feel guilt-free if you are eating the vegetarian zhai version, constructed from savoury wheat gluten and pressed beancurd. Seafood is the logical choice, and includes scallops with ginger, spring onions and chilli, steamed cockles and soft-shell crab. For those who like to wrap their food, mou-shou pork, lent interesting texture by sinewy black mushrooms, is notably well-done. Prices are relatively high: you pay for the illusion of floating. It would be nice if there were even just a little shudder to justify it.

The Fifth Floor £35

Harvey Nichols, Knightsbridge SW1 (235 5250)

+ *superb coffee*
- *hip-hugging blue bucket chairs*

Open
Lunch every day,
dinner Mon–Sat
Hours
12.00–3.00pm
(3.30 Sat/Sun),
6.30–11.30pm
Credit cards
AmEx, Mastercard,
Visa, Switch,
Diner's, Delta
Service charge
12.5%
Set-price lunch
£18.50 & £22.50
**Nearest tube
station**
Knightsbridge
Map 2

A pproached through a bar renowned as the Knightsbridge 'meet market', the restaurant opens out into a long, rectilinear room with widely spaced tables, black shutters and smoked glass to disguise you from the gaze of curious shoppers on the other side of the glass — the whole effect being curiously reminiscent of a well-upholstered airport lounge. Waiters with black bow ties and invisible personalities parade down the wide aisles in fleets: one to take the order, another to pour the wine, a third to refill your glass, a fourth to refill your glass and a fifth to wave your empty bottle with a flourish. The menu comprises some 17 starters and 14 main courses and is constantly changing, with risk-taking, playful innovation and decent grub for grub's sake. Chef Henry Harris capitalizes on the inherent virtues of supremely fresh ingredients: tomato, thyme and Gruyère tart makes use of seasonal sweet Italian plum tomatoes;

steamed fillet of cod, herb and tomato risotto and sauce messine exalts the freshness of the fish, its flesh flaking on the fork and the rice humid with flavour. Less successful were pan-fried scallops with a bouillon-rich Bordelaise sauce and shredded duck confit, which seemed to take a fish-and-meat marriage to breaking point. Desserts can also be hit-and-miss, including a crème brûlée with a curdled custard interior but also a definitive treacle tart – the sticky bee's knees.

ALL THE WINE for 'The Big List' as it is known emanates from the little wine shop adjacent. Thoughtfully indexed and clearly laid out, it allows both quick decisions and more gentle rumination. There is a high regard for bubbles with labels: two pages are given to all the champagnes you could shake a gold card at. Bordeaux and Burgundy start at £30 and march ever upwards. The vintages are well-chosen, however. Turn to Spain, surprisingly, for bargains and F.P.C.C. (flavour per cubic centimetre). The wines of Alella, Guelbenzu, Masia Barril and Marqués de Aragon are all under £15. On the same page, a quintet of treasurable German Rieslings contains Fritz Haag's eloquent Brauneberger Juffer-Sonnenuhr Kabinett and Spätlese. Other than the classic regions, the heart of this list is New World Chardonnay, overshadowing more than the somewhat measly one example of a dry French country wine, the deliciously aromatic Domaine de Triennes Viognier. Don't be taken aback if, when you are presented with the wine, an inch or two is missing – it seems customary here for the sommeliers to take a nip for our benefit.

Fina Estampa £24

150 Tooley Street SE1 (403 1342)

+ *Peruvian food and pisco sours*
- *overwhelming music on occasions*

Finding authentic Peruvian food in a converted pub near London Bridge is the sort of discovery that makes London the fully flavoured melting pot it is. Husband and wife Richard and Bianca Jones, manager and chef respectively, produce a fascinating menu, demonstrating that Peruvian food is by no means small potatoes. Dried, Inca-style (the potatoes, that is), they are the basis of carapulcra; new, covered with a piquant peanut and walnut sauce and served alongside garlic king prawns, they become ocopa. Potatoes layered with avocado and tuna make causa rellena. For the uninitiated, the system of

Open
Mon–Sat
Hours
12.00–3.00pm,
6.00–10.30pm
Credit cards
AmEx, Mastercard,
Visa, Switch,
Diner's
Service charge
10%
Nearest tube
station
London Bridge
Map 1

'Piqueo' at the price of £18 per person gives a well-balanced tasting of the various specialities (not all potato-based). My favourite dish is seco: lamb or chicken in a fresh coriander sauce, served with Peruvian-style beans and salsa criolla. Start the meal with one or two of Mr Jones's potent pisco sours.

La Finezza £35

62–4 Lower Sloane Street SW1 (730 8639)

+ *the porcini season*
- *not much bang for your buck*

La Finezza suits those who yearn for the Italian school of pre-River Cafe. Unashamedly old-fashioned, two of its claims to a sort of fame are the sunny yellow decor and the chef's proficiency with wild mushrooms. In season these star in pastas, risottos, soups and with veal, or are simply sautéed with garlic. Sauces for meat dishes tend to be laced with wine and brandy, but raw ingredients are of the best quality, giving you faith in a dish like steak tartare. Fish and seafood are handled well. To effect an economy on the bill, give vegetables a miss: the chef seems deeply uninterested in them.

Open
Lunch Mon–Fri, dinner Mon–Sat
Hours
12.00–3.00pm, 7.00–11.00pm
Credit cards
AmEx, Mastercard, Visa, Switch, Diner's, Delta
Cover charge
£1.50
Nearest tube station
Sloane Square
Map 2

Florians £28

4 Topsfield Parade, Middle Lane N8 (0181-348 8348)

+ *interesting aperitifs; myriad types of grappe*
- *the decibel count*

Florians nurtures its neighbourhood (Crouch End), offering celebratory menus for events such as Father's Day, the European Cup and Mattanza (the annual tuna catch in Sicily), and holding regular food and wine tastings. The locals repay the thoughtfulness with loyalty, which in its turn is sustained by the rustic Italian food. The latter incorporates modern touches such as lamb carpaccio; cod steak crusted with pine kernels; interesting homemade pasta assemblies such as black tagliolini with octopus and bitter leaves; and fish and game according to market and season. The Italian wine list and grappe collection can also be credited for much customer enthusiasm. The bar area has a life of its own and a separate menu.

Open
Every day
Hours
12.00–3.00pm, 7.00–11.00pm
Credit cards
Mastercard, Visa, Switch, Delta
Set-price lunch
£5.95 & £9.95
Nearest tube stations
Highgate, Finsbury Park

Formula Veneta £30

Open
Mon-Sat
Hours
12.30-3.30pm,
7.00-11.15pm
Credit cards
AmEx, Mastercard,
Visa, Switch,
Diner's, Delta
Cover charge
£1 per person
Set-price lunch
£9.95
**Nearest tube
station**
South Kensington
Map 2

14 Hollywood Road SW10 (352 7612)

+ *the garden in summer; a fine wine list*
− *hoorays in Hollywood Road*

Formula is a reference to motor racing, not to the menu, which concentrates on the food of northern Italy and is particularly alluring − to those who like the gastronomic odds and sods such as eel and pig's trotter − in the list of specials. Owner Gianni Pauro is the quintessential Italian manager, fuelled by high-octane bonhomie which can be put to the test by the loutish (in an upper-class sort of way) clientele. Dishes on the à la carte are far from formulaic, and include broad-bean and chicory soup; tagliolini with oysters; fettucine with raw tomato, garlic and basil; risotto cooked to order for a minimum of two people; and fillet of lamb in mustard, paprika and sherry sauce. Further proof of Italian restaurant authenticity comes from the lack of interest accorded to desserts, and from the seemingly modest pricing jacked up by a cover charge and separately priced vegetables.

Foundation £35

Open
Lunch every day,
dinner Mon-Sat
Hours
10.00am-11.00pm
(5.00pm Sun)
Credit cards
AmEx, Mastercard,
Visa, Switch,
Diner's, Delta
Service charge
12.5%
Set-price lunch
£10.50
**Nearest tube
station**
Knightsbridge
Map 2

Harvey Nichols Lower-ground Floor (entrance in Seville Street), Knightsbridge SW1 (201 8000)

+ *chef Graham Grafton's interesting way of putting things together*
− *the mournful modernity of the basement surroundings*

The relationship between food and fashion is never closer than in the watering holes of department stores and designer shops. Harvey Nichols shot to the forefront of clothing the inner person with the opening of The Fifth Floor (q.v.), with Henry Harris as head chef. The chef of Foundation, which has taken over the lower-ground-floor space (previously Joe's Cafe), is Graham Grafton, who has worked for Harris and also helped Bruce Poole to open Chez Bruce (q.v.) in Wandsworth. The Foundation menu is a familiar modern mix sporting all the latest culinary accessories − Poilâne bread, wild rocket, roasted peppers, garlic mash, smoked chilli, Jersey cream − but, like a good wardrobe, also contains some of the timeless classics like jambon persillé, moules Normandes, salade Niçoise, grilled salmon with sorrel and crème brûlée. Mixed yakitori is offered in the first course and seems something of an aberration, mainly because it is not particularly well-executed. On the whole the cooking is impressive, and features interesting ideas such as a smoked chilli and crab salsa served with rare-grilled tuna; pipérade with roast cod and grilled vegetables; and brandied cherries with vanilla cheesecake. The surroundings – which aim for cool modernity – end up being rather bleak and institutional: eating is supposed to be more fun than this. However, doubtless some customers' idea of a good time is to gaze at themselves in the mirrored walls.

Four Seasons £23

84 Queensway W2 (229 4320)

+ *the house soup, available for the asking*
- *the queues*

The dilemma here is whether to eat in the early part of the evening (i.e., before about 9pm) and risk being mown down in the hustle and bustle of customers and hurtling staff; or to eat in comparative calm later on, only to find that certain dishes have run out. One obvious answer is to go for lunch, a time when the barbecued meats are at their peak of perfection. Chef Wong's char-siu and Cantonese roast duck are renowned. Slow-cooked dishes and entries on the list of specials bring rewards to those who know and love Cantonese cooking. Such folk will want translations for dishes listed only in Chinese characters: on the whole, staff are willing and able to help.

Open
Every day
Hours
12.00-11.15pm
Credit cards
AmEx, Mastercard, Visa, Switch, Delta
Service charge
12.5%
Set-price dinner
£10.50, £13.50 & £16.00
Nearest tube stations
Bayswater, Queensway
Map 6

Frederick's £35

Camden Passage N1 (359 2888)

+ *children's menu featuring goujons of chicken: the new MacFredericks?*
- *service halfway between charm and smarm*

It is appropriate that Frederick's is in Islington, for in the past year it has undergone a blitzkrieg makeover: New Labour, new chef, new decor, new vodka bar, new Frederick's. The stately, plump image of the bourgeois old-timer has been supplanted by the modern Europhile. In the kitchen, Andrew Jeffs – who has worked for Nico Ladenis for eight years – has simplified and invigorated the menu with lively interlopers like brochette of salmon teriyaki with spicy cabbage; tiger-prawn salad with coriander, chilli and lime; and risotto of langoustine with crème fraîche and soft herbs. Interestingly, he rotates his recipes around comparatively few ingredients: herb mustard, garlic, coriander, cabbage, mushrooms of various denominations and foie gras are favoured catalysts. Duck is equally ubiquitous,

Open
Mon-Sat
Hours
12.00-2.30pm
6.00-11.30pm
Credit cards
AmEx, Mastercard, Visa, Switch, Delta, Diner's
Set-price lunch
£12.00 & £13.50 (Saturday)
Nearest tube station
Angel
Map 1

featuring Chinese-style with plum sauce; combined with poached pears and cashewnuts in a salad; sneaking into a sea-bass dish with spiced aubergines (more fish than fowl); and honey-roasted with Savoy choucroute and carrot and parsnip mash. There is a large and mainly French wine list.

Open
Mon-Sat
Hours
12.00-3.00pm,
6.00-11.30pm
Credit cards
AmEx, Mastercard,
Visa, Switch,
Delta, Diner's
**Nearest tube
station**
Leicester Square
Map 5

The French House Dining Room £24

49 Dean Street W1 (437 2477)

+ *generous portions; the revival of the radish (q.v. St John)*
− *don't expect fine saucing (or any saucing, for that matter)*

This is a pleasing little restaurant situated above a pub, decked out in mottled-red wallpaper and determinedly robust in the nature of its cooking, as may be inferred by the symbol of the rampant pig on the menu. The origin of the ingredients may be humble: liver, tongue, herring, sweetbreads, beetroot and chickpeas, but they are cooked to their best advantage and sympathetically presented by Margot Clayton, whose philosophy seems to be: 'If it's fresh, don't muck around with it'. Specialities number stuffed pig's trotter and watercress; Orkney lamb, beetroot and green sauce; and game (such as woodcock) in season. Pig out with hokey-pokey ice cream.

Open
Lunch Tues-Sun,
dinner Tues-Sat
Hours
Tues-Fri 11.00am-
2.30pm (Sat
4.00pm),
6.30-11.00pm;
Sun 11.00-4.00pm
Credit cards
AmEx, Mastercard,
Visa, Switch,
Delta, Diner's
Set-price lunch
£9.50
**Nearest tube
station**
Mile End,
Bethnal Green
Map 1

Frocks £23

95 Lauriston Road E9 (0181-986 3161)

+ *a good weekend hang-out*
− *the mixing of culinary metaphors*

This pretty but cramped restaurant uses good ingredients (free-range meat, vivid vegetables) to modern effect: tuna on scallion and tomato compôte; braised lamb shank with pea and mint sauce; and pan-fried turkey fillet with a coriander and asparagus salsa. An outsider might feel that everyone knows everyone else here, to which the answer may be to bring your entire family for the weekend brunch, when kedgeree or kippers, or a fry-up with bubble and squeak, can be accompanied by jugs of Bloody Mary or Buck's Fizz at prices that make you appreciative of the distance from the West End.

Fung Shing £30

15 Lisle Street WC2 (437 1539)

+ *consistently good Cantonese cooking*
- *winds down relatively early*

Open
Every day
Hours
12.00-11.30pm
Credit cards
AmEx, Mastercard,
Visa, Switch,
Delta, Diners
Set-price lunch &
dinner
£15
Nearest tube
station
Leicester Square
Map 5

There have been two changes since the review in last year's edition of the Guide. A sad one is the death of chef Kwan Fu, who served this restaurant – of which he was one of the owners – so devotedly and artistically. A happier one is the expansion into premises at the back, creating a second ground-floor dining-room that has been decorated an optimistic shade of yellow. If you are interested in life beyond sweet-and-sour pork – and why would you be here otherwise? – ask for the short menu of 'Chef's Recommendations', and also secure, if you can, the advice of the manager, known as Jimmy Jim. From the short menu, try the deeply savoury Fung Shing beancurd-skin-wrapped rolls in pot; spicy boiled chicken (whole or half, depending on numbers); and steamed pigeon with Chinese sausage in lotus leaf. On the main menu, skip the list of appetizers – mostly a sop to Western tastes – and start with a baked or steamed crab; and, from the list entitled 'Chef Special', choose crispy spicy eel or wan nam prawns, where the creatures are fried in a fermented beancurd batter and served with Worcestershire sauce and lettuce for wrapping. Chicken with preserved clam sauce in pot is an interesting main course; beancurd dishes are enterprising; stir-fried milk with scrambled egg white shouldn't be missed; and the seasonal green vegetable is a meaningful gesture towards healthy eating. By the way, if secretly you yearn for sweet-and-sour pork, try barbecued beef which has many of the same hokey qualities. Wine is treated with unusual deference here.

The Gate £22

51 Queen Caroline Street W6 (0181-748 6932)

+ *sexier than most vegetarian restaurants*
- *over-complex dishes can mislay the pure pleasure of vegetables*

Open
Lunch Tues-Fri,
dinner Mon-Sat
Hours
12.00-2.30pm,
6.00-10.45pm
Credit cards
AmEx, Mastercard,
Visa, Switch, Delta
Nearest tube
station
Hammersmith
Map 1

With most restaurants now having the wit to offer interesting vegetarian options on their menus, a wholly vegetarian restaurant suggests a commitment to the orthodoxy that goes beyond mere dietary choice. Located in what was once Brangwyn's studio, connected to a church, the premises of The Gate and the refectory-style dining-room reinforce that suspicion, but the inventive menu strives not to appear wholefoodier-than-thou. Inspiration is taken from all over: nori rolls from Japan; rösti (made with sweet potatoes) from Switzerland; meze from Greece; cornbread and gumbo from the American south; chilli rellenos from Tex-Mexico; and stir-fried noodles served with tom yam soup from Thailand. The list is augmented with daily (seasonal) specials. Desserts uphold the belief that those who renounce the flesh do themselves proud with sweet confections. The reasonably priced drinks list includes organically produced wines and beers.

Gaucho Grill £30

Open
Every day
Hours
12.00-3.00pm,
5.00pm-12.00am
(Sat 12.00-
12.00am, Sun
12.00-10.30pm)
Credit cards
AmEx, Mastercard,
Visa, Switch,
Diner's, Delta
Nearest tube
station
Piccadilly Circus
Map 4

19 Swallow Street W1 (734 4040)

+ *you can have no beef with Argentinian beef*
- *dispiriting decor in the basement dining-room*

The reason to come here is the imported Argentinian beef, which is sent over in vacuum-packs wherein the meat ages without shrinkage, and is stored at precisely 1 degree C, so above freezing. Whether rump, sirloin, rib eye or fillet, at 9oz or 12oz, the steaks are cooked accurately on the asdao (open grill) and served with pepper sauce, garlic sauce or Béarnaise. Add in baked potato and green salad, and you have what many still feel is the definition of a proper meal. Dyed-in-the-wool carnivores can start with a beef carpaccio: wafer-thin slices of South America's finest, served raw. Other items indigenous to the theme include plump empanadas (meat-filled pasties), chorizos (spicy sausages) and a hearty black-bean soup. Flan con dulche de leche is the best of the desserts. Drink Argentinian Cabernet Sauvignon.

Le Gavroche £75

Open
Mon-Fri
Hours
12.00-2.00pm,
7.00-11.00pm
Credit cards
AmEx, Mastercard,
Visa, Diner's, JCB
Set-price lunch
£39
Set-price dinner
£60 & £85
Nearest tube
station
Marble Arch
Map 3

43 Upper Brook Street W1 (408 0881)

+ *set-price lunch at £38, including good wine and service*
- *a hotel feel to the decor of the basement dining-room*

As chefs who once strove for Michelin stars in the well-padded confines of luxury establishments leave to open their own relatively reasonably priced restaurants and brasseries, but take with them their talent, there has to be good reason to spend what can easily become £100 a head. Service is one justification. Led by Silvano Geradin, service at Le Gavroche is truly impeccable: dedicated to its craft: and, like an ancient ritual, fascinating to observe. Space, comfort and quiet this luxuriously but boringly designed dining-room can deliver.

Wines? See below. Food? Michel Roux has taken over as head chef from his father Albert, maintaining links via a section on the menu entitled 'Hommage à Mon Père', which includes l'assiette du boucher (fillet of lamb, veal and beef with three sauces); soufflé Suissesse; oeuf froid la Tzarine (artichoke heart filled with soft poached egg, smoked salmon and caviar); and omelette Rothschild (with apricot and cointreau). Michel's own style is lighter – you could say more modern – but, fortunately for all concerned, he is a chip off the old block and respectful of the classic methods. However, the prices do make any disappointments keenly felt. One reason to visit is that one day – not far off, I suspect – such a confluence of talents dedicated to pleasuring will be unobtainable.

PAGE ONE: 62 CHAMPAGNES. Page two: Meursault, Clos de la Barre, Lafon £129 (Clarke's £51). So it goes. Running down a list of collector's items is all very well, but if you have to buy something, and finances are constrained, the Marsannay from Bruno Clair at £30 and the Château Le Crock, St Estèphe at £28.70 fit the bill. While nearly two-thirds of this grand list is Bordeaux and Burgundy, it makes it difficult for ordinary punters to find anything affordable. Searching California and Italy for respite is fruitless, since the wines furnished in those categories also command the highest prices. The list at Le Gavroche is as institutional as they come, but who can afford to live in an institution? The question is, if customers won't baulk at paying these prices, why should they change? Fewer magnificent and more homely wines please.

Gay Hussar £32

2 Greek Street W1 (437 0973)

+ *the only Hungarian restaurant in London; the bargain lunch*
- *you'll leave heavier than when you arrived*

This year sees the 21st anniversary of chef Laszlo Holecz at the stoves of this historic Soho Hungarian restaurant. Running your finger down the menu, over the dark panelling and red-plush seating, and around the thick red-and-white china, you can barely detect the change of ownership that several years back moved the restaurant away from an individual, Victor Sassie, into the embrace of The Restaurant Partnership plc. Food here must be judged on its own terms. Of course it is substantial, calorific, cholesterol-loaded and completely lacking in political correctness: that is its charm. Left-wingers from the worlds of politics and journalism have

Open
Mon-Sat
Hours
12.15pm-2.30pm,
5.30-10.45pm
Credit cards
AmEx, Mastercard,
Visa, Switch,
Diner's
Service charge
12.5%
Set-price lunch
£16
Nearest tube station
Tottenham Court
Road
Map 5

traditionally felt at home here, as attested by the Labour posters, trophies, cartoons, signed copies of forgotten books and general air of being as resistant to change as The Tribune group. The very pink wild-cherry soup, cold pike with beetroot sauce and cucumber salad, Transylvanian mixed grill, stuffed pancakes (savoury and sweet), roast duck and smoked goose are all favourites. Galuska (thimble dumplings) and tarhonya (egg barley) are side dishes to try; poppy-seed strudel makes a very good dessert.

Gilbert's £28

Open
Lunch Mon-Fri,
dinner Mon-Sat

Hours
12.00-2.00pm,
5.30-10.00pm

Credit cards
AmEx, Mastercard,
Visa, Switch,
Diner's, Delta

Service charge
12.5% optional

Set-price lunch
£7.50 & £12.50

Set price dinner
£17.00 & £21.50

**Nearest tube
station**
South Kensington

Map 2

2 Exhibition Road SW7 (589 8947)

+ *several dessert wines by the glass*
− *dishes on the short menu tend to run out during busy periods*

This is an unassuming restaurant in a small parade of shops, where the values of good, nourishing home-cooking prevail. The interior warm-ochre walls − likened by one critic to the colour of Campbell's condensed tomato soup − have been offset by large gilt mirrors, but the effect is still homely, as if you have wandered inadvertently into someone's dining-room. A set-price menu of five starters and five main courses ranges from a simple salad of baby broad beans, or stilton and walnut tart, to monkfish cooked in a stock-rich tarragon cream sauce. Desserts are from the English nursery repertoire: rum-drenched chocolate tipsy cake, viscid sticky-toffee pudding and Mrs Beeton's (who else's?) lemon tart. Service is endearing.

OWNER JULIA CHALKLEY is usually on hand to guide you through the terrific wine list, but the informative and concise tasting notes are a great help. This serious but not intimidating document is organized by grape variety, and encourages experimentation. The recent innovation on the list of 'guest wines' to complement the dishes on the monthly menu is particularly welcome. In winter you might sample a fine old vines Madiran by the glass with your boeuf en daube, while in summer you can glug Jacky Marteau's exceptionally fruity Gamay de Touraine straight from the fridge or indulge in Jean-Paul Fichet's more substantial Bourgogne Rouge at cellar temperature.

Gitanjli-Mayfair £22

Open
Every day
Hours
12.00pm-3.00pm,
6.00-11.30pm
Credit cards
AmEx, Mastercard,
Switch, Visa,
Delta, Diner's
**Nearest tube
station**
Ealing Broadway

18–19 The Mall, Ealing Broadway W5 (0181-810 0006)

+ *the bombastic owner – when you are in the mood*
- *the bombastic owner – when you are not*

If you can think back to restaurants of the early '70s, you may remember a character called Jetty Singh. He owned a restaurant called Geetanjli (different spelling in those days) in Brook Street, Mayfair. In 1989 he moved to Marbella to open a restaurant there, and then in the summer of 1996 re-appeared in spacious premises in Ealing. In bringing Mayfair (and memories of Marbella) to Ealing, Jetty has not stinted. Marble has been lavishly used in a green marble-topped bar and grey marble-tiled floor. Swinging doors to the kitchen and private room are hand-painted in the Orphism style of Sonia and Robert Delaunay (but executed, I think, by Mrs Singh). A hall at the back called Peter Sellers's Corner is dedicated to the late actor, who was a great fan of the first Geetanjli. Sellers once took out an advertisement in the *Evening Standard* at his own expense to say: 'If you are enjoying birdie num num, you must go to this place.' Jetty is a true enthusiast about food – particularly his own Punjabi cuisine – and he is determined that his customers should enjoy themselves, even if this entails waving joss sticks under their noses and undertaking their ordering. If you are allowed any say in the matter, try to include the street snack gol guppas (stuffed lentil puffs); barra jhinga potphaari (lightly battered king prawns); fish tikka and other tandoor-cooked items; game (only in season); the fish specialities (having checked on what fish is used); baingan bartha (chargrilled aubergines mashed and fried with green peas); the pulau rice; various breads, including the paneeri naan stuffed with cheese; and the definitely superior Punjabi lassi flavoured with almonds and pistachios. As readers have written to say, Gitanjli is a welcome addition to the area.

Il Goloso £24

Open
Mon-Sat
Hours
12.00-3.00pm,
6.30pm-11.30pm
Credit cards
AmEx, Mastercard,
Visa, Switch,
Delta, Diner's
Service charge
12.5%
Cover charge
85p (evenings
only)

204 Fulham Road SW10 (352 9827)

+ *good-value set menus for both lunch and dinner*
- *long waits have been known*

A narrow dining-room packed with tables is perhaps not best-suited to what translates as 'The Glutton'. However, reasonable prices – particularly for the set lunch and dinner – and the family-run service make this a pleasant little tide pool in the 'Beach', as this stretch of Fulham Road has come to be

Set-price lunch
£5.95
Set price dinner
£9.95
Nearest tube
stations
South Kensington,
Gloucester Road,
Earls Court.
Map 2

called. A few dishes are customized, such as melanzane al Goloso (baked stuffed aubergine) and vitello Goloso (veal topped with crab and 'olandese' sauce). Bollito misto with salsa verde is also offered, but otherwise the menu is a slightly old-fashioned, nostalgic list, more inclined to sauces than to salsas, and to frying rather than grilling. The natural home for the desserts is the trolley.

Gonbei £23

Open
Dinner Mon-Sat
Hours
6.00-10.30pm,
(10.00pm Sat)
Credit cards
Mastercard, Visa,
Switch, Diner's,
Delta
Service charge
10%
Set price dinner
£19.80
Nearest tube
station
King's Cross
Map 1

151 King's Cross Road WC1 (278 0619)

+ *something virtuous in King's Cross*
− *it is only open for dinner*

Set dinners start with the tonkatsu dinner at £16, which includes sashimi or sunomono (raw fish with vinegar dressing), agedashi-tofu (deep-fried beancurd), yakitori (grilled chicken on a skewer), tonkatsu (deep-fried pork), rice, miso soup, and fruit salad or ice-cream; and move up to the sashimi or sushi dinner at £19.80, where raw fish, or raw fish and rice, take centre stage. To appreciate the rhythm and balance of a Japanese meal, a set dinner is a wise and economical order, but friendly staff and a laid-back atmosphere encourage à la carte exploration. Sushi is highly recommended. Noodles in soup with tempura make an ideal, quick, one-dish off-to-the-movies or on-the-way-home meal. The table-cooked dishes yose-nabe or suki-yaki are good to share. To go with them, drink saké, Kirin beer or Chivas Regal.

Gourmet Garden £20

Open
Wed-Mon
Hours
12.00-2.30pm,
6.00-11.30pm
Credit cards
AmEx, Mastercard,
Visa, Switch, Delta
Set-price lunch
£10.80
Set price dinner
£14.80
Nearest tube
station
Hendon Central

59 Watford Way, Hendon NW4 (0181-202 9639)

+ *proof that women run a kindlier ship*
− *the eye defeats the stomach*

Exceptionally sweet service is one of the attractions at Gourmet Garden. Malaysian and Singaporean dishes and the laminated list of specials entitled 'Chef's Recommendation' are others. Familiar Chinese assemblies are on offer if you want them, but it would be a great pity not to undertake some gastronomic exploration into what could be new territories, as presented by steamed St Peter with spicy bean sauce; braised pig's trotters with ginger and vinegar; braised quail; and winter pork in claypot. Crabs and lobsters − kept alive, alive O! − are champion when prepared with fiery Malaysian belacan. In a more soothing mode are delicate Hainanese chicken rice, and hor-fun noodles swamped with seafood in a bland but persuasive sauce. Take time to study the different menus: don't let the *embarras de richesses* tilt you towards the set-price deals.

Granita £25

127 Upper Street N1 (226 3222)

+ *'I went to market and I bought...all these things you see on the menu'*
- *some find the furnishings too unforgiving*

I wonder whether chef Ahmed Kharshoum and manager Vikki Leffman, owners of Granita, regret that dinner on 31 May 1994 when Gordon Brown stood back to let Tony Blair take the leadership: the restaurant is forever associated with New Labour. However, if New Labour is, in turn, allied with spare, functional, no-hiding-place decor and honest, vibrant dishes – such as a salad of red oakleaf, shredded Gruyère, croûtons, Dijon mustard and olive oil; crispy chicken, sake, spring-onion marinade, lemon, ginger and soy dipping sauce; linguini, fresh sardines, garlic, flat-leaf parsley and pinenuts; pan-roasted fillet of cod, pea and Parmesan risotto cake, lemon dressing and steamed broccoli; marinated roast chump of new-season lamb (pink), haricot beans, spinach, plum tomato and rosemary; caramel ice cream and biscotti – then neither party loses out. The wine list is short and to the point.

Open
Lunch Wed-Sun, dinner Tues-Sun
Hours
12.30-2.30pm, 6.30-10.30pm
Credit cards
Mastercard, Visa
Service charge
10% (parties of 10 or more)
Set-price lunch
£11.95 & £13.95
Nearest tube stations
Angel, Highbury & Islington

Great Nepalese £19

48 Eversholt Street NW1 (388 6737)

+ *authentic Nepalese cooking at reasonable prices*
- *customers who order onion bhajias and chicken Madras*

A lthough plain and unpretentious in appearance, service here puts some fashionable places to shame. The Great Nepalese has been owned and run by the Manandhar family for 14 years and has two Nepalese chefs in the kitchen. The menu hardly seems to change, but the specialities from the homeland are so under-represented in London that it would be hard to tire of them. Everything labelled Nepalese is recommended: vegetable dishes come lightly cooked; curries are pungent with ginger and herbs (try the duck dish hash ko bhutawa); and there are four different ways with potatoes (all good). To finish, try the delicious rice pudding and a tot of Nepalese rum.

Open
Every day
Hours
12.00-2.30pm, 6.00-11.30pm
Credit cards
AmEx, Mastercard, Visa, Switch, Delta, Diner's
Service charge
10%
Set-price lunch
£5.75 & £11.50
Nearest tube station
Euston
Map 1

Green Cottage £17

Open
Every day
Hours
12.00-11.00pm
Credit cards
AmEx, Mastercard,
Visa, Switch, Delta
Service charge
10%
**Nearest tube
stations**
Swiss Cottage,
Finchley Road
Map 1

9 New College Parade, Finchley Road NW3 (722 5305)

+ *close your eyes and you might imagine you're in Chinatown*
− *open them and you will see an unprepossessing stretch of
Finchley Road*

Among the discerning Cantonese of Swiss Cottage, this restaurant seems to be the one that finds most favour. Meat dishes are particularly well-executed: for example, fragrant Cantonese duck; roasted crispy belly pork; dried shredded beef with chilli; and soy mixed meats for the more adventurous, which include liver, gizzard, squid and duck wings. Zhai 'duckling' made from layered sheets of soy bean and wheat gluten shows that vegetarians are not neglected, a contention supported by the presence of Buddha's cushion vegetables (stewed black moss and mushrooms on Chinese leaves). The virtue of this place lies in delivering cheap and cheerful food in cheap but admittedly not too cheerful surroundings.

Greenhouse £50

Open
Lunch Mon-Fri,
dinner Mon-Sat
Hours
12.00-4.00pm,
6.30-11.00pm
Credit cards
AmEx, Mastercard,
Visa, Switch,
Diner's
Cover charge
£1 per person
**Nearest tube
stations**
Green Park,
Piccadilly Circus
Map 3

27a Hays Mews W1 (499 3331)

+ *the attempt to redefine English cuisine*
− *the cover charge, vegetable charge and wine prices*

The re-invention of British cooking that Gary Rhodes made synonymous with himself and, to some extent, with Greenhouse lives on in the menu, but no longer with Rhodes at the helm. His scholarship has been taken elsewhere (some of it to the back of sugar packets). Signature dishes such as fillet of smoked haddock with Welsh rarebit on a tomato and chive salad, braised oxtails, and steamed treacle sponge with custard are, at the time of writing, being prepared by the brigade trained by Rhodes and headed up by Wayne Tapsfield. Modern (as opposed to post-modern) British dishes include chargrilled pigeon with a sweet pea, bacon and button-onion salad; tuna carpaccio with spicy, crispy (sic) spinach; roast cod on buttered cabbage with wholegrain-mustard butter; orange-glazed confit of duck on a leek and foie gras mash; and rhubarb and honey brûlée. On the whole, the level of expertise in the kitchen is fine, but the prices now set up great expectations − invariably trumped by the bill − and service can be amateurish. Men like this restaurant, with its petrified topiary and jittery waitresses in serving-wench outfits.

The Green Olive £28

5 Warwick Place W9 (289 2469)

+ *neighbourhood restaurant priced for frequent use*
- *bad art on the walls*

Open
Lunch Sat & Sun,
dinner every day
Hours
12.00-3.00pm
(Sat & Sun),
7.00-10.45pm
Credit cards
AmEx, Mastercard,
Switch, Visa, Delta
Set-price lunch
£13.95
**Nearest tube
station**
Warwick Avenue
Map 6

The Green Olive is the Francophile brother or sister restaurant of the nearby Red Pepper (q.v.), an Italian restaurant and pizzeria with the bonus of a wood-fired pizza oven. A mild Italian influence in the shape of various pasta dishes – apparent at the time of opening (February 1996) – has dwindled somewhat, although a ravioli dish still inhabits the first course, and tagliatelle with garlic parsley butter is the partner for roast scallops in the main course. Niçoise is perhaps the correct definition of the cooking: a tian of vegetables underpins lamb fillet; mesclun salad garnishes foie gras parfait; and a soupe au pistou kicked off a May menu. The cooking is competent without being startling. The nature of desserts has gone from being adventurous (as in Amaretto crème brûlée with goat's milk) to conventionally indulgent (as in fine apple tart with Calvados ice cream). The buzz apparent soon after the opening has subsided – something perhaps not unconnected with the move of the original manager, whose liquid, brown-eyed gaze is now directed at the customers of Osteria le Fate (q.v.) – or was at the time of writing. Readers who have been patronizing London restaurants for as long as I have will remember this address as Didier. The Laura Ashley look that I recall – probably inaccurately – has been replaced with a restrained approach, in which unpainted brick walls are a feature. Glassware and napery are of the superior kind that gives you the pleasant frisson of anticipation when sitting down to a crisp white cloth studded with shining empty glasses. To fill them, the wine list is most interesting – and appropriate – in its selection from the South and South-West of France.

FOCUSING ON WINES from southern France is a risky business. It is often asserted that, though the wines may travel, the sunshine in them does not. Here is an opportunity to put that proposition to the test in this short but exciting list. Francois Sack's olive-oily Cassis loses nothing in the transition; the poached-pear fatness of white Lirac and Maurice Conte's red Côtes du Roussillon (available in three vintages: 1979, 1980 and 1986) in their different ways conjure up the heat and dust; while the excellently chosen Rhônes (Chave, Graillot, Château de la Nerthe) dish out the requisitely authentic woodsmoke and spice.

Green's Restaurant & Oyster Bar £40

36 Duke Street, St James's SW1 (930 4566)

+ *Simon Parker Bowles*
- *surroundings are looking shabby*

Open
Every day
Hours
Bar 11.30am-
3.00pm,
restaurant 12.30-
3.00pm; bar &
restaurant 5.30-
11.00pm (Sun
5.30-10.00pm)
Credit cards
AmEx, Visa,
Switch, Diner's,
JCB
Cover charge
£1 per person
**Nearest tube
stations**
Green Park,
Piccadilly Circus
Map 3

L ast year's guide bemoaned the fact that this bastion of Englishness was making too many trips abroad (in cooking terms that is). Happily for everyone, particularly Eurosceptics, the menu has reverted to being staunchly traditional. There is no flamboyance, nor − worst of all the sins − showing off. Native oysters, quails' eggs, potted shrimps, dressed crab, Dover sole, fish cakes, bangers and mash, liver and bacon, Suffolk ham with chutney, cold roast sirloin of beef, Paxton & Whitfield cheeses, bread and butter pudding, baked apple; these are what put the great into Britain. Service is polished. The panelled bar is a good place to meet for a glass or three of bubbly and a tip for the 2.30 at Newmarket.

Green Street £28

3 Green Street W1 (409 0453)

NOW THE OVERSEAS & EMPIRE PRESS CLUB

Open
Mon-Fri
Hours
12.30-3.00pm,
7.30-11.00pm
Credit cards
AmEx, Mastercard,
Visa, Switch
Service charge
12.5%
**Nearest tube
station**
Marble Arch
Map 3

O pen to non-members for weekday lunches only, the basement restaurant of The Green Street Club is useful to know about in a part of town (just off the Marble Arch end of Oxford Street) where eating possibilities may seem limited to fast-food chains, a M&S sandwich or propping up The Brass Rail at Selfridges. Bona-fide members of the louche Green Street would never, of course, be caught frequenting any of those places. The eclectic style of food pioneered by Peter Gordon, now at The Sugar Club (q.v.), has calmed down into (how shall we say?) modern European. There are quite straightforward British items such as smoked-salmon pâté and brown shrimps; smoked herring poached in milk with green beans and roast new potatoes; Cumberland sausage with mash and onion gravy; and steamed chocolate and hazelnut pudding with cream, as well as some Italianate ideas. The decor is colourful and clashing − as is, fairly frequently, the overheard conversation.

Grill St Quentin £35

3 Yeoman's Row SW3 (581 8377)

+ *the sheer size*
- *its formulaic quality*

This large, underground outpost of The Savoy Group offers a schematic French menu served by automatons. However, if an unchallenging but well-executed meal starting with oysters, crab mayonnaise, plateau de fruits de mer or terrine de campagne, and moving on to steak frites or some less contentious choice of grilled item, and finishing with cheese and fruit tart (from 'Spécialités St Quentin') is what you feel like, you will find it here and probably without the fuss of booking. The unexpected expanse of the space is both a pleasure and the reason for finding a table for spur-of-the-moment dining. A few plats cuisinés and daily specials are evidence of there being chefs in the kitchen.

Open
Every day
Hours
12.00-3.00pm,
6.30-11.30pm
(Sun 12.00-
3.30pm, 6.30-
10.30pm)
Credit cards
AmEx, Mastercard,
Switch, Visa,
Delta, Diner's
Service charge
12.5%
Set-price lunch
£11
**Nearest tube
stations**
South Kensington,
Knightsbridge
Map 2

Halcyon Hotel – The Room £45

129 Holland Park Avenue W11 (221 5411)

+ *the terrace enclosed by the villas of Holland Park; Sunday brunch*
- *you being the person picking up the bill*

The Halcyon has cracked the business of outdoor eating with a small, discreet terrace more or less roofed with square, cream canvas umbrellas. In pretty weather, a table outside (book early) acts as a sort of guarantee of enjoyment. In other conditions, high prices set up expectations that Martin Hadden's food often, but not always, fulfils. The à la carte menu (£29 for two courses, exclusive of service) – on which luxury ingredients such as lobster (in ravioli), a sprinkling of caviar (on smoked salmon) or sautéed foie gras (as part of a salad) make an appearance – breaks into supplementary charges. Hadden's training with Nico Ladenis has instilled hard-earned, classical skills, to which he has added a rather peculiar penchant for elaborate construction and fanciful garnishes. Dealing with fish is his strong suit. The American-showbiz element in the clientele who want to eat water-dressed leaves might opt for the vegetarian menu ('I'll take the asparagus and morels – hold the hollandaise') – not minding that it, too, costs £29 for two courses.

Open
Sun-Fri
Hours
12.00-2.30pm
(Sun 3.00pm),
7.00-10.30pm
(Thurs & Fri 4.00-
11.00pm, Sun
7.00-10.00pm)
Credit cards
AmEx,Mastercard,
Visa, Switch,
Delta, Diner's
Set-price lunch
£23
Set-price dinner
£29
**Nearest tube
station**
Holland Park
Map 6

Some pricey wines apart, this is an imaginative list. Schlumberger (a renowned producer, not a make of winter duvet) takes care of

Alsace; Mulderbosch and Frog's Leap supply the Sauvignon blanc interest; and some rewarding New World style Rhône look-and-taste-alikes from Yeringberg and Qupé are bred for the sophisticated palate. Le Sophiste, a beeswax-textured Roussanne/Marsanne blend with a top hat for a cork — it could only come from the prankish Randall Grahm — is £14 more here than at Stephen Bull (q.v.), so prices could be reined in a bit. An extensive list of fine wines reminds us that the clientele are not short of a bob or three.

The Halkin Restaurant   £50

Halkin Street SW1 (333 1234)

+ *the style is the restaurant*
- *faultily faultless, icily regular, splendidly null*

On the front page of the menu runs the epigraph: 'The biggest refinement in all kinds of art is synthesis of simplicity', and at The Halkin minimalist sleek chic runs hand in kid glove with stylized starkness. One might call it the new Milan-imalism: all rectilinear surfaces, cool furnishings, wide-spaced tables and designer-dressed model staff. Precision is evident in the kitchen, where each highly visible grain in a shallow risotto with goat's cheese, courgette flower and red-wine sauce seemed to have been individually attended to. Stefano Cavallini varnishes his canvasses with many deft touches, marshalling a fragment of this, a sliver of that, to confirm that austere definition of style in haute cuisine: that you create time to make more look like less. Roast sea bass is superb, flecked and studded with olives, capers and tomatoes; whereas smoked-haddock and cod quenelles with mashed potato, roasted quail, braised radicchio with Parma ham and broccoli sauce is one of those myriad-minded compositions that you feel is intended as an oblation to the twinkling firmament of Michelin stars: snazzy but utterly pretentious, neither fish nor fowl nor lettuce leaf, where subtle simplicity has yielded to artistic refinement and produced blandness. The wine list stables pedigree Italian stallions and French thoroughbreds to the neglect of more workhorse wines. An entry fee of £25 for the Chianti Classico of Isole e Olena gives you some indication of the territory, but you would pay a fiver less for Gaja's Barbaresco here than at L'Incontro (q.v.): yes, a snip at £155.

Open
Lunch Mon–Fri, dinner every day
Hours
12.30–2.30pm, 7.30–11.00pm (Sun 7.00– 10.00pm)
Credit cards
AmEx, Mastercard, Visa, Delta, Diner's, Switch
Set-price lunch £18.50
Set-price dinner £50
Nearest tube station
Hyde Park Corner
Map 2

Harbour City £24

46 Gerrard Street W1 (439 7859)

+ shark's-fin dumpling; miniature roast pork pie; lamb 'goulas'
- the weekend crowds

This Chinatown restaurant, spread over three floors and seating 160, has many things going for it: superb dim-sum served straight from the kitchen (not left to wilt on trolleys), with 36 exotic options of great appeal to those spellbound by claw of chicken or skin of pig; terrific noodle assemblies, including dough-pulled noodles Shanghai-style; chef's specialities such as hot pots and resonant, anise-imbued stews of lamb or beef 'goulas'; Peking appetizers and Peking duck; helpful, efficient staff; and consistently high standards. It is also open all week, from noon until late.

Open
Every day
Hours
12.00–5.00pm,
7.00–11.30pm
Credit cards
AmEx, Mastercard,
Visa, Switch,
Diner's
Service charge
10%
Set-price lunch
£12.50
**Nearest tube
station**
Leicester Square
Map 5

The Havelock Tavern £18

57 Masbro Road W14 (603 5374)

+ bright, lively atmosphere
- anyone over 30 will feel long in the tooth

Residents of villagey Brook Green have been packing into this converted L-shaped pub, run by young, enthusiastic staff with impressive restaurant pedigrees. The formula — one spawned by The Eagle (q.v.) and The Landsdowne (q.v.) — is simple: old wooden tables, stripped and sealed floorboards, and large windows to give the feel of light and space. The food, ordered from the bar, is 'revived rustic' and includes standards such as penne with tomatoes and chilli, and tuna confit Niçoise. These are supplemented by dishes like warm salad of duck's gizzards and heart with bacon and poached egg, and sauté of lamb's sweetbreads, for those suffering from innard-withdrawal symptoms. Finish off with prune and almond tart or Beaujolais granita. A good selection of wines is scribbled on the blackboard.

Open
Every day
Hours
Mon–Sat 12.30–
2.30pm, 7.00–
10.00pm; Sun
12.30–3.00pm,
7.00–9.30pm
**Nearest tube
station**
Shepherd's Bush
Map 1

Hilaire £39

68 Old Brompton Road SW7 (584 8993)

+ polished service that still manages to be friendly
- hefty prices on the evening à la carte

This oasis of tranquillity, offering a retreat from the fumes and bustle of Old Brompton Road, naturally attracts the well-heeled of South Kensington and punters coming from a hard

Open
Lunch Mon–Fri,
dinner Mon–Sat
Hours
12.30–2.30pm,
6.30–11.30pm
Credit cards
AmEx, Mastercard,
Visa, Switch,
Delta, Diner's

Set-price lunch
£18.50
Set-price dinner
£28.50
Nearest tube
station
South Kensington
Map 2

day's bidding at Christie's. Velour curtains and starched napery soak up the noise, and well-groomed waiters shimmer silently to your table to deliver handwritten menus revealing the best of unadulterated, fresh British produce. Pungent home-smoked eel from Norfolk with Jersey royal potatoes; juicy Scottish divers scallops with a coriander and lime dressing; tender Welsh spring lamb, roasted with a tapenade crust; or sea bass with samphire and laverbread beurre blanc all demonstrate chef Bryan Webb's shrewd ability to source and handle quality ingredients with care and imagination. Although the cooking derives its inspiration from various sources – Spanish, Thai and Welsh influences have been noted – there is a unifying go-for-it approach that renders some meals truly memorable.

THE WINE LIST has been assembled with intelligence and clarity by Neville Blech of The Wine Treasury. An index enables you to nominate the style of wine that you wish to drink (light, dry white or full-bodied red, for example), while the tasting notes are graphic yet concise. Recurrent epithets are balance, elegance, finesse and concentration: these, then, are wines specifically selected to match the food. All the classic regions are well-represented, but look out particularly for a Muscat-like Torrontès from Bodegas Etchart in Argentina, and for a surprisingly steely and refined Welschriesling from Austria.

Humming Bird   £20

84 Stroud Green Road N4 (263 9690)

+ *service so friendly that you will forgive a lot*
– *those occasions when there is a lot to forgive*

Open
Mon–Sun
Hours
11.00am–12.00am
(Sun 2.00pm–
11.00pm)
Credit cards
AmEx, Mastercard,
Switch, Visa
Set-price lunch
£6.95
Set-price dinner
£9.95
Nearest tube
station
Finsbury Park

Mark Ramgoolie took over the Humming Bird from his mother, who set it up, and he is now both 'front of house' and chef. The Caribbean food is authentic and well-prepared: try rich green crab callallo soup, and goat curry with rice and peas. Also ask about fish dishes: the laconically named fried fish is a triumph, as are the homemade breads. It is said that people make the journey from Brixton to enjoy the Humming Bird rum punch, Guinness punch and mauby – and if they don't, they should do. Homemade ice creams and cornmeal pudding are also worth the detour.

Hyde Park Hotel – The Restaurant Marco Pierre White £95

Open
Lunch Mon-Fri,
dinner Mon-Sat
Hours
12.00-2.30pm,
7.00-11.30pm
Credit cards
AmEx, Mastercard,
Visa, Diner's
Set-price lunch
£29.50
Set-price dinner
£75
Nearest tube
station
Knightsbridge
Map 2

66 Knightsbridge SW1 (259 5380)

+ *the best chef in the country*
- *the entrance; the odd disappointment*

Marco Pierre White creates news, waves, ripples and occupies inches of newspaper column space. Just some of the recent rumours, stories and facts concern his buying of a chunk of Mount Street in Les Saveurs and The Mirabelle, entering into partnership with Damien Hirst to revamp Leoni's Quo Vadis in Soho, planning a chain of brasserie-style restaurants across Britain and moving himself and his three Michelin stars to The Oak Room Le Meridien Hotel in Piccadilly. Since he also controls The Criterion (an Eros award this year) any little slips between cup and lip at this his grand showplace would seem easily explicable. When on form, White's cooking is to my mind unbeatable. He has a sorcerer's understanding of ingredients and an innate but well-honed intuition and talent when it comes to dealing with them. The combinations are tantalizing, inviting: ballotine of salmon with herbs, salad of crayfish with caviar, fromage blanc, toasted brioche; galantine of duck and foie gras with walnuts, gelée of Jurançon; roast John Dory with chives and ginger, lentilles du Puy, salad of herbs and truffle, coulis of basil; roast saddle of rabbit with rosemary, risotto of herbs, étuvée of leeks and asparagus, jus of rosemary. Oddly, for such a butch chap, he is at his best when handling fish (which, as the magazines remind us, he also loves to catch). Supplements of as much as £20 on a £70 menu let you know that money should be no object and that he has no objection to receiving your money. But when all goes well and the service manages a smile, and you are with the one you love – or you have just been given a rise – a meal here is a sensational experience.

Ikkyu £20-30

Open
Lunch Mon-Fri,
dinner Sun-Fri
Hours
11.30am-2.30pm
and 6.00-10.30pm
Credit cards
AmEx, Mastercard,
Visa, Diner's

67a Tottenham Court Road W1 (636 9280)

+ *unintimidating Japanese robatayaki*
- *hard to find; slightly shop-soiled decor*

If you find yourself walking up and down Tottenham Court Road looking for the well-camouflaged entrance to this cellar restaurant (it seems to be under Goodge Street station), persevere. In the 1980s this establishment carved out a name for

Service charge
10%
Nearest tube
station
Goodge Street
Map 3

itself as being the perfect place for novices to try sushi — the nigiri set being both authentic and reasonably priced. Today, sushi and sashimi remain excellent; the more adventurous cooked dishes bear examination and Japanese salary men still keep their personal bottles of Chivas locked away behind grilles.

Ikkyu of Chinatown   £15–20

Open
Every day
Hours
12.00–11.30pm
Credit cards
AmEx, Mastercard,
Visa, Switch, Delta
Service charge
10%
Set-price lunch
£4.40–£6.60
Set-price dinner
£5.80–£12
Nearest tube
station
Leicester Square
Maps 4 &5

7–9 Newport Place WC2 (439 3554)

+ *bargains to be had*
- *service sometimes struggles with the numbers*

Part of the Japanese invasion of Chinatown, the new Ikkyu (opposite Tokyo Diner) is closely wedded to the original Goodge Street branch (see above). Even though both share chef Kawaguchi, the Newport Place Ikkyu seems a more modern option in more than just design terms. There are shabu shabu set meals featuring beef teriyaki and tonkatsu (pork chop); a noodle bar with ramen and soba; boxed meals; and, of course, sushi and sashimi. This branch is lighter, brighter and younger in tone. The set meals are very reasonably priced.

The Immortals   £25

Open
Every day
Hours
12.00–11.30pm
(11.30am–
10.30pm Sun)
Credit cards
AmEx, Mastercard,
Visa, Switch,
Diner's, Delta
Service charge
10%
Set-price lunch
£6.50–£13.50
Nearest tube
station
Piccadilly Circus
Map 4 or 5

58-60 Shaftesbury Avenue W1 (437 3119)

+ *set-price menus that depart from the clichés; smiling service*
- *tinned fruit cocktail with the almond-beancurd dessert*

The widely held belief that only saps choose the set menus in Chinese restaurants is a truism that, on the whole, stands the test of tasting. If you wish to eat the most adapted, bastardized dishes — that is, spring rolls, spare ribs, chicken-and-sweetcorn soup, stir-fried chicken with cashewnuts, sweet-and-sour pork and egg-fried rice — you usually need look no further than Menu A. One of the features that allows The Immortals to stand out in Chinatown — a district now spreading down towards Piccadilly — is its interesting set-price menus at the expensive end of the range. Menu D (advertised for a minimum of three people at £25 a head, but graciously served to two) includes pickled vegetables, cucumber and jellyfish; baked soft crab; hot pot of shellfish with glass noodles; beancurd with spicy minced pork; abalone and shark's lips with seasonal vegetables; steamed fish with ginger and spring onion; and fresh fruit among its 10 dishes. When faced with a long, repetitious menu (as should be the case in a Cantonese establishment), giving the order of 'Menu D', and then sitting back and letting the dishes roll in is a luxurious sensation. They roll in disconcertingly quickly, but Hong Kong chef Chung Choy Suen seems, for the most part, to run his kitchen as a tight ship. Seafood is his speciality, and, if choosing à la carte, the penultimate page of the menu — featuring dishes such as whole sea bass with roasted pork belly and garlic, and steamed eel with dried tangerine peel — is one not to pass over. Three pre-theatre menus are offered, of which I would go for 'Water Lily Special' (£13.50 a head at time of writing), starring fried lobster with ginger and spring onion. The location of The Immortals makes it ideal for a pre-theatre meal. The decor is allegedly planned according to principles of feng shui: one to enshrine is the decision to remove the plastic seat covers left over from the days when The Immortals was the Taiwanese Dragon's Nest.

Imperial City £32

Royal Exchange, Cornhill EC3 (626 3437)

+ *the setting: brick-lined vaults of the Royal Exchange*
- *impassive waitresses*

A Square–Mile location, Thai ownership and Ken Hom as consultant result in a sophisticated Chinese restaurant with appeal to business folk who do not wish to waste time wading through long, repetitive lists — they do enough of that at their desks. The provenance of the close–on 60 dishes is Canton, Peking, Chiu Cho and Szechuan, as well as Hong-Kong's new-wave fashions (namely, mango chicken and majestic avocado scallops). To start, Imperial cold platter — for two — is far classier than the hot (mostly deep-fried) version; while mu-shu pork with lettuce makes a nice change from Peking or crispy duck in a pass-the-parcel midway course. Steamed salmon with black-bean sauce, Cantonese pressed duck, Peking braised lamb, spicy beancurd casserole, and Szechuan dan-dan noodles are all recommended main dishes, followed by firecracker sweet won tons with ice-cream. Unusually, the set menus are not the recourse of the sap: the Imperial seasonal set menu, with its second course of lobster, suits celebrations of deals and leaps skyward of the FTSE index.

Open
Mon-Fri
Hours
11.30am-8.30pm
Credit cards
AmEx, Mastercard,
Diner's, Visa,
Switch, Delta
Service charge
12.5% optional
Set-price lunch
£14.95-£24.95
**Nearest tube
station**
Bank
Map 1

Inaho £26

4 Hereford Road W2 (221 8495)

+ *a welcoming Japanese ark*
− *too many arriving two by two*

Going to Inaho is less like invading someone's front room, more like trying to crowd into a ski hut. You will find the owner Mr Nakamura smiling and pleased to see you, although his chances of persuading anyone else to finish up and leave so that you can sit down look pretty slim. Inaho only seats 20, so remember to book. All the elements of the Japanese menu are appreciated: the sashimi, tempura, grills and noodles. An additional list presented on a wooden panel, including dishes such as baked aubergine or salmon and saki soup, is placed on the table. Sushi is only offered on Wednesday to Saturday evenings, but apparently you can have it any time if the chef is given enough notice to prepare the rice.

Open
Lunch Mon–Fri,
dinner Mon–Sat
Hours
12.30–3.00pm,
7.00–11.30pm
Credit cards
Delta, Mastercard,
Visa
Service charge
10%
Set-price lunch
£8–£22
Nearest tube
station
Notting Hill Gate
Map 6

L'Incontro £39

87 Pimlico Road SW1 (730 3663)

+ *gleaming mirrors and glassware*
− *take extra currency with your passport to Pimlico;*
  spaghetti with microscopic lobster

The circumferential Dr Johnson once remarked that he would smile with the wise and eat with the rich, but he might hesitate to dine among the rakishly thin models and suntans to be seen at L'Incontro, Gino Santin's slick and sleek up-market venue. While they might toy with an insalata or a slice of bresaola, there are heartier specialities (mainly Venetian in origin) on the à la carte that include pasta e fagiole (bean and pasta soup), agnello i agrodolce (lamb cutlets in a sweet-and-sour sauce), capasante (scallops) and baccalà mantecato (creamed salt cod). Risottos and pasta have passed muster. At lunch there is a humanely priced, limited-choice set menu for mortals and people not working out in the gym. Nothing will prepare you for the wine list, a catalogue of criminal mark-ups from the average Italian house fodder (£16.50 in red and white) to £33 for a Pouilly-Fumé from Château Favray (cost price £7.65). Read it and weep.

Open
Lunch Mon–Fri,
dinner every day
Hours
Mon–Fri 12.30–
2.30pm, 7.00–
11.30pm (Sun
10.30pm)
Credit cards
AmEx, Diner's,
Mastercard,
Switch, Visa
Cover charge
£1.50 per person
Set-price lunch
£14.50–£18.50
Nearest tube
station
Sloane Square
Map 2

Interlude de Chavot £52

5 Charlotte Street W1 (637 0222)

NOW INTERLUDE

The kiss of Michelin has been bestowed on Eric Crouillère-Chavot's operation. Waiters have multiplied (as if by parthenogenesis); prices have shot up. Chavot's cooking abilities are as sound as ever they were, in fact developing all the time, but no longer can we say that a meal here is a bargain. And some amelioration in price should be mandatory given the surroundings: The front part of the restaurant feels like it is a hallway; the back part feels like Siberia, a condition accentuated by air-conditioning turned up high on cool evenings; the murky green cover plates lower your centre of gravity. However, certain dishes are sublime. Chavot's training with Pierre Koffmann, Raymond Blanc, Nico Ladenis and Marco Pierre White shows in the fundamentals and he is now adding twists of his own. Foie gras and chicken liver parfait with toasted brioche is one of the best versions of this slab of luxury in London; roast quail, herb crostini and truffle dressing puts personality into quail (a Herculean task); roasted scallops and pistou is subtle; panfried foie gras with a tarte Tatin of endives is a marriage made in heaven; roasted leg of rabbit stuffed with squid on a pearl barley risotto has its fans. Desserts are appropriately frivolous. But I'm sure the original roly-poly Michelin man would agree, meals are about more than just food.

Open
Lunch Mon-Fri, dinner Mon-Sat
Hours
12.00-2.30pm, 7.00-11.00pm
Credit cards
AmEx, Diner's, Mastercard, Switch, Visa, JCB
Set-price lunch
£17.50
Nearest tube station
Tottenham Court Road
Map 4

Istanbul Iskembecisi £18

9 Stoke Newington Road N16 (254 7291)

+ *tripe soup, roast lamb's head and kokarec; open until 5am*
- *squeamish companions*

Stoke Newington, where there is a significant Turkish community, is not short of good Turkish restaurants — Mangal and Samsun are two others to look out for — but Istanbul Iskembecisi (meaning Istanbul tripe restaurant) offers a bit more. Be assured, it serves not only items like boiled head-of-lamb soup, but also options such as an extensive, familiar, mainly vegetarian mezeler; kebabs and grilled meat; slow-cooked dishes such as Turkish goulash or braised lamb shank; and the Ottoman Palace speciality of hunkar begendi (lamb stewed with mashed aubergine and cheese). Forget the mealy-mouthed way that the English treat tripe — boiling it with milk and onions — and try it sharpened with salt, vinegar, lemon

Open
Every day
Hours
11.00am-5.00am
Credit cards
AmEx, Mastercard, Visa, Switch
Nearest tube/ railway station
Highbury & Islington/Dalston
Map 1

juice and chilli flakes, added to suit your own tastebuds. Kokarec (charcoal-grilled intestines) is served as an unattributable pile of crisp, golden shreds with salads and spices to mix in: try it. The staff are charming and in favour of children.

I-Thai ⭐ new

Hempel Hotel, 31–5 Craven Hill Gardens W2 (298 9000)

What follows is a prediction: that the restaurant at Anouska Hempel's second hotel (the first is Blakes in South Kensington) will feature a meeting of Thai and Italian cuisines, will be remarkable in appearance, and will be expensive.

The Ivy £40

1 West Street WC2 (836 4751)

+ *the place most likely to provide Brad Pitt at the next table*
- *if you're not Brad Pitt having to book way ahead*

Christopher Corbin and Jeremy King who also own and run Le Caprice (q.v.) are the angels and impresarios behind London's showbiz restaurant par excellence, now into its eighth blockbusting year. The theatreland connection is re-inforced in positive ways: the person taking the booking knows when the curtain comes down on whatever it is you are seeing; the waiters understand how important it is to get a drink immediately after arriving. But The Ivy works even if the meal is your show. The long menu, divided like the classic lists of old, caters for more or less every mood and appetite. There are classic dishes, avant-garde creations, kitchen sink dramas and works in translation. The standard of preparation, if not faultless, is high. For regulars — and there are many — the dishes of the day scribbled in the margins of the menu (fringe productions) give pleasure and diversion. The long, low premises with their Harlequin-patterned stained glass windows are graced by good art.

THE SAME LIST applies to The Ivy as to its sister restaurant Le Caprice (q.v.) one symmetrically divided between reds and whites and split into three further subsections (French; Australian, New Zealand and Californian; Italian and Spanish). A thoroughly modern well-presented package comprising 100 or so wines from around the world at tempting prices most central London restaurants don't begin to match.

Open
Every day
Hours
12.00–3.00pm,
5.30pm–12.00am
Credit cards
Diner's,
Mastercard,
Switch, Visa
Cover charge
£1.50 per person,
Set-price lunch
£14.50 (weekends only)
Nearest tube station
Leicester Square
Map 5

Jason's £30

Jason's Wharf (opposite No. 60 Blomfield Road) W9 (286 6752)

+ *superior seafood by the Grand Union Canal*
- *the tendency towards creamy, boozy sauces*

Here is the best of both worlds: a purpose-built restaurant on land hard by the canal at Little Venice, with a terrace giving on to the water. Chef is Sylvain Ho Wing Chong, who has been associated with several Mauritian fish restaurants including a fleeting, floating one. The 'Arrivage du Jour', as the menu puts it, is displayed in a cold cabinet by the entrance and in front of the open-plan kitchen, immediately instilling an appetite for crab, mussels, oysters, lobster and familiar fish such as cod and turbot, or for more exotic species such as bourgeois, vacqua and red snapper. Treatments range from the conventionally creamy to the more excitingly spicy (the Mauritian input), or, in the case of a noble fish such as sea bass, simple grilling. Lunchtime offers light bites. The canal boat The Lace Plate offers meals to float off with for party bookings arranged in advance.

Open
Lunch every day,
dinner Mon-Sat
Hours
9.30am-5.00pm,
6.30-10.30pm
Credit cards
AmEx, Mastercard,
Visa, Switch, Delta
Set-price lunch
£12.95
Set price dinner
£16.95
**Nearest tube
station**
Warwick Avenue
Map 6

Jimmy Beez £24

303 Portobello Road W10 (964 9100)

+ *creative vegetarian dishes*
- *wobbly tables and tired paintwork*

Refugees from the market and Notting Hillbilly hipsters cram into this tiny, modish brasserie just north of the Westway to tuck eagerly into its remarkably cosmopolitan fare. James Breslaw is one of the more innovative restaurateurs on the scene, and has deservedly built up a substantial following. The earth-girdling menu may comprise such favourites as barbecued Peking duck with red-plum pickle; cumin-roasted red snapper with lime and spring onion chutney; satay prawns; plum tomato tarte Tatin (a classic of Le Caprice [q.v.]); gnocchi and risottos; and comforting steaks and burgers – a choice as diverse and exotic as the music that reverberates through the restaurant. 'Accessorize' your meal with a side order of crispy spinach, kumera potatoes or wok-fried vegetables. Considering the galley-sized kitchen, the standard of cooking is consistently good. Offering brunch until 6pm is an astute wheeze appreciated by the local artists manqués.

Open
Every day
Hours
11.00am-11.00pm
Credit cards
AmEx, Mastercard,
Visa, Switch, Delta
Service charge
Only on Sat & Sun
brunch, 12.5%
(for 6 or more)
Set-price lunch
£12.95-£23.50
**Nearest tube
station**
Ladbroke Grove
Map 6

Open
Lunch Mon–Sat,
dinner every day
Hours
12.00–2.30pm,
6.00–11.00pm
Credit cards
AmEx, Mastercard,
Visa, Diner's
Service charge
12.5%
Set price dinner
£15.50–£19.50
**Nearest tube
station**
Tottenham Court
Road
Map 5

Jin £26

16 Bateman Street W1 (734 0908)

+ *ginseng cocktails; chilli appeal*
− *musak like aural flock wallpaper*

As yet, few Korean restaurants make concessions to Western attempts to come to terms with their cuisine. Jin attracts a mixed crowd of diners who are drawn to the friendly service and to the relatively accessible menu. Bulgogi (slices of beef marinated in chilli and sesame oil), is grilled at the table, wrapped in lettuce leaves and served with kim chee (pickled chilli vegetables). Kim chee is the motor − or should one say the soul − of Korean cooking: an integral accompaniment to all food and an aid to digestion. Also excellent is yuk whe (shredded beef with strips of pear and egg yolk). Experiment too with bi bim bap (rice or vegetables with a raw egg dropped on top); hobak chun (sliced marrow in a light egg batter) and man doo kook (a clear broth with steamed meat dumplings). An interesting range of drinks includes the famous gin ginseng martini cocktail, guaranteed to leave you shaken and stirred.

Open
Tues–Sun
Hours
Lunch 12.00–
2.15pm; dinner
6.00–10.45pm
Credit cards
AmEx, Mastercard,
Switch, Visa
Service charge
10%
Set price dinner
£14.50
**Nearest tube
station**
Victoria
Map 2

Joyful £25

72–3 Wilton Road SW1 (828 9300)

+ *interesting Chinese vegetables (if you ask); no MSG*
− *the awkward, narrow ground-floor dining-room*

The entrepreneurship of Jerry C.C. Tsang, owner of this Chinese restaurant in Victoria, usefully contributes to its menu. From small beginnings in 1976, with 11 acres in Bedfordshire, Tsang is now the largest grower in England of Chinese vegetables, supplying supermarkets as well as Chinatown's greengrocers. His activity in the fish trade is also evident in the dishes on offer. In the first course, lettuce delight wraps iceberg leaves around mixed sautéed fish; oysters and scallops are steamed in the shell with garlic sauce; and octopus grapples with a hot and spicy sauce. Fresh lobster and crabs, eels, squid, prawns, sea bass, oysters and scallops are all starting points for main courses; meat and poultry dishes are, of course, also offered. Vegetarians should note the dedicated section with dishes such as stewed chestnuts, water chestnuts and beancurd puffs; and braised beanthread and vegetables with a red beancurd sauce.

Kalamaras
Mega & Micro   £26 & £18 BYO

76–8 Inverness Mews W2 (727 9122);
66 Inverness Mews W2 (727 5082)

+ *the Beatles ate here*
- *the interiors are looking more tired than Paul McCartney*

Inverness Mews off Queensway does not replicate the streets of Erectheos and Erotokritou in Athens, as pictured on the menu, but, on a warm night with your eyes half-closed, the noise spilling out and the scents of chargrilling can transport you at least some of the way there. The new ownership (since Stelios Platanos retired) has kept the formula going, offering tangibly Greek – as opposed to Greek/Cypriot – dishes. It is good to see horta (wild greens), although I think it is a pretty penitential dish; and the plate of psaria fresca (fresh fish) outdoes what might be plucked from the overfished seas around Greece and its islands. Some of the casseroles, such as that of young lamb with spinach and lemon, are agreeably light. Pastries satisfy a sweet tooth.

Open
Lunch Mon-Fri,
dinner every day
Hours
12.00-2.30pm &
5.30pm-12.00am
Credit cards
AmEx, Mastercard,
Visa, Diner's
Service charge
10%
Cover charge
Mega 75p,
Micro 95p
Set-price lunch
£14-£20
Set-price dinner
£16-£22
Nearest tube stations
Bayswater,
Queensway
Map 6

Kartouche   £26

329–31 Fulham Road SW10 (823 3515)

+ *desserts demonstrate 101 uses for a dead chocolate bar*
- *lurid colour scheme; lurid noise*

High tide on the heaving strand of Fulham Road is approximately 8.30pm, when the jeunesse dorée of Chelsea wash up in Kartouche. However, there is more to it than mere fashion: the consistency of the product makes this a venue worth returning to. The reasonably priced menu is eclectic to say the least, and certainly a bountiful and varied bestiary has been raided to create unusual taste sensations: fillet of kangaroo, bison sausages and sheep's balls with capers have all figured, and emu – something of a favourite here – has been described as 'literally flying out of the door' (a surreal thought). The cook's tour ranges far and wide for its influences: Thailand for spicy fishcakes and tom yum, and north Africa for houmus, babaganoush and so forth. For the less adventurous there is always a trad. roast such as pork with really good crackling, or Cumberland sausages with bacon and mash. Desserts are worth saving room for. Service is brisk and well-organized, and doesn't force you to leave.

Open
Every day
Hours
12.00-2.45pm
(Sat & Sun
3.15pm), 6.00pm-
11.45am (Sun
11.00pm)
Credit cards
AmEx, Mastercard,
Visa, Switch
Service charge
Optional 12.5%
(parties of 5 or
more)
Nearest tube stations
South Kensington,
Gloucester Road
Map 2

133

A 90-BIN WINE list, neatly laid out by style, intrepidly explores the outer limits of unusual tastes: Alicante Bouschet from California, Marzemino from north-east Italy and Pacherenc du Vic-Bilh from Gascony are rarely-seen visitors to planet Chelsea. Meanwhile, the structure of the list poses further interesting choices: for example, a fruit-drenched Chenin Blanc from Australia versus Daniel Jarry's more traditionally styled Vouvray. In the aromatic-white section you can balance the claims of Malvasia Bianca ('like Gewürztraminer on acid' – Randall Grahm, winemaker) and a melon-fresh Albariño from Galicia. Four rosés, 20 half-bottles and five well-chosen dessert wines round off the impressive portfolio.

Kassoulet

127 Ledbury Road W2 (792 9191)

At the time of going to press, the owners of Kartouche (q.v.) are opening a second restaurant, Kassoulet, a pub conversion on the corner of Talbot Road and Ledbury Road. Michael Weiss, who has worked at the Hotel Intercontinental and at 192 (q.v.) is at the stove. The menu could be described as 'eclectic French': a mixture of rootsy peasant dishes (such as traditional cassoulet) and those of a more Mediterranean disposition.

Kastoori   £18

188 Upper Tooting Road SW17 (0181-767 7027)

+ *Indian 'cuisine grandmère' in Tooting*
- *very functional dining-room*

Vegetarian Indian food has become almost mainstream. Tooting's large Asian population is now witnessing fusion cuisine from the Thanki family, who come from Gujarat but also spent several years in Africa – the result being dishes such as matoki (green banana curry); kasodi (sweetcorn in coconut milk); drumstick curry (fiddly to eat but worth it); and green-pepper curry with sesame and peanut sauce. Potatoes, aubergines and tomatoes are the foundation of many dishes, and the spicy fresh tomato curry, originating in the Gujarati region of Katia Wahd, is a speciality. Meals should start with bhajias and bhel pooris, and be mopped up with puran puri – a chapati stuffed with lentils, saffron, nutmeg and cardamom. Service is from the heart, and gentle encouragement and explanation accompany each dish. The Sunday special thali at £6 underlines Kastoori's reputation for good value food with a difference.

Open
Lunch Wed-Sun, dinner every day
Hours
12.30-2.30pm, 6.00-10.30pm
Credit cards
Mastercard, Visa
Set-price lunch
£8
Set-price dinner
£13
Nearest tube stations
Tooting Bec, Tooting Broadway

Kavanagh's ⭐new £26

26 Penton Street N1 (833 1380)

+ *colourful, good-humoured neighbourhood restaurant*
- *the appurtenances of lollo rosso and aerosol spray cream*

Michael Kavanagh, one of the chefs and co-proprietor of this bouncy little restaurant, has cooked in almost as many kitchens as he has made hot dinners. After leaving school he followed a swift trajectory through restaurants as diverse as Clarke's, Langan's Brasserie, Simpson's-in-the-Strand, Mulligan's of Cork Street and Ballymaloe House (Eire), and is still the optimistic side of 30. He describes his weekly-changing menu as modern British, although there is the odd appropriate Irish incursion such as Noreen Curran's black pudding, here served in filo parcels with grain-mustard sauce. Irish coffee is made with a large Jamieson's. His cooking — and that of his co-chef Catherine Fogarty — tends towards the good-hearted rather than the meticulous, with some evidence of clumsy garnishing, yet a detail such as a vegetable dish of mashed green peas can suddenly delight. Favourites with the customers include roast rump of lamb with spiced vegetables and a cumin, yoghurt and walnut dressing; risotto of goat's cheese, marjoram and broad beans; ricotta and white-chocolate cheesecake; and the aforementioned black pudding. The interior of the small restaurant — seating 38 — has the innocence of a playgroup. Naïve paintings that could have been carried out by the offspring of a union between Beryl Cook and Stanley Spencer dot the walls, which are themselves coated in primary colours. School-hall chairs with a ledge at the back to take the hymn books provide seating. Close geographically but far in spirit from some of the self-consciously trendy restaurants of Islington's Upper Street, Kavanagh's is there for the crack (in the Irish sense of the word, you understand). The Sunday brunch menu includes a 10-item Irish breakfast.

Open
Lunch Tues-Fri, dinner Tues-Sat & Sunday brunch
Hours
12.30-2.30pm, 7.00-10.30pm (Sunday brunch 12.00-3.30pm)
Credit cards
Mastercard, Visa, Switch, Delta
Set-price lunch
£7.50-£10
Nearest tube stations
Angel, Kings Cross
Map 1

Kensington Place £30

201 Kensington Church Street W8 (727 3184)

+ *griddled scallops with pea purée and mint vinaigrette*
- *pressure to turn tables around*

This massive glass display cabinet — in which characters are caught in suspended animation of delight like figures on a Grecian urn, their lips formed in words never to be heard (which is certainly true) — reveals itself inside to be a slick, up-market

Open
Every day
Hours
12.00-3.00pm, 6.30-11.45pm (10.15pm Sun)
Credit cards
AmEx, Mastercard, Visa, Switch, Delta
Set-price lunch
£14.50

canteen showcasing Rowley Leigh's excellent cooking. This, as readers of his column in Saturday's *The Guardian* will know, is based on having a line to the best suppliers and buying whatever is in season: for instance, a spring menu appropriately featured samphire and purple sprouting broccoli. Leigh embraces clear, uncomplicated flavours: wild sea trout with salt lemons and sorrel sauce, and grilled venison steak with juniper butter are conventional combinations elevated by the quality of the ingredients and the simplicity of the conception. Some dishes — sorrel omelette, morels on toast, cod with mustard sauce — are deceptively simple, and rarely are they done better. Service is willing, although it does become stretched mid-session when the variegated demands of customers pull it hither and thither.

THERE IS NO doubt about the quality of the wines on this mid-length list, which begins with wonderful Bruno Paillard as the house champagne and works its way diligently around the globe, exploring Argentina, South Africa, California and Australia (but not New Zealand, which appears to be out of fashion this year). There are some terrific bargains: Château de Fieuzal 1986 is only £30, at which price you can also buy August Clape's earthy Cornas. One minor carp is that the list is formatted in an undifferentiated block of print that makes it difficult to read, especially as there is no division into categories.

Open
Mon-Sat
Hours
12.00-3.00pm,
5.00-10.30pm
Credit cards
Mastercard, Visa,
Switch, Delta
Nearest tube
station
Piccadilly Circus
Map 5

Kulu Kulu £10

76 Brewer Street W1 (734 7316)

+ *kushi katso (deep-fried pork and onion)*
- *inscrutable service*

For a 'kaiten' (conveyor-belt) sushi operation, Kulu-Kulu, situated in the street in which Japanese restaurants first flourished, is on the small side: even crammed full, it would accommodate only 50 diners. The sushi chugs around on colour-coded plates, and all the favourites are there — salmon, prawns, mackerel and octopus — plus more arcane choices such as sea urchin. As always with kaiten, there are times when it seems as though the only sushi coming round are the ones you don't fancy, but catch chef Fukuda's eye and he will fashion your favourites to order. Non-purists will be pleased with the punctuation of the occasional plate of hot, cooked food, such as deep-fried chicken, or pork and onion.

Lahore Kebab House £10 BYO

2 Umberston Street E1 (481 9737)

+ *the best chicken tikka in town*
- *in and out in a trice*

Established in 1976, this simple outfit is a name passed around among those in the know about Indian — or, more precisely, Pakistani — food. Other restaurants have tried to help themselves to a piece of the magic by incorporating the word Lahore into their names, but here is the original and best. Kebabs, tikkas, curries and karahi dishes (cooked in an iron pan) have a freshness and vitality that outstrips much grander places. Lamb, mutton and chicken are supplemented by quail, kidneys and brain masala, according to availability. Dhals are well-spiced; bread is brought hotfoot and puffed straight from the tandoor and replenished unasked throughout the meal. Try homemade keer (cardamom-flavoured rice pudding for dessert). The first-floor room is air-conditioned, but up there you miss out on the cooking action.

Open Every day
Hours 12.00pm-12.00am
Credit cards None
Nearest tube station Aldgate East/Whitechapel
Map 1

The Lansdowne £20

90 Gloucester Avenue NW1 (483 0409)

+ *mobile-free zone*
- *language from the kitchen is at times as colloquial as the food*

Located in a residential street in Primrose Hill, The Lansdowne is one of those pubs where you mark your seat, crane your neck to peer at the specials of the day chalked on a blackboard, and order and pay for your food at the bar. Despite the inconvenience of such an arrangement, and the brusqueness of the staff behind the bar, the cooking is worth delving into. Duck and pistachio terrine, served with cornichons, homemade bread and a nicely dressed salad, makes for a hearty starter, or in the summer tangy chilled soups are a good option. The rest of the menu is proficiently put together, and includes a pasta dish, a chargilled fish (red mullet, for instance) and either lamb or steak with perms and coms of chilli, tapenade, pesto, couscous and so on. The atmosphere — particularly at weekends — is lively, with small children running amok and a peripatetic cat investigating the ankles of all and sundry.

Open Lunch Tues-Sun; dinner Mon-Sun
Hours 12.00pm-11.00pm
Credit cards Delta, Mastercard, Switch, Visa
Set-price lunch Sunday lunch £15.00
Nearest tube station Chalk Farm
Map 1

Launceston Place £33

Open
Lunch Mon-Fri &
Sun, dinner Mon–
Sat
Hours
12.30-2.30pm
(Sun 3.00pm),
7.00-11.30pm
Credit cards
AmEx, Mastercard,
Visa, Switch, Delta
Set-price lunch
£14.50-£17.50
**Nearest tube
stations**
Gloucester Road,
High Street
Kensington
Map 2

1a Launceston Place W8 (937 6912)

+ *Condrieu for £27; comme il faut service*
- *ingredients smothered by clumsy combinations*

Entering the tastefully furnished dining-rooms located on the ground floor of this charming period townhouse, there is a genteel, clubby atmosphere. Locals, in their proprietorial way, refer to it as 'No.1, The Place'. Unfortunately, the conservatism spills over into the menu, where the rarefied prices are not really justified by a sophistication or lightness of touch in the implementation. Asparagus with rocket and Parmesan was, from the start, an erratic concept, while rubbery blinis took half the pleasure out of a starter of smoked salmon. Duck confit with plum and chilli jam is a stratospheric £15, while a main-course portion of canneloni [sic] with morels, ricotta and Parmesan weighs in at £12, and neither is as exciting as the prices suggest. Better value are the set menus available at lunchtime and in the early evening. What you lose on the swings you gain on the roundabouts: the wine list offers plenty of good bottles at below £20.

Laurent £20

Open
Mon-Sat
Hours
12.00-2.00pm,
6.00-11.00pm
Credit cards
AmEx, Mastercard,
Visa, Delta
**Nearest tube
station**
Golders Green
Map 1

428 Finchley Road NW2 (794 3603)

+ *the choice is more or less made for you*
- *being with someone who doesn't like couscous*

Owner, manager and chef is Laurent Farrugia. His speciality is couscous, and should you want anything different you will be disappointed. Start with brique à l'oeuf, an envelope of deep-fried, paper-thin pastry posting you a soft-centred egg, and then decide between couscous complet, royal (too much for the average appetite), chicken, fish or vegetarian. The grain is well-cooked, fluffy and golden, the harissa galvanizingly hot. For dessert there is sorbet, ice cream, crème caramel or crêpes Suzette. North African wines include a Gris de Boulaouane rosé. The surroundings are sweet and simple.

Leith's   £45

92 Kensington Park Road W11 (229 4481)

+ *bargain lunch menu; clarets*
- *constipated service*

The dish – salad of quail and pancetta with chicken and truffle mousse – was exquisitely presented, deserving not be eaten but to be framed. And there is the conundrum of Michelin decorations: if as a chef you aspire to their glitter, your cooking by definition becomes high art. High art is expensive, and, except at lunch (or luncheon as they call it here), it is beyond the reach of most purses. The vegetarian menu is still superb: a meal of tortellini of goat's cheese and herbs with asparagus and leek broth, followed by feuilleté of roasted cèpes with truffled scrambled egg and chive butter elevated this downtrodden sphere of eating to gourmet levels. Alex Floyd's cooking is modern, inventive and adept, aimed at contriving clean and elegant flavours such as in the sterling conjunction of roasted scallops and spiced lemon couscous with artichokes and light curry butter. Desserts are the forte of patissier Michael Strong, and, like an Englishman on the Continent, are mad, bad and dangerous to know: prune, orange and marzipan pyramid with passionfruit sauce; banana fritters with liquorice ice cream and butterscotch sauce; and rhubarb and vanilla soufflé are all alluringly death-defying in intent and execution.

LEITH'S HAS ONE of the most seriously enjoyable wine lists in London. On the one hand there are mouthwatering clarets and burgundies of impeccable provenance; then there are wines selected for their individuality: a zippy, fresh, mango-drenched Albariño from Galicia, an extraordinary barrel-fermented Viognier from La Jota in the Napa Valley, and Philippe Salasc's rarely seen Domaine Capion 'Futs de Chêne', a densely structured Cabernet/Syrah blend from an estate in the Languedoc adjacent to the renowned Mas de Daumas Gassac. Whatever you try you will be in safe hands – Nick Tarayan's notes are lucid, humorous and persuasive, and contain a guarantee that if you don't like the wine they recommend they will replace it and drink the other with their supper.

Open
Lunch Tues-Fri, dinner Mon-Sat

Hours
12.15-2.15pm, 7.00-11.30pm

Credit cards
AmEx, Mastercard, Visa, Switch, Diner's, JCB

Service charge
12.5%

Set-price lunch
£16.50

Set-price dinner
£27.50

Nearest tube station
Notting Hill Gate

Map 6

Open
Lunch Mon-Fri &
Sun, dinner Mon-
Sat
Hours
12.00-3.00pm,
6.00-11.30pm
Credit cards
Mastercard, Visa,
Switch, Delta
Set-price lunch
£5 & £7.95
Nearest tube
station
Chalk Farm
Map 1

Lemonia £20

89 Regent's Park Road NW1 (586 7454)

+ *no bazouki music; extrovert but not histrionic service*
– *commercial taramasalata*

Difficulty in getting a table is testimony to Lemonia's popularity with the denizens of Primrose Hill and elsewhere. Booking in advance in the evenings is therefore de rigueur. There are various reasons for coming here: the friendly atmosphere, the knowledge of continuity provided by the fact that it is a family-run establishment, and the endeavour to provide appetizing food at reasonable prices (you can best explore this by mixing and matching between the regular menu and the daily specials to compose your own meze of starters and mains). Fish is always fresh and prepared with minimal fuss: beautifully crisp-skinned red mullet, tender octopus salad and grilled swordfish are commendable. One of the pleasures is watching the legerdemain of waiters working at breakneck speed while retaining their charm: controlled topsyturvydom.

Open
Lunch Mon-Fri,
dinner Mon Sat
Hours
12.00-3.00pm,
6.00-11.30pm
Credit cards
AmEx, Mastercard,
Visa, Delta, Diner's
Set-price dinner
£10
Nearest tube
station
Piccadilly Circus
Map 5

The Lexington

45 Lexington Street W1 (434 3401)

At the time of going to press, Antony Worral Thompson has bought Martin Saxon's relaxed west Soho restaurant, seemingly continuing a policy of buying up disparate, unrelated going concerns (see also the entry for De Cecco). It may be that the usual eclectic cooking will be offered, but it could be that Wozza will surprise us. It has been known.

Open
Every day
Hours
12.00pm-4.00am,
Sun 12.00-
11.30pm
Credit cards
AmEx, Mastercard,
Visa, Switch, Delta
Cover charge
£1 per person
Nearest tube
stations
Tottenham Court
Road, Leicester
Square, Piccadilly
Circus
Map 5

Little Italy £29

21 Frith Street W1 (734 4737)

+ *something of the spirit of old Soho carried on, complete
  with long hours*
– *slow service; lack of finesse in cooking details*

If anyone can claim this name as a synonym for Soho it is the Pollidri family, owners since the 1950s of Bar Italia, which for decades was one of the very few places to provide properly made espresso. Next door to Bar Italia and part-owned by the Pollidris, the restaurant is an agreeable mix of the new wave in Italian food with old-fashioned family values. If you want to read 'family' as 'mafia', some of the more louche, medallioned male clientele might lend justification (at an agreed rate). In an area in which the mega-restaurants seem to attract cloned designer-designed customers, and others make clear a preference for particular sexual proclivities, the motley crowd that fetches up in Little Italy is a welcome sight. The menu – a long list – is often most interesting in the handwritten dishes of the day, which might feature market fish in a Mediterranean soup; an elaborate (perhaps over-elaborate) pasta dish such as fusilli with roasted peppers, smoked chicken and wild mushrooms; and something homely like polpettone in umido in salsa pomodoro (meatloaf steamed in a tomato sauce). Fashionable grilled vegetables tend to be unfashionably oily, and deep-fried squid and zucchini are battered with a heavy hand. Italian sausages or a simply grilled veal chop make a sensible order, and roast potatoes with garlic and rosemary the perfect accompaniment. The short Italian wine list – innocent of vintages – is not greedily marked up, leaving room on the credit card for the array of grappe. Photographs of boxers, including my hero Rocky Marciano, decorate the walls. When the tape played is Sinatra, the final piece of this only mildly themed jigsaw is in place.

Livebait £28

43 The Cut SE1 (928 7211)

+ *a vindication of casting your net far and wide*
- *too many people chasing too few tables*

Fish restaurants in London have tended to fall into the categories of chippy (including superior ones such as Brady's and Two Brothers); clubby (for example, Bentley's and Wilton's); and continental (such as Le Suquet and Poissonnerie de l'Avenue). Livebait, which opened on the cusp of 1996, has broken new ground and done it in an area – Waterloo – not known for gastronomic excitement (excepting The Waterloo Fire Station). Its ceramic-tiled decor – with a proportion of the seating given over to booths divided by opaque, ribbed-glass screens and lit by glass globes – makes a workmanlike statement, but the bank of crustacea winking and waving at the rear of the premises, and the offering of inventive, worldly-wise dishes such as barbecued, chilli-marinated octopus served with spider endive leaves and cucumber raita; or pan-roasted sea bass served with braised Florence fennel in white wine and saffron, with a poached egg, beetroot risotto and Parmesan cheese, quickly alert you to the fact that the times they have a-changed. Livebait has succeeded in making the concept of a fish

Open
Lunch Mon-Fri,
dinner Mon-Sat
Hours
Lunch 12.00-
3.00pm, dinner
5.30-11.30pm
Credit cards
Mastercard,
Switch, Visa,
Diner's
**Nearest tube
station**
Waterloo
Map 3

restaurant saucy and provocative, through the medium of imaginative treatments of sparklingly fresh ingredients. Prices are not high for what has become one of the most costly sources of protein: half a pint of prawns is £2.80 at time of writing; rock oysters start at 90p apiece; a chilled soup made of melon, chilli, coriander, orange, yoghurt and Atlantic prawns served with croûtons and sea-hen caviar is £4.45; and a main course of half a Cornish lobster served with potato and tarragon salad is £14. Desserts are beguiling: namely chocolate-marshmallow tartlet with mixed berries, and boiled orange cake with caramel oranges and crème fraîche. Breads are also good. Service is cheerful. Well-chosen wines are presented by style and body, and there is beer, cider and draught Guinness to mix with a half-bottle of champagne to accompany those oysters.

The Lobster Pot £35

3 Kennington Lane SE11 (582 5556)

+ *the Régent family*
- *priced above its station?*

Hervé Régent's temple to fish cooking has a strange logic all of its own. It is more French than France, more nautical than a day at the seaside and all in the worst possible taste. It is hard to be discerning about the food when the musical accompaniment is sea shanties. That said, the fish lover will be content here. Bouillabaisse, moules, fruits de mer, soles, sea bass and monkfish are all carefully cooked – often with rich sauces – but at prices that seem steep despite the high cost of the raw materials. And that decor: it is a bit like the theme tune of Desert Island Discs brought to life.

Lou Pescadou £26

241 Old Brompton Road SW5 (370 1057)

+ *'Plateau Pescadou': an altar to bivalves*
- *smoky atmosphere; 15% service charge*

Mock-nautical metaphors abound in this trattoria-like restaurant situated on a dingy stretch of Old Brompton Road, and you half-expect the waiters to be wearing stripy Breton shirts and to sport flat fishermen's caps. They certainly contribute to the convivial atmosphere, which turns to desperate hilarity when you try to decipher the whimsical, higgledy-piggledy menu. This trawls up various options: one page lists crustacea prepared in a variety of styles, clams ticking with

Open
Tue-Sat
Hours
12.00-2.30pm,
7.30-11.00pm
Credit cards
AmEx, Mastercard,
Visa, Switch,
Diner's, Delta
Service charge
12.5% inclusive
Set-price lunch
£15.50
Set price dinner
£22.50
Nearest tube
station
Kennington
Map 1

Open
Every day
Hours
12.00-3.00pm,
7.00pm-12.00am
Credit cards
AmEx, Mastercard,
Visa, Switch,
Diner's, Delta
Cover charge
£1 per person,
Service charge
15% optional
Set-price lunch
£9

thyme, and moules à la creme; or there is the daily selection of fish which may comprise turbot roasted with garlic, or cod with a green sauce. Bourride contains a flotilla of dreadnought monkfish slabs swimming in an (over) creamy fish-stock reduction. There are alternatives: pasta, pissaladière (the Provençal version of pizza, made with onions, tomatoes, anchovies and studded with black olives) and a few meat dishes for the carnivores. Desserts are very much an afterthought. One minus point: the very ordinary bread — presumably supplied to justify the £1 cover charge — should be made to walk the gangplank and fed to the fishes.

Luna ⭐ new £23

Nearest tube station
Earls Court
Map 2

48 Chalk Farm Road NW1 (482 4667)

+ *Italian food as a community service*
- *less-than-perfect pasta*

The crescent moon provides a decorative icon; the predominant colour in the two-storey premises is the purple of a mythical night sky. Run by agreeable young women, Luna exemplifies the positive face of the revolution that has taken place in our eating-out expectations. Neighbourhoods — this one is Chalk Farm/Camden Town — should have places where you can eat innovatively and healthily at a reasonable price, and as simply or elaborately as the mood dictates. Luna's mainly Italian menu offers 'big salads' and tempting sandwiches on homemade focaccia, as well as the usual appetizers, pastas, fish and meat courses. Recipe ideas are not contrived or contorted, but quite often turn out more interesting on the plate than on paper. This was true of a first course of polpettine, warm vegetable croquettes served with rocket and goat's cheese, and spicy squid with a marinated mixed-bean salad. Mixed antipasti is a well-balanced, well-dressed selection of items; a vegetarian version is available for those who choose to go through life without the consolation of Parma ham. A lapse from Italian into Esperanto occurs with main courses such as spicy scallops (queenies) with lime, coriander and stir-fried vegetables, or sausages with garlic mash and onion marmalade, but both dishes are well-prepared. Oddly, pasta assemblies seem the least successful items. Desserts include baked peaches with mascarpone, and espresso and chocolate terrine. A dessert wine is on offer for those occasions when you want to splash out a bit. Reports of standards wavering under pressure have come in — but these did come immediately after a favourable review in the *Evening Standard*.

Open
Every day
Hours
12.00-11.30pm
Credit cards
Mastercard, Visa, Switch
Set-price lunch
£6.95
Nearest tube station
Chalk Farm, Camden Town
Map 1

Magno's Brasserie £32

Open
Every day
Hours
12.00-2.30pm,
5.30-11.30pm,
(Sun 12.30-
10.00pm)
Credit cards
AmEx, Mastercard,
Switch, Visa,
Delta, Diner's
Service charge
12.5%
Set-price lunch
and dinner
£13.95 & £16.95
Set-price dinner
£16.95
Pre-theatre menu
£10.95
Nearest tube
station
Covent Garden
Map 4

65a Long Acre WC2 (836 6077)

+ *set menus*
− *suits galore*

Covent Garden is near theatreland, as you are unceasingly reminded, and as such the pre- and post-theatre menus play an even larger role in shaping the style and ambience of Magno's. A combination of bustly service and no-nonsense food makes this a useful addition to the area. Cooking fluctuates between old-fashioned recipes − such as baked Roquefort in puff pastry, and coq au vin − and creative juggling with punchier ingredients, with anchovies, salt cod and spicy sausages giving impetus to dishes. The menu is adaptable in other directions, embracing risottos and ravioli, but never quite achieves a convincing balance. In one meal both fish and chicken were overcooked, and cream sauces accompanying a pair of dishes were identical and bland. The wine list is about average for French restaurants of this type: i.e., fairly average. Useful in the area as they say.

Ma Goa £20

Open
Dinner Mon-Sat
Hours
7.00-11.00pm
Credit cards
AmEx, Mastercard,
Visa, Switch,
Diner's, Delta
Nearest tube/
railway stations
East Putney/
Putney

244 Upper Richmond Road SW15 (0181-780 1767)

+ *Indian food unlike any other*
− *their claim that Goa is unspoilt is, sadly, not true*

Owned and run by the Kapoor family, with Mrs Kapoor in charge of the kitchen, the menu here changes and evolves as if in response to customers' increasing interest and knowledge. Goan Goan gone are silly titles like strip-steak sizzler and beach-party barbecue, and in their place are intricately spiced dishes incorporating Goan ingredients and techniques, such as palm vinegar for piquancy and hundee (sealed-pot) cooking for intensity of flavour. The best way to approach the first course is via a selection to share, which gives a taste of chicken-liver chaat, Goan sausage and shrimp balchao. Basmati rice cooked in vegetable stock is delicious. There are some interesting, sweet, soothing South Indian desserts.

Maison Novelli £36

29 Clerkenwell Green EC1 (251 6606)

+ *top-class cooking at a reasonable cost*
- *the small kitchen leads to long waits*

Jean-Christophe Novelli is not the first chef to leave behind the lavish food budgets and pension plans of luxury-hotel working life to go it alone. Bruno Loubet, his predecessor at The Four Seasons Hotel, now at L'Odéon (q.v.), is one who showed the way. Novelli has bought what was Cafe St Pierre in up-and-coming Clerkenwell, and opened a brasserie on the ground floor and a more ambitious restaurant above. It is with the latter that we are concerned, as Novelli seems temperamentally unable to work successfully outside the ethos of haute cuisine, and the customer reaps the benefit more dramatically in the first-floor restaurant where, at time of writing, the menu of the day is priced at £19.50 for three courses and coffee. À la carte, two courses are £18, a price lower than many first courses in fancy hotels. The menu is short, largely because the kitchen has severe physical limitations. It vividly reflects Novelli's passions — notably his enthusiasm for meat cooking of a bawdy, gutsy kind. Confit of goose neck stuffed with foie gras; poached pork knuckle cervelas with white beans; and stuffed braised pig's trotter convey the idea. His energetic approach to fish cooking lags not far behind. Two examples are tartare of marinated salmon and asparagus topped with a cucumber crown and a poached quail's egg, accompanied by chilled gazpacho and truffle oil; and roast sea bass with aubergine caviar, olives, fennel, sun-dried tomato and paper-thin slices of chorizo, plus chorizo-flavoured oil. Desserts as ravishing as the work of a couturier milliner are another of Novelli's strengths: admire and then consume the tiramisù Kaluha. The dining-room is quite bizarrely decorated, which is fine. Service can be lacklustre.

Open
Lunch Mon-Fri,
dinner Mon-Sat
Hours
12.00-3.30pm,
Mon-Thurs
6.00pm-10.30pm,
Fri-Sat 6.00pm-
12.00am
(brasserie
11.00am-11.15pm)
Credit cards
AmEx, Mastercard,
Visa, Switch, Delta
Service charge
10% brasserie,
15% restaurant
**Nearest tube
station**
Farringdon
Map 1

Malabar £25

27 Uxbridge Street W8 (727 8800)

+ *Indian ordering made easy*
- *authentic but uncongenial stainless-steel dishes*

The motto here could well be: 'If it ain't broke, don't fix it'. The local Notting Hill clientele seems not to tire of the more or less static menu, on which the same dishes stand out as slightly unusual: devilled chicken livers; venison marinated in tamarind; prawns fried in potato flour; long chicken (cooked with cloves and ginger); stick prawns (skewered

Open
Every day
Hours
12.00-2.45pm,
6.30-11.15pm
Credit cards
Mastercard, Visa,
Switch, Delta
Set-price lunch
£15

shellfish with a lemon sauce); and, among the vegetables, green banana and pumpkin. It should be noted that prices — which seem to be on the high side — include both tax and service. The previous incarnation as an Italian restaurant lives on restfully in the decor.

Open
Lunch Wed-Sun,
dinner every day
Hours
12.30-2.15pm
6.00-11.00pm
Credit cards
AmEx, Mastercard,
Visa, Diner's, Delta
Set-price lunch
£4.95
Set price dinner
£7.25-£11.50
Nearest tube
station
Parsons Green
Map1

Mamta   £20

692 Fulham Road SW6 (371 5971)

+ *karma in the world of Coke*
− *curry-sauce-coloured decor*

The quiet subtlety of Indian vegetarian food is unexpected but very welcome in Fulham Road. The owners Mr Kamdar and Mr Daudbat are also managers and chefs, which lends a pleasant personal air but can make for long waits. Puris, uttapam and dhosa are as good as ever to those in the know, and a reliable revelation to those coming fresh to mouth-bombs of savouriness and dramatic pancakes. Vegetables come curried with sauce, dry-spiced or without spices (for whom, I wonder?). The most interesting assemblies are the chefs' specials, which have daft names but profound content. For example, À la carte Mombai is an excellent potato curry; Aubergine Sparkle buries the fried slices in a rich sauce; and Undhiu (served on Wednesdays and Saturdays, in limited amounts) is a highly satisfactory mix of soft vegetables and crisp gram balls. Sweet and sticky characterizes the desserts.

Open
Mon-Sat
Hours
12.00-3.00pm,
6.00-11.00pm
Credit cards
Mastercard, Visa,
Diner's
Set-price lunch
£4.90
Nearest tube
station
Edgware Road
Map 6

Mandalay   £15

444 Edgware Road W2 (258 3696)

+ *authentic Burmese dishes cooked and served with charm*
− *thoughts inevitably turn to the plight of the Burmese people*

We should not — at time of writing, anyway — travel to Burma, but there is nothing to stop us from making a sortie up Edgware Road to this modest little cafe run by two Burmese brothers, Altaf (Dwight) and Iqbal (Gary) Ally, whose slightly improbable previous place of work was Oslo. Taking it in turns to cook and wait, the reassuringly well-covered brothers conduct themselves with engaging seriousness and serenity: they are clearly concerned that their customers get the best from the eminently reasonably priced menu. Appetisers should comprise some deep-fried parcels — they might be spring rolls, samosas or fritters — plus a soup and a salad. Unusual and interesting components in these dishes include calabash, raw papaya, fermented tea leaf, red lentils with beanthread noodles and bottle gourd, but there are straightforward mixtures such as egg and potato, or chicken with shrimp and lime for those who do not wish to venture too far down the Irrawaddy. Main courses reveal an Indian influence on the cuisine, but curries and barbecued meat can be partnered with mild noodle- or rice-based assemblies. Vegetarians are well-served here, and for those who like those sweet Eastern dessert confections seemingly designed for the young and/or toothless there is coconut agar agar jelly, semolina in coconut cream, tapioca and faluda. Surroundings are as basic as the wine list, but even formica tables and a very generic Chardonnay can be invested with a sort of nobility when intentions are so palpably good.

Mandarin Kitchen £26

14–16 Queensway W2 (727 9012)

+ *sparklingly fresh seafood*
- *you need friends — a couple cannot do justice to the menu*

If you neglect to book for dinner, your party must line up on a bench like naughty schoolchildren and inch towards the unsmiling prefect in charge of reservations as those in front are found accommodation. However, the Chinese element in the clientele eats early, so at about 9pm there is a mass exodus. The strength of this Cantonese kitchen is seafood. Lobsters from Scotland and crabs from the south-west coast snap their fingers with freshness; while pot of crab with bean noodle and dry shrimps in chilli has a profoundly delicious liquor in which the glassy noodles are steeped. Roast eel fillets with garlic; pure king-prawn meatballs; New Zealand mussels in chilli and black-bean sauce; Cantonese roast duck; spicy beef-goulash casserole pot; and shredded pork on fried noodles are all recommended. Interest in the menu is repaid with involved service.

Open
Every day
Hours
12.00-11.30pm
(last orders lunch
5.30pm)
Credit cards
AmEx, Mastercard,
Visa, Switch,
Diner's
Set-price lunch
£9.90
**Nearest tube
stations**
Queensway,
Bayswater
Map 6

Mandeer £18

21 Hanway Place W1 (323 0660)

+ *the flour power of Indian vegetarian food*
- *dishes arrive too quickly for the contemplative life*

It will be a sad day when Mr and Mrs Patel's Mandeer (established in 1961) is no longer there to transport customers away from the transistor radios of Tottenham Court Road to the peaceful, benign world of Gujarati and Punjabi vegetarian food and ayurvedic remedies. Hindu deities winked at by twinkling

Open
Mon-Sat
Hours
12.00-3.00pm,
5.30-10.00pm
Credit cards
AmEx, Mastercard,
Visa, Switch,
Diner's, Delta
Service charge
12.5%

Set-price lunch
£10
Nearest tube
station
Tottenham Court
Road
Map 3

fairy lights oversee the dining-room, which is romantically candle-lit in the evenings. There are five thalis – complete meals – some of which are ideal for diet bores. The no-dairy contingent can choose the vegan version and also be deprived of onions and garlic. Dishes on the long à la carte are well-described, and staff are helpful. At least one dish should be selected from the 'Special Vegetable' chapter. Fans of evaporated milk will love the desserts.

Open
Mon-Fri
Hours
12.00pm-10.30pm
Credit cards
AmEx, Mastercard,
Visa, Switch,
Diner's, Delta
Service charge
Optional 12.5%
service charge
Set-price lunch
£23
Set price dinner
£19.85
Nearest tube
station
Farringdon
Map 3

Mange 2 £30

2–3 Cowcross Street EC1 (250 0035)

+ *the lipstick-red paintwork*
- *silly name, silly mannerisms*

In an area where restaurants, bars and cafes multiply almost daily, Mange 2 is an oddity. Somehow you can't imagine all those desiccated architects and photographers leaving their bare, spare Clerkenwell lofts and ending up in the gothic clutter here – although perhaps they might be desperate for a bit of untidiness. The menu is quite intricately French, sometimes producing something decent like sea bass with roasted vegetables; at other times over-reaching itself with, for example, a lobster and mango salad with truffle dressing. The adjacent bar area, with its shorter, sharper menu offering mussels, smoked salmon, sirloin steak, and spinach and bacon salad, is in fact the part of the operation that is most to the point.

Open
Dinner Tues-Sun
Hours
6.30-11.00pm
Credit cards
AmEx, Mastercard,
Visa
Set price dinner
£12.95-£16.00
Nearest railway
station
Norwood Junction

Mantanah Thai £22

2 Orton Buildings, Portland Road, South Norwood SE25 (0181-771 1148)

+ *Thai cooking with vision*
- *the journey there*

Quality of food at the Yeoh family's simple Thai restaurant stands out dramatically against what has become the monotonous, unsubtle background provided by the proliferation of Thai establishments. The long menu has much that is familiar but also many evolved and experimental dishes, plus others informed by home-cooking. A rough guide is that dishes with fanciful English names – Golden Triangle, Ocean Green, Dragon Dance, Crying Dracula, Hot Pork, Midnight Curry, Highland Tribe and so forth – are the more unusual or original assemblies. The menu from the north and north-east of Thailand, and the comprehensive, inventive vegetarian list (printed in green), repay study — and tasting. Thai food lovers who live far from South Norwood wish that Mantanah would move towards the centre.

Maze ★ new £30

Open
Lunch Mon-Sat
Hours
12.00pm-3.00pm
(bar food 10.30-
1.00am)
Credit cards
AmEx, Mastercard
Visa, Diner's
Service charge
12.5%
Nearest tube
stations
Piccadilly Circus,
Green Park
Map 5

29 Old Burlington Street W1 (437 9933)

+ *useful in the area*
- *just another modern menu*

This review is based on one visit just after Maze, the lunchtime restaurant of the club Legends, opened in late July 1996. The chef had been sacked, the executive chef Eddie Baines was busy opening Randall & Aubin (q.v.) and the pastry chef was struggling to manage the whole of the menu. By the time you read this, things should have settled down. I hope so. The long ground-floor space with a bar at the back has been designed by Eva Jirinca, who was responsible for the monochrome interiors of the original Joe's Cafe and Le Caprice (q.v.). The menu is written as if words like rouille, rocket, marinated, squid, lentils, sorrel, ravioli, ricotta, carpaccio, shaved, brioche, tuna, glass noodles, chicory, braised, smoked haddock, ribboned, boudin noir, teriyaki, crème fraîche, seaweed, zucchini, lavender, compôte, brownies, and amaretto had been written on cards, shuffled and dealt out in order to create the dishes. When it works, it is appetizing and suits the potential lunchtime clientele of smartly suited working girls in this part of the West End. When it doesn't, cut the pack and shuffle again.

McClements £33

Open
Mon-Sat
Hours
12.30-2.30pm,
7.00-10.30pm
Credit cards
AmEx, Mastercard,
Visa
Service charge
10%
Nearest railway
station
Twickenham

2 Whitton Road Twickenham (0181 744 9610)

+ *would be a discovery anywhere, but Twickenham!*
- *chef has a short fuse*

Chef/proprietor John McClements has concentrated his efforts at this one address conveniently close to Twickenham main line station and his menu is now à la carte. McClements' special subjects are seafood and offal but the two are only once paired — in the salade gourmande of lobster, quail and foie gras — and the meat dishes less rip-roaring in their embrace of entrails than once they were. Scare headlines and customer timidity must have played their part. However, the cooking remains robust, earthy or briny and above all tempting. Consider black pudding en croûte with Dijon mustard sauce (something of a signature dish); oyster fritters with celeriac and sauce tartare; duck rillettes and a terrine of brawn, sauce ravigote; open ravioli filled with roast lobster and baby spinach with a lobster sauce; roast grouse with whisky sauce and trimmings; cassoulet of confit of duck, ham, sausages and beans. Desserts include a hot soufflé with Calvados sauce – a version of le trou Normand might be just what you are needing – and tarte Tatin of pears with homemade ice cream. The room is small (30 seats), slightly kitschily decorated, but charming.

Meson Bilbao £22

33 Malvern Road NW6 (328 1744)

+ *lots of hake on the menu*
- *lots of hake on the menu*

A Basque outpost in NW6. Jose Larrucea has 'retired' from mainstream restaurants and done just what he would have done back home in Spain: opened his own small tapas bar and restaurant. The wine list indicates his own favourites, as does the menu. Chorizo busturia (a grilled aubergine sandwich with a filling of the spicy sausage) is delicious; various mussel dishes are good; there is fine jamón de Serrano and, as befits a Basque establishment, fresh and well-cooked fish. Try to view the sometimes haphazard service as similarly authentic.

Open
Lunch Mon-Fri, dinner Mon-Sat

Hours
12.00-2.30pm, 6.00-11.00 (Fri & Sat 6.00-11.30)

Credit cards
AmEx, Mastercard, Visa, Switch, Delta, Diner's

Nearest tube stations
Maida Vale, Queen's Park

Map 1

Le Metro £24

28 Basil Street SW3 (589 1213)

+ *le vin*
- *vin de Levin*

Tucked away in a small basement room with gleaming white walls, white tiles, bold lines and polished mirrors, the enterprise that this Guide has previously described as resembling a starship caters to resident earthlings and pan-galactic giggle-blasters (the Silk Cut sorority) alike. One might boldly bounce in to seek breakfast or afternoon tea as well as for lunch or dinner, perhaps for a glass of one of the many wines on the very fine list, or simply to blow off some Knightsbridge post-shopping steam over a cappuccino. Should you wish to eat, the menu accents contemporary cooking. Starters might be Caesar salad, bruschetta of roasted peppers, marinated salmon with dill and crème fraîche, pressed terrine of sole interleaved with leek and mint, grilled mackerel, warm salad of chicken livers, chump of lamb with glazed turnips, honey-glazed duck with ginger and soy, diverse

Open
Mon-Sat

Hours
7.30am-11.15pm

Credit cards
AmEx, Mastercard, Visa, Switch, Diner's

Nearest tube station
Knightsbridge

Map 2

risottos, summer pudding or British cheeses – in short, a deft delving into the current modern British repertoire. Portions suggest that they respect your current waist measurement.

FORTY-THREE WINES are offered by the glass, and an honourable attempt to divide the wines into flavour categories is vitiated by the arbitrariness of the arrangement. Wines are accorded designer labels. From the 'Clean and Classic' section, to 'Metro Everyday' for what the man or woman in the street is drinking, to the 'Hedonistic', there are wines for every special occasion. Where the arrangement fails is in the nomenclature, not in the choice of wines: when a dry yet buxom Rully from Louis Jadot finds itself modelling on the same catwalk as the brash, nectarine-flavoured Shaw & Smith Sauvignon and the delicate, waif-like attractions of Schloss Johannisberg, while a minerally Montagny from Louis Latour is meant to be flaunting its 'hedonistic' charms, one might suspect that someone has got their grapevines crossed.

Mezzo £40

100 Wardour Street W1 (314 4000)

+ *dishes that lay siege to the most jaded appetite*
- *the noise; quick turning of tables; bar staff with attitude*

Mezzo may or may not be 'the biggest restaurant of its kind in Europe' (and if it is, so what?), but it almost certainly had the most prolific media coverage ever for its launch in the autumn of 1995. Few were left unapprised of the amount of money invested, the number of staff employed, the famous artists commissioned, the quantity of cigars consumed by Sir Terence Conran (owner), the trays of rocket used per week, the laundry bill and the name of the chef's mother. Hard-boiled restaurant critics naturally rushed along to find fault, but that fractious, captious crew were more or less unanimously enthusiastic about John Torode's feeding of the 350 (at any one sitting). More impressive still, the high standard of cooking has been maintained. Problems there may still be with getting a booking, eating at a time and for a length of time that suits, catching the eye of a receptionist or hearing yourself speak (particularly once the live music starts at 10.30pm), but when the food is brought to the table – usually efficiently and graciously – it is gratifying. Democratic is a word that the chef has used to describe his cooking: presumably by this he means that he gives the same care and attention to scallop spring roll with nori, cucumber and chilli water as he does to jambon

Open
Lunch Mon-Fri &
Sun, dinner every
day
Hours
Mon-Thu
12.00pm-1.00am,
Fri & Sat
12.00pm-3.00am,
Sun 12.00-
11.00pm
Credit cards
AmEx, Mastercard,
Visa, Switch,
Delta, Diner's
Service charge
12.5%
Cover charge
£5 only after
10.30pm Thurs, Fri
& Sat for bands
Set-price lunch
£19.50
Set-price dinner
£14
**Nearest tube
station**
Piccadilly Circus
Map 5

persillade with cornichons and Dijon mustard. Principles of social equality seem slightly strained when pairing artichoke vinaigrette with houmus, but for the most part the ideas and ideologies are blameless. Some to savour are English asparagus, egg raviolo and lemon butter; grilled veal cutlet with white beans and gremolada (served for two); Vietnamese fried fish, chilli tamarind and shallots; breaded pig's trotter, sauce gribiche and frites; rotisserie peppered rib of beef with mustard; and rhubarb and champagne jelly. Vegetarians are cherished with dishes such as potato and thyme rösti with onion, rocket salad and Parmesan; and goat's cheese in cabbage with tomato broth. Carved from a space that once housed The Marquee Club, the basement dining-room has a suitably nightclub feel. The sort of person who rhapsodizes about restaurants being a branch of theatre finds vindication here – although the walls of chefs working behind glass are pure TV. Those who value quiet, intimacy and a familiar face among the staff should think twice before trying to book.

SHORT AND SWEET. The product is largely commercial, but the list is well-constructed. White wines feature some quality producers, including Vouvray from Didier Champalou, Riesling from Zind Humbrecht, and Sauvignon Blanc from Ignacio Recabarren's award-winning Casablanca winery. Among the reds, pick up a Pic Saint Loup (a sort of liquid summer pudding) from the Languedoc, this being one of the most exciting wine-producing regions in the world; or have a punt at the bitter raspberry-flavoured Cline Cellars Zinfandel from Sonoma. There are two examples of Tokaji, a Muscat de Rivesaltes and a Recioto di Soave by the glass, and a good list of eaux de vie for those who are inclined to linger.

Mezzonine £24

100 Wardour Street W1 (314 4000)

+ *Two dishes for £7 between 5.30pm and 7pm*
- *cramped seating; some ditsy waiters*

The ground floor of Mezzo features a long bar and a refectory-style dining area comprising the orientally themed Mezzonine. The no-bookings policy implemented at the outset has been revised, and bookings are now taken for lunch and early evening (pre-theatre or cinema). Sitting down to eat across the road from Chinatown and in close proximity to some creditable Thai and Vietnamese establishments serves to sharpen critical faculties when tasting items such as lamb salad with

Open
Every day
Hours
Mon-Thurs 12.00-2.30pm, 5.30pm-1.00am (Fri-Sat 5.30pm-3.00am)
Credit cards
AmEx, Mastercard, Visa, Switch, Delta, Diner's
Service charge
12.5% optional
Nearest tube station
Piccadilly Circus
Map 5

lime leaf, chilli and basil; wok-fried crab with garlic and ginger (served for two); red-cooked pork belly, bok choy and spring onions; or roast duck, red-curry sauce and fragrant rice. There is an element of fast food in this hybrid that is based, some say, on the menus of The Rock Pool and The Wok Pool in Sydney; but what quite a few dishes lose in authenticity, some others gain from there being an understanding of contemporary appetites, as demonstrated by the interesting vegetable-centred assemblies such as pumpkin with noodles and spiced coconut dressing. What is missing is the atmosphere and the large portions of true oriental restaurants, which no amount of 'good design' can replace. The menu is divided into small dishes and larger dishes, and dishes for two. One course plus dessert is the idea, so that customers can be squeezed in and squeezed and out of the conveyor belts of tables more efficiently. A note on the menu warns that you may be ordered into the bar with your dessert and coffee if other people are waiting for a table.

Ming £26

35-6 Greek Street W1 (734 2721)

+ *the effort made to match wines to Chinese food;*
  one-dish meals
- *flights of fancy occasionally crash with a dull thud*

Being in Soho proper rather than in the narrow enclave of Chinatown, you sense that Ming is trying to appeal to a more cosmopolitan (i.e., Western) audience. Both the decor — pleasing sea-green pastel shades — and the articulate staff suggest this, as do the loftier prices compared to t'other side of Shaftesbury Avenue. There is a commitment to clear and original flavour, which lifts the food above many of the Cantonese clones. Where Ming scores is in its intelligent pairing of unusual vegetables, such as kohl rabi (fennel and salted turnips); in its accent on fresh seafood (you know it's fresh because it lives on the premises), sizzling with garlic and spice and all things nice; in its resurrection of provincial dishes such as lamb ta tsai mi or Tibetan garlic lamb; and in the single 'Ming bowl' menus — complete meals in themselves, which may feature mantou, a northern Chinese bread. As with other Chinese restaurants, Ming swings most on the specials page: try hot fish mousse and crab on a bed of soft noodles.

Open
Mon-Sat
Hours
12.00-11.45pm
Credit cards
AmEx, Mastercard,
Visa, Switch,
Diner's, Delta
Set-price lunch
£8
Set price dinner
£14-£30
Nearest tube
station
Leicester Square
Map 5

Mitsukoshi £50

Open
Every day
Hours
12.00-2.00pm,
6.00-9.30pm
Credit cards
AmEx, Mastercard,
Visa, Diner's
Service charge
15%
Set-price lunch
£15
Set-price dinner
£30-40
Nearest tube
station
Piccadilly Circus
Maps 3 & 4

14–20 Regent Street W1 (930 0317)

+ *exquisitely light, healthy, carefully constructed Japanese meals*
– *not so conducive to financial health*

One of London's de luxe Japanese restaurants, Mitsukoshi's bland, modern decor seems a drawback, but to counterbalance there is vivid cooking based on the very best ingredients. Simmered dishes such as shabu shabu or suki yaki – which can be vapid elsewhere – are satisfying because they begin with good broth and progress to the very best beef. Make sure that you see the chef's short list of extra seasonal dishes and ko kaiseki set meal. Set meals (£30–£40), the backbone of the dinner menu, are beautifully thought out to contrast taste, texture and temperature according to Japanese precepts – and are served at a perfect pace.

Monkeys £40

Open
Lunch every day,
dinner Mon-Sat
Hours
12.30-2.30pm
(Sun 1.00-
3.30pm), 7.30-
11.00pm
Credit cards
Mastercard, Visa,
Switch, Delta
Set-price lunch
£15
Set-price dinner
£20-30
Nearest tube
station
South Kensington
Map 2

1 Cale Street SW3 (352 4711)

+ *grouse, snipe, woodcock, teal, mallard, partridge, pheasant*
– *hee-hawing hoorays*

Tom and Brigitte Benham, proprietors and chef and manager respectively at this long-serving, pretty, comfortable, Anglo-French Chelsea restaurant know their customers (mostly locals) well. They provide them with what they want; foie gras, lobster ravioli or caviar for luxurious meals, salmon in summer, game in autumn and winter, rich desserts such as millefeuille of pancakes and Cointreau at all times, interesting wines (see below). Long practise at dealing with the bag from shoots, means that this restaurant is a sage choice for the enjoyment of game. As well as the timing of cooking being right, the traditional accoutrements are all present and correct. Fish eaters are also well catered for with, for example, scallops and ginger, grilled sea bass or baked fillet of cod with herbs and breadcrumbs. Set-price dinner menus are down in price this year – something to be applauded – and the cost includes mineral water and coffee. The seemingly pointless name of the restaurant has some justification in the pictures on the walls.

THIS WINE LIST is a hand-scripted labour of love brimming with red corpuscles. Loire is sketchily represented; Beaujolais has seven delegates. Chapoutier, Guigal, Fèvre plus a solid wedge of mainly junior clarets comprise the remainder of the list, including a double magnum of Grauad-Larose 1984 that has the distinction of being nearly 100% Cabernet Sauvignon – for those who get a kick out of chewing tannin.

Mon Petit Plaisir £28

33 Holland Street W8 (937 3224)

+ *a French bistro from central casting*
- *efforts to suit vegetarians fall rather flat*

Prices have been rationalized – by which we mean reduced somewhat – at this little bistro, très typique, located on one of Kensington's prettiest streets. The cost of the set-price deals unequivocally includes a service charge, a fact that in no way dulls the smiles of the energetic, committed staff. The cooking style is French as we were taught at school – soupe de poissons; parfait de foie de volaille; cassolette de crevettes; gratinée de St Jacques au Champagne; baron d'agneau grillé Béarnaise; suprême de volaille à l'estragon; glaces ou sorbet – and is competently handled. Its (in catering terms) yester-year quality induces a nice feeling of relaxation; there is no need to be on the qui vive to recognize the latest leaf or grain. The terrace is a bonus in summer.

Open
Lunch Mon-Fri,
dinner Mon-Sat
Hours
12.00-2.15pm,
7.00-10.30pm
Credit cards
AmEx, Mastercard,
Visa, Switch,
Diner's, Delta
Service charge
12.5%
Set-price lunch
£12.50-£15.50
Set price dinner
£18.00-£22.00
**Nearest tube
station**
Holland Park
Map 2

Mon Plaisir £32

21 Monmouth Street WC2 (836 7243)

+ *the quintessential French bistro*
- *themes are not what they used to be*

Relentlessly old-fashioned and convivial in the Gallic way, Mon Plaisir has seen decades of worthy service. The almost choreographed period confusion – a jumble of ancient blue soda siphons, bric-à-brac, posters new and old and the laissez-faire attitude of the staff – is part of the brasserie charm, although the sound of Piaf still warbling her classics makes one wonder whether this piece of ersatz Montmartre is a homage to, or a parody of, an original. Heritage is affirmed at the stove in a menu of classic signature dishes: gratinée à l'oignon; coquilles St Jacques Meunière; steak tartare; and crème brûlée. From the à la carte menu, boudin noir et blanc with mashed potatoes and apples has the requisite earthiness; while tasty seared calf's liver with a tarragon jus reposes on a nest of spruce spinach. A further option is the Menu Parisien, served to couples in the evening, involving cassolette d'éscargots followed by côte de boeuf with Béarnaise and choux Chantilly, whose agglomerated

Open
Lunch Mon-Fri,
Dinner Mon-Sat
Hours
12.00-11.30pm
Credit cards
AmEx, Mastercard,
Visa, Switch,
Diner's
Service charge
12.5%
Set-price lunch
£13.95
**Nearest tube
stations**
Covent Garden,
Leicester Square
Maps 4 & 5

aphrodisiac properties doubtless lead to subsequent consummation of *ses plaisirs*. After 50 years Mon Plaisir needs galvanizing, for, as the French say: '*Tout passe, tout casse, tout lasse.*'

Monsieur Max £34

133 High Street, Hampton Hill (0181-979 5546)

Open
Every day
Hours
Mon-Sat 12.00-
2.30pm, 6.00-
11.00pm Sun
11.00-4.00pm,
7.00-10.00pm
Credit cards
None
Nearest railway
station
Hampton

After the untimely, tragic death of his twin brother Marc in November 1995, Max Renzland has decided to leave behind both Chez Max and Le Petit Max and open a new operation. Premises are larger than Le Petit Max and are licensed, but the BYO tradition lives on in a corkage charge of only £4. French provincial food – much appreciated, incidentally, by the late Elizabeth David herself – is the inspiration for the menu.

Montana £32

125–7 Dawes Road SW6 (385 9500)

Open
Lunch Sat-Sun,
dinner every day
Hours
12.00-3.30pm,
Mon-Thurs 7.00-
11.00pm, Fri-Sat
7.00-11.30pm
(Sun 10.30pm)
Credit cards
AmEx, Mastercard,
Visa, Switch, Delta
Service charge
12.5% optional
Set-price dinner
£17 & £21
Nearest tube
station
Fulham Broadway
Map 2

+ *the closest we get in London to Arizona 206*
- *waiters anxious to be your bestest friend*

This self-styled American south-western restaurant only really got into gear when chef Daniel McDowell joined the team in the spring of 1996. McDowell, who in last year's guide was cooking at Jones (now Detroit [q.v.]) in Covent Garden, understands the language of chillies, without which you cannot speak south-western food. Chilli need not, however, be synonymous with macho burning. Some varieties have muted frenzy and emit a low, steady hum: just such can be found in the first course of Rhode Island fish chowder (yes, it's the wrong part of the country, but Montana isn't the South-West either). A rival soup is fashioned from butternut squash, pasilla chilli, coconut and cilantro; another chilli (chipotle) revs up steamed mussels with orange zest and roasted garlic. Roast breast of guinea fowl with spicy pumpkin salad and pumpkin-seed sauce has made the transition from Jones. McDowell is right to keep pumping this out: understanding just how the sweet vegetable contrasts with the oily, funky seed demonstrates once more that he has the smarts. There are dishes for the non-meat and -fish eater (such as a cumin-roasted vegetable and tortilla stack with goat's cheese and red beans), and cool-hand ways with fish (such as baked snapper with palm oil, dried prawns and long-grain rice). Given the American passion for desserts in general and for baking in particular, desserts are oddly low-key. Montana the restaurant is self-consciously groovy, which can be rather wearing – as can the live jazz.

Moshi Moshi Sushi   £15

Unit 24, Liverpool Street Station EC2 (247 3227);
7–8 Limeburner Lane EC4 (248 1808)

+ *sushi à la conveyor belt at bargain prices*
- *pesto sushi is a clash of cultures*

Moshi Moshi Sushi, perched high in the vaulted glass confines of Liverpool Street station, was the first establishment to introduce conveyor-belt sushi – a popular concept in Japan and the USA – to Britain. The company's stated aim is to revolutionize the way Japanese food is regarded in this country, and eventually to provide a healthy fast-food alternative nationwide. Certainly the baggage-carousel delivery obviates language difficulties and breaks down inhibitions. Different-coloured plates denote the price of a sushi portion (two pieces), which ranges from 90p for, say, tuna salad roll to £1.90 for, say, scallop. Sashimi fashioned from tuna and salmon is £2.50. A recent development is the vegetarian menu of sushi. It strikes me as dubious that sun-dried tomato with cheese, baby corn and mayonnaise sushi is the best way forward, but I suppose this is less alarming to some than sea urchin or dried gourd shavings. The newer Limeburner Lane branch has a mezzanine bar, but trainspotting at Liverpool Street station is more atmospheric. Lunch boxes are provided for take-away.

Open
Every day
Hours
11.30am-9.00pm
Credit cards
Mastercard, Visa, Switch, Delta
Nearest tube stations
EC2: Liverpool Street
EC4: Blackfriars, St Paul's
Map 1

Mr Chow   £40

121 Knightsbridge SW1 (589 7347)

+ *ethnic without tears*
- *the Italian waiters*

When Michael Chow opened his London restaurant in 1968, it was a phenomenon. Attention paid to design, art, lighting, greeting, graphics and making comfortable a starry, starry crowd is part of the package of any ambitious new restaurant opening these days, but nearly 30 years ago the significance of such elements was seldom grasped – and was certainly not in the realm of restaurants serving Chinese food. Mr Chow became the place to be seen to be eating. But glamour is perishable, and after Chow left to live in the States, his restaurant gradually lost its magic. In the autumn of 1995 he returned to London to relaunch himself. He set himself a hard –

Open
Lunch Mon-Sat, dinner every day
Hours
12.30-3.00pm, 7.00pm-12.00am
Credit cards
AmEx, Mastercard, Visa, Switch, Delta, Diner's
Cover charge
£1 per person
Set-price lunch
£9.50
Nearest tube station
Knightsbridge
Map 2

if not impossible – task. Times have changed. However, the easy-to-grasp menu with its playfulness and puns – first course is followed by 'Of Course' – is based on fine ingredients, and there is a classic restraint to the northern style of cooking that can be subtle and pleasing. The 'Complete', based around Peking duck, is tempting. Everyone these days can knit one, purl two, with chopsticks, but cutlery is still offered. David Hockney, Peter Blake and Jim Dine (paintings by) are still faithful.

Mr Kong £24

Open
Every day
Hours
12.00pm-1.45am
Credit cards
AmEx, Mastercard,
Visa, Diner's, JCB
Service charge
10%
Set-price lunch
£8.80
**Nearest tube
station**
Leicester Square
Map 4 or 5

21 Lisle Street WC2 (437 7341/9679)

+ *accommodating waiters*
- *feeling the eyes of hungry queuers boring resentfully into your back*

Mr Kong still ranks as one of the kings of Chinatown, where inspiration generally ranks as thin as the meat on a scrawny spare rib. Dispense with the mundane set menus and the boundless à la carte and head for the chef's specials, whereupon you will earn some measure of respect from the staff who probably think the gwai lo are incapable of imagining anything more exotic than a sweet-and-sour prawn ball. The formerly alluring statty ells (sic) are uncompromisingly weird in texture, even when they appear as the correctly spelled satay eels; sautéed frogs' legs in ginger wine are chewily interesting; stewed lamb with beancurd sticks in the pot sounds a statement of fact but is, in reality, a deliciously tender slow-cooked dish, as is braised duck web with abalone for those seekers of recondite pleasures. But don't expect any firebreathing from the sautéed dragon wistlers, which transpire to be nothing more exotic than pea shoots cooked with dried scallops. Beancurd stuffed with meat had a mature-cheese smell and arrived as pillows bursting with shoots, gelatinous mushrooms, dried pork and surrounded in an egg-white and oyster sauce; it elicited an approbatory grunt of 'good dish' from the waiter. It was. Stick to tea or beer unless Piesporter Michelsberg is your idea of heaven.

Le Muscadet £33

Open
Lunch Mon-Fri,
dinner Mon-Sat
Hours
12.30-2.30pm,
7.30-10.45pm
Credit cards
Mastercard, Visa,
Switch, Delta
Service charge
12.5%

25 Paddington Street W1 (935 2883)

+ *the place for gravy-training?*
- *a limited wine list*

Le Muscadet may be under the new ownership of Ana and Claude Paillet, but this discreet little restaurant remains loyal to its French provincial forbears. A profusion of dried flowers, variegated shades of pink and arcadian tapestries set the middle-aged tone whilst cream and stock sauces reduced to an artery-lining intensity are the raison d'être of the place. Typical first courses are moules marinière; escargots de Bourgogne; feuilleté de légumes et champignons au Cognac; and a saffron-drenched fish soup made with red mullet. Les Plats Principaux continue the theme: lotte au citron vert (monkfish with lime butter) was accomplished, meaty yet moist, and was one of the less elaborate dishes on offer, although nicely pink noisettes of lamb with a rosemary jus are cooked with mimimum fuss, otherwise la crème is compris in dishes from Dover sole with asparagus spears to boned baby quails filled with a chicken, herb and Armagnac mousse. Vegetables come across as an afterthought. A beguiling array of cheeses will detain you more than the conventional desserts.

Nearest tube station
Baker Street
Map 3

Museum Street Cafe $30

43 Museum Street WC1 (405 3211)

+ *home-baked breads*
- *whatever happened to vegetables?*

A bstinence in moderation by all means. Surroundings may be spartan, tables are undoubtedly small, chairs encourage you to sit up straight, but the atmopshere is amiably laid-back. The no- smoking policy that reigns supreme in the restaurant (the adjuration is now a temperate 'Thank you for not smoking') doesn't apply to cooking methods, at the heart of which is chargrilling. The formula is simple: a limited choice of three starters and three main courses served with a salsa, a herb butter and vegetables, or a few leaves piled on to the plate. Starters include a soup − yellow pepper and sage with blanched garlic cream is one example − and a tart or salad combo; main courses are straightforward, allowing the ingredients to do the talking. Chargrilled salmon with soy, ginger and coriander; leg of lamb skewer with tapenade; and sautéed breast of guinea fowl stuffed with thyme, garlic and parsley are so liberally endowed with healthy connotations that you may find yourself inadvertently unbuckling over a dessert such as Valrhona chocolate cake with crème fraîche, chocolate sorbet with biscotti or wonderful cheeses from nearby Neal's Yard.

Open
Mon-Fri
Hours
12.30-2.15pm,
6.30-9.15pm
Credit cards
AmEx, Mastercard,
Visa, Switch, Delta
Set-price lunch
£13-£16
Set-price dinner
£18-£22
Nearest tube stations
Tottenham Court Road, Holborn
Map 4

A SMALL BUT perfectly formed wine list consisting of 10 whites and nine reds is notable for the enlightened policy of simply doubling the cost price of the wine. In concrete terms this means you are paying 10–15% less for your wine here than in the majority of West End restaurants. Suddenly Jean-Philippe Fichet's Meursault becomes relatively affordable (£26.50), and the peppery-fruity Crozes Hermitage from Cave des Clairmonts appears excessively reasonable at £13.50. Treat yourself.

Nico Central £36

Open
Lunch Mon-Fri,
dinner Mon-Sat

Hours
12.00-2.00pm
7.00-11.00pm

Credit cards
AmEx, Mastercard,
Diner's, Visa,
Switch, Delta

Set-price lunch
£21 & £25

Set-price dinner
£27

Nearest tube
station
Oxford Circus

Map 3

35 Great Portland Street W1 (436 8846)

+ *sound value*
– *central to the garment district*

As at Simply Nico (q.v.) there has been a change of ownership – from Nico and Dinah Jane Ladenis to Roy Ackerman's Restaurant Partnership plc – but Nico's chef André Garrett remains and so do the good deal, fully inclusive set-price menus. Three-star chefs – Nico is one – like luxurious ingredients to play with and thus there are dishes such as pan-fried foie gras with toasted brioche and caramelized orange which attract supplements – £6 in that instance. But a wide choice and interesting ideas such as boned devilled quail on braised red cabbage, risotto of cep mushrooms, and home-salted cod with crushed new potatoes and Dijon mayonnaise in the first course, and roast monkfish with herb risotto and basil oil, and best end of lamb with aubergine and tomato gâteau in the main course, mean that you can get the point about masterly cooking without paying the extra. The fact that set prices encourage the eating of desserts is celebrated by the tempting array; caramelized lemon tart; chocolate marquise with orange confit; poached pear sablé with caramel sauce; crisp rhubarb crumble with iced crème fraîche to name a few.

Nicole's £34

Open
Lunch Mon-Sat,
dinner Mon-Fri

Hours
Mon-Fri 10.00am-
10.45pm,
Sat 10.00am-
6.00pm

Credit cards
AmEx, Mastercard,
Visa, Switch,
Delta, Diner's

Cover charge
£1 per person
(12.00-4.00pm)

Service charge
12.5%

Nearest tube
stations
Bond Street,
Green Park

Map 3

158 New Bond Street W1 (499 8408)

+ *the bar is a great place to eat alone*
– *feeling too poor or too fat*

Annie Wayte has been chef since this restaurant opened in the basement of the Nicole Farhi shop in autumn 1994. Implicit in her respectful approach to food is gentle, subtle change, with a different emphasis on details from season to season. Whether deliberate or not, it is an attitude that matches well the style of the designer clothes sold above. She knows what women want – chargrilled vegetable salad; grilled scallops with spicy cream lentils; grilled chicken breast and goat's cheese with pinenut and black-olive relish – but this is not niminy-piminy food and there are robust dishes – duck rillettes with beetroot, celeriac salad and grilled toast; and salt beef with borlotti beans and mustard fruits – which doubtless women like too but, pursuing a sexist line, may account for a significant male presence among customers. Everyone falls for the desserts.

Evenings can be quiet, but parking is easy and you can fantasize about having a shop opened after hours for your convenience. Just like Virginia Bottomley at M & S. Not.

O'Conor Don–Ard–Ri Dining Room £26

88 Marylebone Lane W1 (935 9311)

+ *smiling Irish eyes*
- *when was anything sun-dried in Ireland?*

This is no pub conversion with restless Antipodean chefs fusing their need to go on a culinary walkabout with the necessity of earning money. This is a sweetly fusty, formal dining-room on the first floor of an Irish pub owned by the O'Callaghan family, who employ a chef called Conor Fitzpatrick. The natural response – and a sound one – is to order hot buttered Irish oysters followed by traditional Irish stew, or beef and Guinness casserole, then baked treacle (using black treacle not golden syrup) tart and cream. More dishes in this idiom would suit the mustard-plush-upholstered chairs and standard lamps with their tasselled shades better than do alternatives such as mousseline of scallops and sun-dried peppers, or roast boneless quail stuffed with apricots and roasted garlic. Prices are reasonable. Staff are charming. The downstairs bar takes a daily delivery of Donegal oysters and provides good bar food and occasional live Irish music.

Open
Lunch Mon-Fri, dinner Mon-Sat
Hours
12.00-10.00pm
Credit cards
AmEx, Mastercard, Visa, Switch, Delta
Service charge
10%
Set-price lunch
£15
Set price dinner
£18
Nearest tube station
Bond Street
Map 1

L'Odéon £40

65 Regent Street W1 (287 1400)

+ *Bruno Loubet...*
- *...cannot be everywhere, all the time*

When L'Odéon opened in December 1996 a gust of air blew forth, as those who had been holding their breath for the previous 18 months waiting for this mega-restaurant to happen were able to exhale. Various set-backs to do with planners and builders had held up the launch of Bruno for the masses: Loubet had most recently been cooking at Bistro Bruno in Soho (q.v.), before that he was chef of The Four Seasons Restaurant in The Four Seasons Hotel, and before that he was chef of Le Petit Blanc, in its original incarnation, in Oxford. He is a singular cook: French down to his fingernails but able to see the point of something as battily British as piccalilli and then get down to

Open
Every day
Hours
12.00-3.00pm
5.30pm-12.00am
(Sun 1.00-4.00pm,
6.30-10.30pm)
Credit cards
AmEx, Mastercard, Visa, Switch, Diner's, Delta
Cover charge
£1.50 per person
Service charge
12.5% (for 6 or more)
Set-price lunch
£14.50-£17.50
(incl cover charge)

the job of improving it. And serving it with mackerel whose innate oiliness it reprimands. His approach is idiosyncratic but intuitive, as can be inferred from dishes such as roast scallops and black pudding with mashed potato, garlic and parsley coulis (a best-seller); pumpkin tortellini with chorizo cream sauce; caviar jelly with soured cream and chives; monkfish feuillantine with orange and cardamom; roast Hereford duck breast with beetroot and rhubarb marmalade, and fruit-tea jus (duck is a favourite starting point for this chap from the South-West); and mascarpone and basil ice cream with prune sauce (desserts, it must be said, are not his strong point). When the dishes work, it is exciting eating. When Loubet is not there – and he has to have time off sometimes – standards have been known to waver. What is less thrilling is the context. A former British Airways first-floor office and innoculations centre has been rather drably converted by Fitch Associates, seemingly celebrating the extraction system and not making the best use of the half-moon windows and the view. Standards in service have declined since Marian Scrutton went to The Avenue (q.v.). Prices are those suited to an up-market intimate restaurant, not to a large, linoleum-floored restaurant that you might hope to use on a fairly casual basis.

THIS LIST IS a ramshackle affair that has lurched from classifying wines according to region to having a tentative stab at putting them into grape varieties. So, it was nice to see Alain Brumont's Pacherenc-du-Vic-Bilh, a surprise that it is listed as a Sauvignon. To have wines from Italy, Germany, the Rhône, the Loire, South Africa and Spain classified under 'Native Regional Varieties' smacks of laziness. How about something more disingenuous like 'best of the rest'? A diverse array of grapes: Zinfandel, Pinotage, Tannat (both a straight and super cuvée) and even a Petite Syrah from Mexico, will attract snapper-uppers of unconsidered trifles.

Odette's £32

Open
Lunch every day,
dinner Mon-Sat
Hours
12.30-2.30pm,
7.00-11.00pm
Credit cards
AmEx, Mastercard,
Visa, Switch,
Delta, Diner's
Set-price lunch
£10

130 Regent's Park Road NW1 (586 5486/8766)

+ *£10 set menu at lunch; the desserts*
– *some ambitious dishes suffer from mutually exclusive ingredients*

Odette's romantic reputation continues to flourish in its idyllic location just opposite Primrose Hill. Cool, efficient service smooths your meal, whether you are sitting in the front of the restaurant where, in summer, the tables spill on to the street; in the middle where dark green walls are covered with myriad gilded mirrors; or in the light-drenched balcony-cum-conservatory at the back. The menu achieves solidity rather than subtlety: hare with a juniper sauce, kidneys with a red-onion gravy, and salmon trout with aubergines and fennel strike all the grace-and-flavour notes. Someone evidently has a sweet tooth, because the desserts are outstanding: in particular, the chocolate espresso tart. The wine bar downstairs serves restaurant-quality food at a price that affords you the wallet space to wade freely into the sumptuous wine list.

BOTH COMPREHENSIVE AND fairly priced, the list ranges jauntily across the world. It offers numerous half-bottles and wines by the glass, and is punctuated by amusing tasting notes that are sometimes more pluperfect praise than pithy description. Nevertheless, there is a laudable commitment to suggesting food-and-wine matches, and a disarming lack of pomposity in the service of wine (other restaurants please note). The categorization of the list by style is thoroughly commendable, although including a clean, spritzy Gavi and a New Zealand Sauvignon in the full-bodied section is not. For the adventurous there is a list of offbeat guest wines, allowing the opportunity to steer into comparatively uncharted territory.

Nearest tube station
Chalk Farm
Map 1

Ognisko £26

55 Exhibition Road SW7 (589 4635)

+ *tackling a stuffed dumpling on the terrace in summer*
- *uninspiring wine list, but turn to the vodkas*

Not far from the museums is this exhibit of slightly foxed and faded Eastern European grandeur. Ognisko, restaurant of The Polish Hearth Club, is open to non-members and to anyone weary of fashionable, minimalist cooking. Sitting on gilded chairs at pink-clothed tables, tuck into blinis with smoked salmon, Sevruga caviar and soured cream; salad of smoked eel and avocado; bortsch with kolduny dumplings; stuffed fillet of beef with buckwheat; knuckle of pork Bavarian-style; bigos (Poland's national dish of smoky sausage, stewed pickled cabbage and dried mushrooms); and pancakes stuffed with sweet cheese, rendered crisp by frying. Calories are not counted here, nor are the glasses of vodka you knock back.

Open
Every day
Hours
12.30-11.30pm
Credit cards
AmEx, Mastercard, Visa, Diner's
Nearest tube station
South Kensington
Map 2

Old Delhi £32

Open
Every day
Hours
12.00-3.30pm,
6.00-11.00pm
Credit cards
AmEx, Mastercard,
Visa, Diner's
Service charge
15%
Nearest tube
station
Marble Arch
Map 6

48 Kendal Street W2 (723 3335)

+ *Iranian and Indian dishes side by side*
- *egregious service for which you are charged 15%*

The crown of the late Shah of Iran is carved in gold on the front door of Old Delhi, embossed on the menu and printed on the bill. Mr Shaghaghi, owner of this apparently Indian establishment is, as he would put it, Persian. Formerly an art dealer, after the revolution he bought Old Delhi and introduced into the Indian repertoire some Persian dishes. The resulting menu is an alluring mingling of two compatible cuisines, with the Indian dishes benefiting from a high standard of raw ingredients. Among the Persian dishes, try in the first course kufteh (meatballs) and mirza-ghasemi (based on aubergine and egg); in the main course gaimeh (lamb with yellow split peas and dry limes) and fesenjune (chicken in a potent walnut and pomegranate sauce); and in the dessert course ice cream flavoured with rose water and pistachios. Wines are overpriced.

Oliver's Island £26

Open
Lunch Sun-Fri,
dinner Mon-Sat
Hours
12.00-2.30pm,
6.30-10.30pm
Credit cards
AmEx, Mastercard,
Visa, Switch, Delta
Service charge
12.5%
Set-price lunch
£9.95
Nearest tube
station
Gunnersbury

162 Thames Road, Strand on the Green W4 (0181-747 8888)

+ *good fish dishes*
- *leaden puddings*

By the end of its first year of trading, this restaurant had shed the Australian chef who opened it and replaced him with the sous-chef Shane Cattermole. Fish is the dish here, and there are usually four daily specials which could be anything from cod to skate. The field mushrooms (a feature of the original chef's menu) are still in evidence, as are loyal customers who can be summarized as middle-aged, married and conservative with a small 'c'. Risotto with peas and crispy black pudding is good; desserts are not.

Oliveto ★ new £28

Open
Every day
Hours
Mon-Fri 12.00-
3.00pm, 7.00-
11.30pm; Sat-Sun
12.00-4.00pm,
7.00-11.00pm
Credit cards
AmEx, Mastercard,
Switch, Visa,
Delta

49 Elizabeth Street SW1 (730 0074)

+ *pizza, pasta, precise, unpretentious*
- *eaten here tends to be as in Square, Place, Terrace, Gate, Mews*

The brother or sister of Olivo (q.v.) in nearby Eccleston Street attracts the same sort of expensively shod clientele who appreciate the thin, crisp pizzas and calzones and the imaginative pasta assemblies. Shellfish pasta dishes which please include black tagliatelle with ragoût of cuttlefish; tortelloni stuffed with prawns; linguine with crabmeat, garlic and chilli. The Sardinian influence is felt here — as it is in Olivo — in spaghetti bottarga (with dried grey mullet roe) and spada marinato (carpaccio of marinated swordfish). Main course dishes of meat and fish tend to be char-grills with scant adornment. The interior is cool, but the service warm.

Nearest tube stations
Victoria, Sloane Square
Map 2

Olivo   £25

21 Eccleston Street SW1 (730 2505)

+ *happy holiday atmosphere*
- *tight-lipped service*

Open
Lunch Mon-Fri, dinner Mon-Sun
Hours
12.00-2.30pm, 7.00-11.00pm
Credit cards
AmEx, Mastercard, Visa, Switch, Delta
Cover charge
£1.50 per person
Set-price lunch
£4 & £16
Nearest tube station
Victoria
Map 2

Sardinian dishes particularize this popular Italian restaurant, as does the blue and yellow decor which gives the feeling of sitting in an empty swimming-pool with a molten sun above. Insalata di fregola (salad made with couscous, cucumber, capers and basil); malloredus (baby gnocchi) with a sausage and tomato sauce; spaghetti all bottarga (with grated, dried grey-mullet roe); sebadas (deep-fried pastries filled with soft, sweet cheese and painted with honey) are all Sardinian-inspired. The chargrill takes centre stage in the cooking process, and rocket zooms all over the plates. The set-price lunch (exceedingly popular) is good value. The irritating Italian habit of adding a cover charge (here £1.50) covers greeny-gold olive oil into which to dip the good bread. Sardinia also infiltrates the wine list.

192   £29

192 Kensington Park Road W11 (229 0482)

+ *happy hour for champagne*
- *unhappy hour waiting for main courses*

Open
Every day
Hours
12.30-3.00pm
(Sat-Sun 3.30pm),
7.00-11.30pm
(Sun 11.00pm)
Credit cards
AmEx, Mastercard, Visa, Switch, Diner's
Service charge
12.5% (for parties of 6 and over)
Set-price lunch
£9.50 & £12.50
Nearest tube stations
Ladbroke Grove, Notting Hill Gate
Map 6

The revamped interior of pastel oranges and purples, jazzy lighting and eye-level celebrity-surveillance mirrors might have been designed with the intention of maintaining a vaguely Bohemian feel, but instead comes across as a form of muted psychedelia for 30-somethings. The kitchen has seen a roll call of London's finest, and Albert Clarke's menu is an up-to-the-minute lexicon of modern British favourites such as crab, avocado and bacon salad; veal chop with green-olive tapenade; and duck liver, duck confit, baby spinach and a poached egg. There is probably too much choice in an extensive menu that changes twice daily; quality control tends to suffer as a consequence. Tough breast of pigeon and overcooked liver have been two complaints. When Clarke is on form there is much to enjoy: plaice with broad beans, girolles and pearl onions was described enthusiastically as 'cooked in accordance with the laws of fish'. Service has been known to affect the personae of the Seven Dwarfs, particularly Dopey.

THE FACT THAT 192 is the restaurant outlet for John Armit wines has distinct advantages for the consumer. Tempted by Château Rieussec 1983, an unctious cru-class Sauternes at £25 (considerably cheaper than you would be able to purchase it retail), you would probably wish to order a case on the spot and drink it like a camel. Bargains proliferate, most notably in the sections 'Grand White Wines' and 'Grand Red Wines', with the brilliant Nuits St Georges Blanc from Domaine de l'Arlot (made from mutated pinot noir vines) a steal at £39, and the plummily approachable Château Certan Giraud 1985 a financially approachable £30. 40 wines are available by the glass in two sizes: large and standard.

L'Oranger ⭐ new £34

5 St James's Street SW1 (839 3774)

+ *a good deal for superior cooking*
- *the static feel to the menu*

Open
Lunch Mon-Sat, dinner every day
Hours
12.00-2.30pm, Mon-Fri 6.00-10.45pm, Sat-Sun 6.00-11.15pm
Credit cards
AmEx, Mastercard, Visa, Switch, Diner's, Delta
Set-price lunch
£16.00-£19.50
Set-price dinner
£22.00 & £29.00
Nearest tube station
Green Park
Map 3

Just as Marco Pierre White and Claudio Pulze (when they were partners in The Canteen) joined forces, financially and otherwise, to launch Gordon Ramsay at Aubergine (q.v.) in 1993, so three years later Ramsay and Pulze have established Marcus Wareing as chef at L'Oranger (the site was previously Overton's of St James's). As at Aubergine, the pricing system consists of set-price deals at both lunch and dinner. Considering the area and also the level of professionalism, it could be successfully argued that these deals are a bargain: at the time of writing, three courses at dinner cost £22 with no supplements to trip you up. Wareing has learned his lessons well, and there is a reliable expertise in the preparation of dishes such as marinated tuna and white radish in a sesame-oil vinegar; chilled tomato soup with basil; ragoût of mussels with parsley and handrolled pasta; pan-fried cod with a wild-mushroom duxelle; rabbit-leg confit with frisée salad and pommes sautées; and pork fillet with parsnip purée, spinach and wild mushrooms; but several visits to L'Oranger set you wondering what Wareing might cook on his day off, left to his own devices. A dish cited as a speciality is certainly a feat of technical expertise: potato 'scales' are wrapped around a fillet of brill and the whole cooked in such a way that the scales are crisp-edged but the fish not overdone; while a savage reduction gives the brill a wine-dark sea in which to swim. Creamed leeks provide light relief. An alluring dessert is tarte fine of plums or figs (according to season), served with vanilla or cinnamon ice cream respectively. Service is formally attired, led by a manager who has worked at Aubergine. Only subtle changes have been made to what was a revamped interior for Overton's. It remains clubby in feel, as suits St James's, which – perhaps unfortunately – also suits suits. Nigel Davies, who was the talented chef of Overton's in its last incarnation, will be opening a restaurant in Dulwich in 1997: very good news for SE21 and thereabouts.

AS WITH THE list at Aubergine (q.v.), this is one of those infuriating French undertakings that could be so much better. When no information is given on grape variety or style, you tend to cavil at minor faux pas. Why is a Sauvignon de Touraine listed separately under 'Regionales White' (an interesting example of Franglais) and not under the appellation Loire Valley? Why are so many producers merely dignified with the slapdash title of Mr? Why are there so many spelling mistakes? Despite all these criticisms, there are some good-value buys: Teiller's gooseberry and mint-leaf Ménétou-Salon (£18), Robert (his friends call him Mister) Michel's tarry Cornas (£25) and the selection of offbeat châteaux from less fashionable vintages that allows plenty of happy grazing for under £40.

Orsino £28

119 Portland Road W11 (221 3299)

+ *a damn fine range of coffees*
- *the pomodoro and rocket show; prosciutto con melone at £7.50*

The sequel to Orso (see below) shares many of its sibling's traits. Modern Italian dishes are served on pottery plates; the surroundings are terracotta-peach; an easy breeze of cool sophistication wafts through the room. But somewhere in transmission the genetic blueprint of the food gene has gone missing between Covent Garden and Shepherd's Bush, resulting in a dilute imitation. If the BBC, located nearby, had commissioned this second series, they might have thrown more money into the casting of essential and appropriate ingredients. Among the antipasti, grilled squid came with watery tomato mush; other salads were mere assemblies or lists of non-complementary ingredients rather than dialogues of flavour.

Open
Every day
Hours
12.00-11.00pm
Credit cards
AmEx, Mastercard, Visa, Switch, Delta
Set-price lunch
£11.50-£15.50
Nearest tube station
Holland Park
Map 6

Diced pieces of raw red onion, tomatoes and black olives do not a £7.50 salad make. Taglierini with mussels, leeks, tomato and white wine also missed the mark; shrivelled shellfish sitting oddly in tandem with undercooked leeks. A rather better option would be to concentrate on the small pizzas, on a creamy fennel risotto or on something from the top end of the menu, such as roast sea bass with lime leaves and new potatoes.

Orso £30

27 Wellington Street WC2 (240 5269)

+ *glamorous customers; glamorous waiters*
− *(for the uninitiated) playing hunt the entrance on Wellington Street*

Open
Every day
Hours
12.00pm-12.00am
Credit cards
AmEx, Mastercard,
Visa, Switch, Delta
Set-price lunch
£11.50-£13.50
Nearest tube
station
Covent Garden
Map 4

A recent visit found Orso firing on all cylinders. The 'Pizzeta Giovanni' had real pizzazz: small and crispily crusted with moist nuggets of goat's cheese, whole roasted cloves of garlic and fresh oregano; while risotto with grilled asparagus was rippling with butter. Other first courses included tagliatelle with roast lamb, canellini and puntarelle; and a summer salad of artichokes, peas, peeled baby broad beans, asparagus and mint. Reports suggest that standards still slide alarmingly − less-than-fresh ingredients, oily flavours, small portions − when the first team isn't in situ. Nevertheless, if you are in the mood the whirl and glitz will seduce: the food is clean, healthy, colourful and sometimes memorable (meat dishes stand out), and you may bask in the glow of celebrities. Vin Santo and cantucci is the recommended coda to a meal.

ORSO AND ORSINO (q.v.) share the same list. Every year we make the same criticism of it − nothing changes. Crammed on to a single page, unannotated, with no indication of grape variety, style or even region, it is anonymous to anyone who is unfamiliar with Italian producers, which is a pity when there are occasional pearls. Sylvio Jermann's Vintage Tunino is an amazing kitchen-sink blend of Sauvignon, Chardonnay, Ribolla Gialla, Malvasia and Picolit. Quality reds characterized by Tedeschi, Antinori, Masi and Lungarotti. The inclusion of five wines from the Chianti Classico region and not a single one from southern Italy is an imbalance that should be rectified.

Oslo Court £32

Charlbert Street (off Prince Albert Road) NW8 (722 8795)

+ *pink grapefruit grilled with brown sugar and sherry*
- *location in a characterless block of flats*

Most of Oslo Court's customers are regulars; to mark the various rites of passage in life it is to its comforting continental menu that they turn. The current Spanish fraternal ownership has kept alive something of the style originated by the Yugoslavian Katnic family who opened the apartment-block restaurant over a quarter of a century ago. Set-price menus at both lunch and dinner encourage a soup-to-nuts approach to dining, including the many vegetable garnishes and a trawl through the dessert trolley. There are old-fashioned, rich, celebratory dishes such as seafood crêpe with cheese sauce; Coquilles St Jacques served with the shell padded with mashed potatoes; veal Holstein, the breadcrumbed cutlet served with fried egg, anchovies and capers; and duckling Montmorency (with cherry sauce); but there is also fresh fish simply grilled. And where else nowadays could you find grilled grapefruit with brown sugar? Service is also of the old school.

Open
Mon–Sat
Hours
12.30–2.30pm,
7.00–11.00pm
Credit cards
AmEx, Mastercard,
Visa, Switch,
Diner's
Set-price lunch
£19
Set price dinner
£26.50
Nearest tube station
St John's Wood
Map 1

Osteria Antica Bologna £25

23 Northcote Road SW11 (978 4771)

+ *large portions; low prices*
- *success breeds carelessness*

There was a time when most South Londoners would have sold their birthright for a mess of pottage — or even a pasta dish — here. That moment has passed, but this casual, wood-lined, cramped restaurant remains popular for what it does well — when it does it well. Assagi (small dishes that can be ordered as first courses or in greater quantity as complete meals) are a nice facility. Pastas are interesting and sometimes quite convoluted, reflecting the traditions of Emilia-Romagna. Fusilli is sauced with octopus, ricotta and chilli; garganelli comes with a shepherd's sauce of lamb, rosemary and pecorino. The house-speciality main course is goat partnered with polenta and a rich tomato and almond pesto. Desserts — including a dark chocolate cake with espresso cream, and warm apple and walnut cake served with cream — are a high point. Wine is an interest of the owners (c.f., Del Buongustaio), and the wholly Italian list is both well-chosen and reasonably priced.

Open
Every day
Hours
12.00–3.00pm,
6.00–11.30pm (Sat
10.00am–11.30pm,
Sun 10.00am–
10.30pm)
Credit cards
AmEx, Mastercard,
Visa, Switch
Cover charge
70p per person
Set-price lunch
£7.50
Nearest railway station
Clapham Junction
Map 1

Osteria le Fate £30

Open
Mon-Sat
Hours
12.00–3.00pm,
7.30pm–11.30pm
Credit cards
AmEx, Mastercard,
Visa, Switch, Delta
Set-price lunch
£14.50–£17.50
Set-price dinner
£17.50–£20.50
**Nearest tube
station**
Sloane Square
Map 2

5 Draycott Avenue SW3 (591 0071)

+ *Ligurian first courses and pasta*
− *the main courses*

Opened by Sandro Caponnetto − a chef who in Genoa owned a restaurant called Capun Pascia, and a chap so truly, madly, deeply, Italian that he is a former professional footballer − this Chelsea restaurant cleaves to its regional Italian identity in offering various Ligurian dishes. The best-known speciality of the area is undoubtedly pesto, made in its homestead with particularly sweet, aromatic basil and pale, delicate olive oil. Served here not with the traditional pasta (trenette or piccage) plus green beans and potatoes, but with a sheet of lasagne folded around those vegetables, it is notably good. It also adds extra distinction to the minestrone, which is served as a room-temperature purée of vegetables and herbs, resembling sublime baby food. Another purée, this one a slightly grainy soup based on chickpeas, vigorously spiced and garnished with grilled king prawns, is also a stellar dish. Among the antipasti, monkfish tartare with artichokes, spinach fried in a thin, crisp pastry (delizia in crosta), and mozzarella in carrozza are all recommended. Another suggestion is to confine your order to first courses, pasta dishes and dessert, since the main courses tried on two occasions were universally disappointing: overcooked, under-seasoned, dull. It seems almost as if different kitchens handle the different courses. The house in which the restaurant is located provides three small dining-rooms on two levels. Decorative themes are patterned chinaware and crowds of bottles: some containing alcohol, some olive oil. Pretty-boy waiters exhibit a sort of benign fecklessness.

Oxo Tower Restaurant £40

Open
Mon-Sun
Hours
12.00pm–3.00pm
5.30–11.00pm
Credit cards
AmEx, Mastercard,
Visa, Switch,
Delta, Diner's
Service charge
12.5%
**Nearest tube
stations**
Blackfriars,
Waterloo
Map 3

8th Floor, Oxo Tower Wharf, Barge House Street SE1 (803 3888)

+ *the sensational view − London laid out anew*
− *where are Oxo Katie and Phillip?*

Although it opened just as this Guide was going to press, making only one preview meal possible, I suspect that the Oxo Tower Restaurant − and the brasserie and bar − will create waves up and down the Thames for some long time to come. The development of the restaurant is by Harvey Nichols, a fact hammered home by the well-designed teas and what-have-you on sale. The elegant restaurant design − featuring double-sided louvres on the curved ceiling that change from white during the day to blue as night falls, affecting not just atmosphere but acoustics – is the work of a design firm, Lifschutz Davidson, who happily have been involved with local housing projects (there are five floors of community housing below the restaurant). Head chef Simon Arkless has worked for the McCoy brothers, for Simon Hopkinson at Bibendum (q.v.) and for Henry Harris at Harvey Nichols' The Fifth Floor (q.v), where he was sous-chef. The menu is – how did you guess? – eclectic but put together with considerable gastronomic intellect. Consider oyster, cucumber and chive soup with Gewürztraminer and caviar Chantilly; crab and sweet-pork salad with Thai dressing; acorn-fed black-pig charcuterie with purple figs; pan-fried fillet of cod, black-truffle dressing and wilted greens; roasted partridge with verjus and celeriac purée; pot-roast rabbit with butterbeans, thyme and chorizo; elderflower cake with blackberry compôte; and blue-cheese Bavarois with poached pears. The ideas bode well. It is a pity that vegetables are priced as an extra – and are necessary to the main courses. The wine list is magisterial. At night, with your sight-line in line with the sky line, clocking the panorama from St Paul's to the Houses of Parliament, you can fall in love with London all over again.

Le Palais du Jardin £35

136 Long Acre WC2 (379 5353)

+ *a true brasserie, open all day from breakfast to midnight*
- *so crowded it is hard to get from front to back*

In the general excitement about large restaurants this Covent Garden brasserie and crustacea cafe/bar rarely gets a mention, perhaps because no celebrity chef or knight of the realm is involved. Like a Parisian brasserie, it has a welcoming democratic, egalitarian air – it is not, in other words, populated by the cloned customers who in London dominate the overtly fashionable places. The sheer size of the place – not immediately apparent upon entering – and including the glazed extension at the back, lends excitement. The menu offers a wide range of styles and prices, from workaday (bangers and mash) to diet day (half a cold lobster) to special event (breast of duck with cabbage-wrapped duck confit and wild mushrooms). Desserts are a high point, one being basil brûlée with soft fruit and a pistachio macaroon. Generally, standards of cooking, presentation and service are high. Extraction is powerful; there is no problem with smokers.

Open
Every day
Hours
12.00pm-12.00am
(Oyster bar),
12.00-3.30pm,
5.30pm-12.00am
Credit cards
AmEx, Mastercard,
Visa, Switch, Delta
Service charge
Optional service
charge of 12.5%
**Nearest tube
station**
Covent Garden,
Leicester Square
Map 4 & 5

Palio £24

Open
Lunch Mon-Fri &
Sun, dinner every
day
Hours
11.30am-11.30pm
(Sun 10.30pm)
Credit cards
AmEx, Mastercard,
Visa, Switch,
Diner's
Set-price lunch
£8.50
Set price dinner
£9.50
Nearest tube
station
Notting Hill Gate
Map 6

175 Westbourne Grove W11 (221 6624)

+ *Wozza's palliest restaurant*
- *the loos*

Running ahead of the AWT med-cred pack is Palio, a bar/restaurant whose exterior looks as though it has undergone a severe mango-juice respray. Why the formula succeeds here is perhaps due to the fact that the menu has a straightforward appeal borne out of not trying to be all things to all people. The matchmaking focuses on Italy, with a tranche of pastas (penne with chicken, avocado and mascarpone; or rigatoni with pancetta and butternut squash), risottos and bruschettas. Plates are thatched with copious greenery; generous herbal assistance lifts quotidian dishes of squid, mussels, lamb and cod. Sticky toffee pudding has the requisite wickedness factor on the dessert front. Service is largely care of agile Antipodeans and, more than at Antony Worral Thompson's other joints, this one has the feel of catering to a local and regular clientele.

Patio £16

Open
Lunch Mon-Fri,
dinner every day
Hours
12.00-3.00pm,
6.00pm-12.00am
Credit cards
AmEx, Mastercard,
Visa, Switch,
Diner's, Delta
Set price dinner
£9.90
Nearest tube
stations
Shepherd's Bush,
Goldhawk Road
Map 1

5 Goldhawk Road W12 (0181-743 5194)

+ *genuine warmth and generosity*
- *the English menu — ignore it*

According to the owners Ewa and Kas Michalik, a review of their restaurant in the *Evening Standard* in November 1995 brought about a revolution in their lives. After working in relative obscurity for nine years, suddenly the world (i.e., *Evening Standard* readers) found out about the Polish home-cooking served at the incredible price of £9.90 for three courses including Polish vodka, and began beating a path to the rather unlovely doorway in Goldhawk Road. To think that prices would have subsequently risen is to underestimate the Michaliks' irrepressible spirit of generosity and hospitality. The same deal stands. You might start with smoked salmon and blinis or herrings with soured cream, go on to duck à la Polonaise or homemade pierogi served with about five different vegetables, and finish with lemon mousse, fresh fruit, chocolates, sugary cookies and, of course, more vodka. The atmosphere is of an Eastern European front room in the home of a family that loves food and drink and flowers.

Pearl of Knightsbridge £34

22 Brompton Road (Knightsbridge Green) SW1 (225 3888)

+ *dim-sum at lunchtime; first courses at dinnertime*
- *drab decor; awful muzak*

Keen followers of up-market Chinese restaurants might notice in the typography and content of the new menu at Pearl a distinct similarity to those of Zen Central (q.v.) in Mayfair. As part of some convoluted change of ownership, two of the former managers in the Zen group are now running this Knightsbridge establishment. Another Zen connection is chef Cho-Ka Law, who has come from Zen in Hong Kong. Whatever the machinations, the food — self-styled modern Cantonese — is notably well-prepared and shows some interesting deviations from the usual lists of dishes. First courses exemplify this best. Try grilled oriental dumplings; cold-smoked, herb-marinated fish; quail in an intense brown, shiny sauce or with peppercorn salt; spring-onion cake; rice-wine marinated chicken; and pig's trotter served with a dab of English mustard. Modern Cantonese is obviously all-embracing, as Peking and Szechuan dishes are also offered. Weight the meal towards starters, but leave some room for fried crispy egg-yolk buns and wok-fried red-bean paste for dessert.

Open
Every day
Hours
12.00–2.45pm,
6.00–11.15pm
Credit cards
AmEx, Mastercard,
Visa, Switch,
Delta, Diner's
Service charge
12.5%
Set-price lunch
£10
Nearest tube station
Knightsbridge
Map 2

The Peasant £24

240 St John Street EC1 (336 7726)

+ *the mission: to boldly blow sophisticated flavours into bucolic cooking*
- *the inclination to decorate dishes with more than a peck of pickled peppers*

A restaurant within a pub, serving food with Italian leanings which blows hot and cold within a dish, let alone a meal. Certain concepts are flawed: wild mushrooms, toast and tapenade was an odd, mud-coloured starter for summer — a selection of new season's vegetables might have served the purpose better — and a yellow pea dahl flavoured with cumin and coriander suffered from defective spicing. More to the peasanty point are a chilled tomato soup with bread, basil and chorizo sausage; warm frittata with lemon, courgettes, mint and potato; and braised lamb shank with butternut squash and rosemary risotto. Chocolate praline ice cream with coconut biscotti, and pear and amaretti tart with ginger custard, conclude the meal on a high. The wine list traipses merrily into

Open
Lunch Mon-Fri,
dinner Mon-Sat
Hours
12.30–3.00pm,
6.30–10.45pm
Credit cards
AmEx, Mastercard,
Visa, Switch, Delta
Service charge
12.5%
Nearest tube stations
Angel, Farringdon
Map 3

the New World with delegates from Thelema, Mount Langi, Firesteed, a token nod to France and, more surprisingly, only one Italian red. Service is sympatico.

The People's Palace £28

Open
Every day
Hours
12.00-3.00pm,
5.30-11.00pm
Credit cards
AmEx, Mastercard,
Visa, Switch,
Delta, Diner's
Nearest tube
station
Waterloo
Map 3

Royal Festival Hall, South Bank SE1 (928 9999)

+ *food to go with the room to go with the view*
- *who coined the name — Gary Robespierre?*

Earth hath not anything more fair to show than the location of this restaurant on the south side of the appositely named Hungerford Bridge. Except The Oxo Tower Restaurant (q.v.). The People's Greenhouse, as it might be renamed, has undergone a quiet revolution: there is less headless-chicken scurrying; the kitchen brigade seems to have settled into a routine under chef Steven Carter (ex Stephen Bull [q.v.]) and the prices have gone up to cover the new-found maturity. Ceviche of tuna with coriander chutney; crab, cardamom and orange salad; and terrine of puy lentils with a curry vinaigrette demonstrate a fascination with spices. Grilled fillets of mackerel dusted with cumin, served with a zesty cucumber and red-onion salad, where coolness and acidity matched the latent oiliness of the fish and the dryness of the spice, is a dish where flavours converge while retaining their subsidiary role. Smoked rump of lamb with Tuscan-bean stew was flavoured with mustard-rich anchoïade croûtons. Given the proximity of the arts complex, we can only conclude: 'If music be the food of love, eat on.'

Le P'tit Normand £26

Open
Lunch Mon-Fri,
dinner every day,
Sunday lunch
Hours
12.00-2.00pm,
7.00-10.00pm
(7.00-10.30pm Fri
& Sat)
Credit cards
AmEx, Mastercard,
Visa, Switch,
Diner's, Delta
Service charge
12.5%
Set-price lunch
£5
Nearest tube
station
Southfields
Map 1

185 Merton Road SW18 (0181-871 0233)

+ *cheerfully old-fashioned*
- *side salads*

With little culinary competition in Wandsworth — apart from Chez Bruce (q.v.) — this French bistro is gratefully appreciated by the locals. However, the owners should not push their luck quite so far where service is concerned. The menu, although fleshed out with daily specials, is short to the point of being curt, but perhaps the chef is wise to keep his repertoire limited and thus seemingly authentic. Moules, soupes à l'oignon and de poisson, côte de veau and entrecôte aux cinq poivres fulfil the expectations set up by red-checked tablecloths and other accoutrements of an 'Allo 'Allo approach. It is probably customers' unwillingness to ingest the cholesterol, or the fashionable stance of being 'dairy-free', that accounts for the meltdown in what was once a notable cheeseboard.

The Phoenix Bar & Grill £25

162 Lower Richmond Road SW15 (0181-780 3131)

+ *a culinary breath of fresh air*
- *traffic spoils the peace of the terrace*

Opened in the early summer of 1996, this light, bright, white conversion of two adjacent houses is the latest restaurant enterprise of Rebecca Mascarenhas and her husband James Harris, who own Sonny's (q.v.) in neighbouring Barnes. The menu is a clever modern mix, ideally suited to a local meal of no big deal but containing dishes that tickle the palate of the professional (constant and therefore mildly jaded) eater out. One such is the first-course salad of spicy pecan, gorgonzola and pear, in which mealy nuts glazed in a peppery caramel contrast with pungent, creamy cheese and semi-sweet fruit, all on a heap of leaves. It deftly sees off any virtue from the notion of salad. Spanish charcuterie is another good way to begin, as are Rossmore oysters with red onion, chilli and lime relish. Grills make up a section that stands alone. B.b.q. pork belly, served with corn-on-the-cob rubbed with chilli butter, features here: a dish in which fat-rimmed, crisp-skinned slices of meat, treated much like spare ribs, are served with a powerful sauce. A more delicate appetite might choose grilled sea bream with rocket, lemon and roasted chillies. Lobster club sandwich enclosed in layers of toasted brioche – the dish that began life at the restaurant Arcadia in New York – costs a hefty £15 (about twice the price of most main courses). Vegetable side orders are unusually carefully prepared. The desserts are enticing: a summer menu offered blackberry and strawberry sundae served with blueberry sauce, frozen tequila sunrise, and cold rice pudding with cinnamon biscuit. James Harris's wine knowledge ensures an interesting list, and the mark-ups are held in check. This stretch of road used to sport some slightly dog-eared English bistros. The Phoenix is the sassy new kid on the block wearing all the latest gear.

THIS LIST IS brief, bright and brotherly, offering some quirky things by the glass. Start with André Ostertag's unconventional barrique-aged Pinot Blanc, and then try either an alluring Santenay from the Côte d'Or or a rasping Sangiovese from California. An enlightened marking-up policy means that you can sample Sylvio Jermann's fabulous and fabulously expensive

Open
Lunch Mon-Fri, dinner every day, Sunday brunch
Hours
12.00-2.30pm, (Sun 12.00-3.30pm) Mon-Thurs 7.00-11.00pm, Fri-Sat 7.00-11.30pm, Sun 7.00-10.00pm
Credit cards
AmEx, Mastercard, Visa, Switch, Delta
Set-price lunch
£10
Set-price brunch
£16
Nearest tube stations
Putney Bridge, East Putney
Map 1

Chardonnay at £35, which is only a tenner more than you would theoretically pay in the shop − if you could find it. It's called 'Where the dreams have no end...', and I dare you to order it with a straight face.

Pied à Terre £60

Open
Lunch Mon-Fri,
dinner Mon-Sat
Hours
12.15-2.15pm,
7.15-11.00pm
Credit cards
AmEx, Mastercard,
Visa, Switch,
Delta, Diner's, JCB
Set-price lunch
£22
Set-price dinner
£29.50, £39.50,
£46
Nearest tube
station
Goodge Street
Map 4

34 Charlotte Street W1 (636 1178)

+ set-price lunch menu
− the chef wot won the stars has gone

This business of Michelin stars can lead to what in some legal circles might be called 'passing off'. When Richard Neat was cooking at Pied à Terre he got first one, then a second Michelin star. Almost immediately after getting the second, much to everyone's surprise, he decided to up and go. He is, at the time of writing, executive chef of Fables (q.v.). Neat's sous-chef Tom Aikens is now cooking for this ostensibly Michelin two-star establishment. Prices have not lessened but increased. Two courses are £38 (with supplements); the menu dégustation is £52, not including service. Quite a few of the dishes, for example one based on snails with morille, asparagus and garlic purée, another on saddle of rabbit with rabbit leg confit, another on braised pig's head and trotter, retain Neat's imprint. It would not matter if the cooking was as good, but reports suggest it is not.

TWO FEET ON the ground seems to be the motto with all the endless duplication on this list. There are two Pouilly-Fuissés, two Gewürztraminers, two Mercureys, two Condrieus, and otherwise a serious selection of mainly French classics featuring an assortment of great names: Dageneau, Bonneau du Martray, Guigal, Rousseau and Coche-Dury. 'White Wines from The Rest of the World' (sic) unveils a prosaic manifest of Sauvignons and Chardonnays. A good touch is 14 dessert wines − six by the glass − including Banyuls, a rancio- (or cooked-) style vin doux naturel with a flavour of burnt caramel and brandy-soaked raisins. The list ends with its head in the clouds with '*Derrière les Fagots*,' some rare, mature Bordeaux and Burgundy at astronomical prices.

Poetry Cafe £20

22 Betterton Street WC2 (240 5081)

+ *romance rather than commercialism in Covent Garden*
- *when the chef is away, standards waver*

Open
Every day
Hours
12.00-3.00pm,
6.00-11.00pm
Credit cards
Mastercard, Visa,
Switch, Delta
Service charge
12.5% optional
**Nearest tube
station**
Covent Garden
Map 4

To join The Poetry Society as a friend costs £10 a year. For this modest sum you are entitled to eat in the small ground-floor cafe and also to use the reading room and web site located in the basement. So reasonably priced is the cafe menu that a few meals soon earn you back your sub. Chef Rebecca St John Cooper has worked at Mélange (now Mars) in nearby Endell Street and at Andrew Edmunds (q.v.). As at both those places, a gathering of like-minded customers and a short, modern menu responsive to the market are features of Poetry Cafe. The atmosphere is sympathetic, as suits the fuelling station of a benign, worthwhile body dedicated to spreading the insidious benefit of phrases and images that crystallize experience. Some of the vocabulary used in the menu conveys the gist of the cooking: salsas, tapenade, focaccia, caponata, lemongrass, chorizo, fishcake, couscous, granita. They may not rhyme, but the words are used mellifluously and in the appropriate context, so that squid with lemongrass is also flavoured with chilli and ginger, while cod and parsley fishcakes come with a tomato relish. Happy endings are provided by items such as lavender and honey ice-cream, and apple and blackcurrant crumble. The room is simply decorated – the brick walls are white-painted – but images of poets add an intricacy of their own.

Poissonerie de L'Avenue £38

82 Sloane Avenue SW3 (589 2457)

+ *a stable buoy in choppy seas*
- *slightly disapproving service charged at 15%*

Open
Mon-Sat
Hours
12.00-3.00pm,
7.00-1.30pm
Credit cards
AmEx, Mastercard,
Visa, Switch,
Diner's
Service charge
15% optional
Set-price lunch
£18.50
**Nearest tube
station**
South Kensington
Map 2

Peter Rosignoli's Poissonerie has been trading for over 30 years in an area transformed – in catering terms – by Joseph Ettedgui's Joe's Cafe, Terence Conran's Bibendum, and Mogens Tholstrup's Daphne's and The Collection. Holding firm with his somewhat old-fashioned fish restaurant formula, he has held on to a loyal core customer base some of whom doubtless buy their fresh fish at La Marée, the next door shop that is part of the business. Prices are confident but you get some cooking for your money, for example in the first course croustade de crabe frais au gratin; raviolis de homard et saumon, sauce tomate au basilic; risotto aux fruits de mer et légumes crus, and in the main course filets de sole 'Clara-Ward', célériac et artichauds (Clara Ward would seem to like lemon juice); brochette de coquilles Saint-Jacques au riz Créole; bouillabaisse maison avec son rouille. However, noble fish such as turbot and wild salmon are also served simply grilled or poached. Vegetables priced separately and a 15% service charge help to pad out the bill. Oysters can be eaten by themselves in the oyster bar or – a nice touch – chosen as a savoury in anges à cheval (angels on horseback).

Le Pont de la Tour £45

36d Shad Thames SE1 (403 8403)

+ the sun shining, a table on the terrace, a picture-postcard view and a glass of champagne in your hand
- for the money, the vista should include the Taj Mahal and the Pyramids

Open
Lunch Mon-Fri & Sun, dinner every day
Hours
12.00-3.00pm, 6.00-11.30pm (11.30-11.30pm bar & grill)
Credit cards
AmEx, Mastercard, Visa, Switch, Diner's
Service charge
12.5%
Set-price lunch
£27.50
Set-price dinner
£19.50 (pre-theatre)
Nearest tube stations
Tower HIll, London Bridge
Map 1

There is one theory afloat that London needs to expand dramatically to fit in the number of restaurants that Conran intends to open, and another that, as the population of London is contracting, maybe everybody could be snugly fitted in under the roof of the Gastrodrome complex by Tower Bridge. At this, the first of the restaurants, lunch prix fixe is within the realm of affordability. Unfortunately, however, the cooking tends not to fire on all cylinders, and reports of soggy vegetables and overcooked fish make this a bridge too far, especially when one throws in the cost of a taxi journey. In the evening, it is a case of in for a penny, in for a bank account. Aside from the fruits de mer, first courses are familiar if you have dined at Bibendum (q.v.): poached egg with asparagus, black truffle and Parmesan; ballotine of foie gras and brioche toast; and spiced crab salad with avocado and coriander. Main courses number roast leg of rabbit with pancetta, buttered leeks and mustard sauce (the up-market chicken Kiev of our times); Châteaubriand grill with sauce Béarnaise; and roast wild salmon with aïoli, roast peppers and basil. It can be a gastronomic experience, especially in the evening when subtle lighting, beautiful glassware and cosseting waiters contribute to the feel-good factor and you have sufficient time to study the wine list... and time yet for a hundred indecisions and revisions before you alight on the right page.

IT IS OTIOSE to remark that it requires skill to assemble a bad list of this magnitude. Every base is exhaustively covered, but to me a massive list is like one of those modern trawlers which hoovers up sprats and dolphins regardless. Inspecting this volume, there is little pleasure that derives from a sense of discrimination or even prejudice. There are no tasting notes except for a house selection at the front of the wine list, and scanning the tracts of virgin clarets and burgundies is like looking at hieroglyphics in the snow. Much relies on the quality of the sommeliers to interpret and recommend, and they are spending a large proportion of their time ferrying bottles from the shop. Look to Alsace and Loire for whites, and to the Rhône, Italy and Spain for reds. There – that's reduced the choice no end.

Poons £20

4 Leicester Street WC2 (437 1528)

+ *steamed Dover Sole at £9.80*
- *the set menus*

Open
Every day
Hours
12.00-11.30pm
Credit cards
None
Set-price lunch
£14
Nearest tube station
Leicester Square
Maps 4 & 5

The description 'wind-dried meats' does not refer to the less-than-fragrant zephyrs that puff through Chinatown, but to a way of curing duck, pork and pork sausages, rendering them the Chinese equivalent of charcuterie. This is Poons' unique selling point. These various meats are best sampled in a hot pot with rice. Another speciality of Poons is the slow-cooked meats or fish in a casserole. Alternatively, there are one-dish meals with minced pork and salted fish, and the wind-dried-duck mix (available in small and large portions), barbecued meats, chicken baked in a salt crust, boneless chicken sandwiched with wind-dried pork, and wind-dried-duck slices with celery (that's enough wind-dried – Ed.); an extensive list that distinguishes this venture from the majority of the one-tone Cantonese rivals. Relatively recent refurbishment of this branch, and of the caff in Lisle Street, allows more comfortable eating, but it's not a place for long-term residence.

The Popeseye £24

108 Blythe Road W14 (610 4578)

+ *real meat for real men*
- *only real men need apply*

Open
Dinner Mon-Sat
Hours
6.30-10.30pm
Credit cards
None
Service charge
12.5%
Nearest tube station
Olympia
Map 1

This is the place that put the 'un' into unpretentious. Sometimes chaotic and disdaining the notion of comfort, it still draws a following. The customers here are carnivores – not the discreet and guilt-ridden kind, but red in tooth and claw. The name Popeseye is shared with a Scottish cut of steak – we'd probably call it rump – and that is what you should order. The only other things you need are the first-rate chips and sound clarets. This is a simple menu that may be short on variety, but is long on passion.

La Porte des Indes ⭐ new £45

Open
Every day
Hours
12.00-2.30pm,
7.00-12.00am
(Sun 12.00-
3.00pm, 6.00-
10.30pm)
Credit cards
AmEx, Mastercard,
Visa, Switch,
Diner's
Service charge
12.5%
Set-price lunch
£15 unlimited
buffet lunch
Set-price dinner
£34 & £29
**Nearest tube
station**
Marble Arch
Map 1

32 Bryanston Street W1 (224 0055)

+ *the dramatic sweep of space behind an almost domestic façade*
- *peanut shells on the bar floor; inept service; nothing very
French about the Indian food*

From the folks who brought you The Blue Elephant (q.v.), here is a celebration of the French presence in India. 'The French presence where?' you might ask. (Surely it was we British who taught the Indians all they know about cooking? How else would they have discovered kedgeree, mulligatawny soup, Major Grey's chutney and chicken tikka masala?) As it turns out, the fact that in the 17th century the French established a settlement in Pondicherry, south of Madras, and later controlled for a time the kingdom of Hyderabad, is too remote a one on which to settle a 350-seater restaurant behind Selfridges. The Frenchified name and the inevitable handful of 'jealously guarded' recipes handed down in Pondicherry families through the centuries make little headway in what is otherwise a fairly standard but unusually expensive Indian menu, albeit with Thai ideas applied to presentation. The premises are a surprise: nothing from the outside prepares you for the vastness within. Unused for the past 20 years or so, the space which has housed ballroom and banqueting suites once rejoiced in the name of The Mayfairia Rooms. Some striking elements have been introduced into the interior, including a white-marble staircase, a chevron-patterned marble wall at two-storey height, down which water runs, and elaborately carved pink-sandstone balustrades. However, the effect is spoiled by cheap furnishing fabrics and bemused staff dressed in drab uniforms of cheap brown-and-beige man-made stuff. The obvious use for La Porte des Indes as a party venue is made less attractive by the high cost of a meal. An uninspired wine list is also shockingly overpriced. As at The Blue Elephant, the set-price menus (and, here, the house thalis) deliver the best value, as well as a fairly broad sampling of the product.

The Prince Bonaparte £22

Open
Lunch Wed-Mon,
dinner every day
Hours
12.30-3.00pm,
6.30-10.30pm
Credit cards
None

80 Chepstow Road W2 (229 5912)

+ *vivacious food in a tumultuous pub*
- *the music can be overbearing*

There is scarcely a pub left in Notting Hill Gate where you can get a half of mild and a packet of stale crisps. At The Prince Bonaparte sustenance takes the shape of carrot, roast-fennel and sage soup; six Rossmore oysters with shallot vinegar; chicken-liver, chorizo, spinach, basil and Parmesan pasta; grilled salmon, coriander couscous, red-hot pesto and rocket; roast chicken, roast pepper, Gruyère and tomato sandwich with cress and basil vinaigrette; toffee-fudge ice cream and caramel sauce – just to name a few dishes from summer menus. However, in other respects the management holds on firmly to the pub ethos, and there is plenty of space for eaters and drinkers alike in an interior done up not so much to the nines as perhaps to the high fives.

Nearest tube stations
Notting Hill Gate, Westbourne Park, Bayswater
Maps 1 & 6

The Prince of Ceylon £20

39 Watford Way NW4 (0181-203 8002)

+ *Sri Lankan hoppers and devilled dishes*
- *impassive staff; Watford Way*

Open
Every day
Hours
12.00-3.00pm,
6.00pm-11.15pm
Credit cards
AmEx, Mastercard, Visa, Switch, Diner's
Set-price lunch
Buffet £7 (Sunday)
Nearest tube station
Hendon Central

None of the handful of Sri Lankan restaurants is centrally located and this one in Hendon is no exception. However, aficionados of spicy food should make the detour (if detour it is) because Sri Lankan food, with its input from the Dutch, Portuguese, Malays, Arabs and South Indians, offers some interesting departures from standard Bangladeshi menus. Hoppers (lace-edged, bowl-shaped pancakes made from fermented rice flour), pittu (steamed rice flour mixed with coconut) and godamba (a version of roti bread) are a foil to devilled meats (try chicken livers), fish curries, and Singhalese mutton curries. Seeni sambol is a particularly good onion-based, sticky, sweet-sharp chutney. Interesting vegetable dishes include devilled potato, cashew-nut curry and green-banana curry. Commit this paragraph to memory; staff are not blessed with the gift of the gab.

Quaglino's £35

16 Bury Street SW1 (930 6767)

+ *the grand entrance down the stairs as the auditorium unfolds before you*
- *'I want others to hear myself speak'* (The Evening Standard London Restaurant Guide 1994)

Open
Every day
Hours
12.00-2.30pm,
5.30pm-12.30am,
(Fri & Sat 1.00am,
Sun 10.30pm)
Credit cards
AmEx, Mastercard, Visa, Switch, Diner's
Service charge
12.5% optional

Quags' gigantism may have been dwarfed by Mezzo; it still functions nevertheless as the ultimate hybrid between an ocean liner and an art-deco cathedral of eating and a hymn to technology. The downside is negotiating with a machine: booking here is still an aggravating experience, and service by squads of waiters is robotic to the point of inflexibility – the sensation of being processed in a vast pecuniary mangle is never

Set-price lunch
£13.95
Nearest tube
stations
Green Park,
Piccadilly Circus
Map 3

far away. The size and style are breathtaking. As a Captain Strahan said of the battle of Bastogne: 'Oh my dear fellow, the noise... and the people!' The menu, printed on a slim pistachio-green sheet, divides into starters, crustacea, main courses, grills and rotisserie, with specials highlighted in red type. Remarkably, given the volume of people being served (400+ covers per session), the standards in the kitchen remain high. Although you can eliminate margin for error by ordering crustacea from a counter extravagantly piled with raw shellfish on ice, be assured that virtually all dishes are carefully cooked and presented. Shoulder of pork came with tooth-crunching crackling; osso buco with haricot beans and saffron, enriched by that slightly sticky sauce characteristic of stewed veal, was topped with a zesty gremolada. Desserts are equally enticing: pavlova with passionfruit; Sauternes custard with Armagnac prunes; and roast pear with ginger ice cream.

THE LOPSIDED WINE list has some curious omissions. Loire reds, white Rhônes, and most of regional France and Spain are ill-served; and two cheap Italian reds versus four wines from Beaujolais is disproportionate. As many ports are offered by the glass as white wines. The latter include the quirky Charbono from Duxoup Wineworks (£24.25), pronounced as in the Marx Brothers film, a Dolcetto relative with Rhône-ish attitude; and the pineapple-ripe Collard's Chenin Blanc (£15.95). That popping sound you can hear is the directors of Quaglino's celebrating every time you buy a bottle of champagne – the mark-ups are punitive.

Quality Chop House £25

94 Farringdon Road EC1 (837 5093)

+ *quality chips*
- *bring a cushion to sit on*

Open
Every day
Hours
12.00-3.00pm,
6.30-11.30pm
(Sun 12.00-
4.00pm, 7.00-
11.30pm)
Credit cards
None
Nearest tube
station
Farringdon
Map 3

With its cafe (sorry, caff) exterior and tiled floor, hard wooden benches and long narrow tables, this is a place that is not a sentimental harking back but a venue that places the emphasis fairly and squarely on simple food. Objections that eggs, bacon and chips and lamb chops have been supplemented by less rootsy Modern European favourites such as fish soup and rouille, bang-bang chicken and grilled tuna steak with salsa rossa miss the point; the two are not mutually exclusive, nor are the trad. Brit. dishes mere tokenism. There is room for the vernacular cravings of Toulouse sausages, mash and gravy, or corn-beef hash with fried egg, as well as for sampling the creative dimensions of a mushroom, celeriac and coriander soup, and straddling the divide are the London staples that Charles

Fontaine helped to put on the map at Le Caprice (q.v.): salmon fishcake with sorrel sauce, Caesar salad, duck confit and so forth. Unless you are a party of six you may well be asked to share a table, which encourages people to be sociable – an unusual dining out experience. Democracy is further reinforced by the drinks list, where the selection of mainly French wines shares equal billing with spirits, beers, ciders and soft drinks.

Quincy's £30

675 Finchley Road NW2 (794 8499)

+ *food as daring as Delia's*
- *vegetables may be cooked al denture*

Open in the evenings only on Tuesdays to Saturdays, this cosy, candle-lit restaurant holds an ongoing, longstanding dinner party with host David Wardle and cook David Philpot. A set-price menu that changes monthly always offers a homemade soup of the day, plus other first courses such as ballotine of duck with chicory and orange salad, and spiced aubergine salad with grilled sardines. In the main course will be a fish dish according to the market, and perhaps roast lamb with pea and mint purée and jus navarin; as well as noisettes of venison with pear and juniper sauce and crushed potatoes. Vegetarians are looked after: a suitable main course might be asparagus and herb cannelloni with olive oil and balsamic vinegar. Puddings assume equal importance in the set-price menus and are much looked forward to by the clientele, many of whom are regulars who have become friends of the management.

Open
Dinner Tue-Sat
Hours
7.00-11.00pm
Credit cards
AmEx, Mastercard, Visa
Set price dinner
£25
Nearest tube station
Golders Green
Map 1

Randall & Aubin £22

16 Brewer Street W1 (287 4447)

+ *the interior; almost a traiteur*
- *the service when eating on site*

Eddie Baines, formerly chef at Daphne's (q.v.), and James Poulton have saved Randall & Aubin, a venerable butcher's shop and grocery store, from going the way of many Soho addresses – into designer cafe or designer boutique. The original tiled interior has been preserved and enhanced, and food is still the focus. A rotisserie provides spit-roasted chickens and roasts of the day, such as a slab of belly pork; a crustacea bar offers oysters, crab, lobsters and langoustines, plus humbler creatures like whelks; sandwiches are made up from the roasts with the customer's choice of extras such as

Open
Mon-Sun
Hours
11.00am-11.00pm
Credit cards
AmEx, Mastercard, Visa, Switch, Delta
Nearest tube station
Piccadilly
Maps4 & 5

apple sauce, yoghurt, watercress, pickles, mustard and cress; there are soups and salads. It is a terrific concept and potentially a great boon to those living or working in the area, but at time of writing there are still hiccups in both cooking and service. The seating is arranged in a way that suits lone diners much better than convivial couples, but the English tendency to make a three-course meal out of every event militates against the brisk turnover that the place invites. However, by the time you read this I trust the system will be working smoothly. It is such a good idea.

Rani £20

Open
Sunday lunch,
dinner Mon-Sun

Hours
6.00-10.30pm,
12.15-2.30pm Sun

Credit cards
AmEx, Mastercard,
Visa, Switch, Delta

Service charge
10% optional (for
5 or more)

**Nearest tube
station**
Finchley Central

7 Long Lane N3 (0181-349 4386); 3 Hill Street, Richmond, Surrey (0181-332 2322)

+ *the menu offered in braille*
- *the risk of diet bores at the next table*

Anyone who has just spent good money on having their blood or a strand of hair analysed for allergies should rush along to these mainly Gujarati vegetarian restaurants owned and run by the enterprising Pattni family. Symbols alert you to the presence in dishes of sugar, dairy products, wheat, nuts, onions and garlic. While this is interesting – and occasionally invaluable – information, it might serve to detract from the main point, which is the excellent Indian vegetarian food encompassing pooris, bhajias, masala dhosas, vadas, and pulse and vegetable curries (including a slow-cooked assembly of spice-stuffed Kenyan aubergines and potatoes), homemade chutneys, excellent breads (plain and stuffed), and syrupy, milky desserts. The newer branch at the foot of Richmond Hill offers particularly attractive minimalist surroundings.

Ransome's Dock £28

Open
Lunch every day,
dinner Mon-Sat

Hours
11.00am-11.00pm
(12.00am Sat),
11.30am-3.30pm
Sun

Credit cards
AmEx, Mastercard,
Visa, Switch,
Diner's, Delta

Set-price lunch
£11.50

35–7 Parkgate Road SW11 (223 1611)

+ *the drinks list; the puddings*
- *the colour of the walls (dock-egg blue?)*

A thriving restaurant in a modern dockside development, a microcosm of all that is best in the modern British movement: ignore the decor and concentrate on a menu that combines Mediterranean and Thai with more traditional British ingredients, and labels its sources proudly (Morecambe Bay potted shrimps, Loch Fyne scallops, Rocombe Farm ice cream). Dishes are well-executed by chef/proprietor Martin Lam and his capable team, and range from saddle of rabbit stuffed with pancetta and foie gras for the hungry carnivore, to Moroccan spiced chicken breast with carrot salad and couscous for the fashion-conscious. Equal attention goes into the list of desserts, wherein the hot prune and Armagnac soufflé with Armagnac custard, and a blood-orange millefeuille, reveal Vanessa Lam's delicate hand in pastry. The professional service reinforces the commitment to excellence, and also helps you to negotiate the model wine list.

PRICES ARE REASONABLE, although you may wish to bump up your bill by starting with one of the fine range of Lustau sherries on offer and finishing with a glass of dessert wine (such as a Coteaux du Layon). In between, a cornucopia of goodies includes Cloudy Bay Sauvignon '95 (a bargain at £18.50), for which amount you can also snaffle a bottle of Alain Graillot's deliciously smoky Crozes-Hermitage. This is a list that doesn't miss a trick, with plentiful half-bottles, magnums, dessert wines and even a dazzling array of sparklers from around the world.

Rasa   £17

55 Stoke Newington Church Street N16 (249 0344)

+ *vegetarian delights from Kerala*
- *too many other tourists*

Owner Siva Das Padmanabhan (Das for short) comes from Cochin, capital of the southern Indian state of Kerala, and his colourful little restaurant might be a one-man tourist board for this most tranquil of areas. However, you would be hard put to find the range of vegetarian dishes when visiting Kerala that you can taste by trekking to Stoke Newington. Some emanate from the home kitchen. Among the specialities are appams and iddiappams (hybrids of pancake and crumpet, made with fermented rice-flour batter thinned with coconut milk); kappa and kadala curry (two separately spiced mixtures based on chickpeas and cassava root); and nadam dhosa (thick pancakes made of rice and black gram batter mixed with onions, chillis and tomatoes, served with a lentil sauce and coconut and ginger chutney). Green banana and green papaya introduce intriguing sour-sweetness into some of the vegetable curries. One of the thoran (dry vegetable assemblies flavoured with black mustard seeds, chilli, curry leaves and fresh coconut), acts as a madeleine for anyone who has travelled in Goa or Kerala. Tea-shop snacks such as acchapam and pappadavadai – a poppadum taken to new heights of crunch – are good to nibble on while deciding your menu. Both the menu and the staff give helpful guidance. Rasa is licensed but proscribes smoking.

Nearest tube stations
Sloane Square, Battersea Park
Map 2

Open
Lunch Tues-Sun, dinner Sun-Thurs
Hours
12.00-2.30pm, 6.00-11.00pm (12.00am Fri & Sat)
Credit cards
AmEx, Mastercard, Visa, Diner's, Delta
Nearest railway station
Stoke Newington
Map 1

Red Fort £32

Open
Every day

Hours
12.00-3.00pm,
5.40-11.30pm

Credit cards
AmEx, Mastercard,
Visa, Switch,
Diner's

Cover charge
£1 per person

Set-price lunch
£12.50 buffet

Set-price dinner
£20

**Nearest tube
stations**
Tottenham Court
Road, Leicester
Square

Map 5

77 Dean Street W1 (437 2115)

+ *buffet lunch popular with hungover film executives*
− *delusions of culinary grandeur*

Assiduous PR and the fairly high public profile of owner Amin Ali, who must be credited with once getting backing from Camden for a Bangladeshi workers co-operative, has given The Red Fort a gastronomic reputation it does not always live up to. Tandoor dishes are reliable; whole pomfret marinated in caraway seeds with spiced yoghurt, and a Rajasthani smoked kebab of fresh salmon are relatively unusual and good; and the whole leg of lamb − akbari raan − makes a special centrepiece for two people. Shali tukra (a delicious Indian version of bread-and butter-pudding) is topped with edible silver leaf. A wise move might be to time your visit to The Red Fort to coincide with one of its food festivals, when chefs are brought over from India. A refurbished interior and a certain slickness to the service (some of it, unusually, from women) may help you to forgive what seem to be demanding prices.

The Red Pepper £22

Open
Lunch Sat-Sun,
dinner every day

Hours
12.30-2.30pm,
6.30-10.45pm
(Sun 3.30-
10.30pm)

Credit cards
Mastercard, Visa,
Switch,Delta

Service charge
12.5% (for 5 or
more)

**Nearest tube
station**
Warwick Avenue

Map 6

8 Formosa Street W9 (266 2708)

+ *wood-fired pizza oven*
− *cramped and uncomfortable seating*

Pizzas are better when baked in a wood-fired oven, and at The Red Pepper they may also benefit from the refinement of toppings being added at different stages: some baked on, some added fresh as a garnish. Also, apart from the heretical pizza pollo featuring smoked chicken, the chefs understand that the best pizzas don't stray far from tomato, mozzarella, and something salty and/or hot such as ham, anchovies, salami piccante or chilli oil. Antipasti are well conceived. Consider octopus salad with French beans and roasted onions; or goat's cheese, asparagus and new-potato salad. Pastas are good: for example, ricotta gnocchi with tomato and smoked mozzarella; and black tagliolini with scallops and saffron. The tiramisu has a grown-up attitude to sweetness, underlined by its espresso-coffee-flavoured sauce. The Red Pepper is understandably popular and can get too crowded for comfort, but lissom waiting staff serve quickly. Try to get a table on the ground floor.

The Ritz Restaurant   £65

The Ritz Hotel, Piccadilly, W1 (493 8181)

+ *finding yourself inside a Boucher painting*
- *hotel pricing with a vengeance, especially à la carte*

The Louis XVI dining-room is London's − if not the world's − most stunning belle époque restaurant interior. No-one could fail to be seduced. Chef David Nicholls does his best − and his best is pretty good − with a raft of different menus aimed at different events, different appetites, different age groups. He has to suppose that, while one person may want steak-and-kidney pie (offered at Thursday lunchtime), another may prefer to toy with a lobster poached in elderflower wine. Choosing luxury ingredients left well alone is one way of approaching the overwhelming choice, but it seems a pity not to discover what the kitchen does with fillets of Dover sole Ritz. Answer: prepares it with leeks, truffles and sprue asparagus. There are dinner dances at weekends. Tables on the terrace, although battered by noise from Piccadilly, are another version of romance. If you want to open children's eyes to elegance, treat them to Sunday lunch at The Ritz.

IF YOU CAN pawn a diamond as big as the Ritz you might be able to afford some of the clarets; otherwise play the tedious game of hunt the decent bottle under £30. Thanks to Tollot-Beaut's Chorey-les-Beaune (£29.50) and the Palliser Estate Pinot Noir from New Zealand (£25.50), or by trying one of the 'Sommelier's Selections' − which turn out to be bin ends − at the front of the list, you might just succeed. The house wines are as mediocre as they are expensive. As with all the other hotel lists reviewed in this Guide, you feel when you open the beautiful leather-bound volume that a colony of moths will fly out − evidence that time and wine fashion have bypassed the contents of this cellar.

Open
Every day
Hours
12.30-2.30pm,
6.00-11.15pm
Credit cards
AmEx, Mastercard,
Visa, Switch,
Diner's
Service charge
12.5%
Set-price lunch
£28, £36.50 & £43
(£49 Fri & Sat)
**Nearest tube
station**
Green Park
Map 3

Riva   £30

169 Church Road, Barnes SW13 (0181-748 0434)

+ *Andrea Riva*
- *cramped seating*

Andrea Riva has the look of controlled power and passion that you see in orchestra conductors; the restaurant − albeit with an awkwardly shaped and slightly drably designed set − is his production. If we the customers are mere players, he strives to bring each one in at the right time to enjoy a moment of his benign attention, and thus do Riva customers become regulars. Chef Francesco Zanchetta specializes in food of the Veneto.

Open
Lunch Sun-Fri,
dinner every day
Hours
12.00-2.30pm,
7.00-11.00pm
Credit cards
AmEx, Mastercard,
Visa, Switch, Delta
Service charge
10%
**Nearest
tube/railway
station**
Hammersmith,
Barnes
Map 1

Specialities from another northern Italian region, Lombardy, are Andrea Riva's subject. Grilled vegetables are slicked with the finest olive oil; gnocchi tossed with cured black olives and a deep, verdant pesto; breast of duck is marinated in grappa and juniper berries, and served with roasted pumpkin. One of the antipasto assemblies features San Daniele ham with pears, goose with truffled oil, cornmeal pancake with speck and asiago cheese; while the more Mediterranean sapori sports salt cod and polenta, perch fillet and a salad of baby octopus. Dessert should not be skipped. Outstanding are sgroppin (liquidy lemon sorbet with grappa and prosecco) and sbrisolona (maize and almond crumble soaked in vin santo with mascarpone). Should he offer, let Riva choose the wine: he often produces interesting bottles not on the list.

The River Cafe £45

Thames Wharf Studios, Rainville Road W6 (381 8824)

+ *delectable simplicity; the wood-fired oven; the setting*
– *the cost*

Open
Lunch every day,
dinner Mon-Sat
Hours
12.30-3.30pm,
7.30-11.00pm;
Sun 1.00-4.00pm
Credit cards
AmEx, Mastercard,
Visa, Switch, Delta
Service charge
12.5%
**Nearest tube
station**
Hammersmith
Map 1

The best Italian restaurant in Europe (as nominated by New Yorker magazine)? Of course not; the best Italian restaurant will be in Italy. However, neither is it, as A.A. Other restaurant reviewer put it, the best Fulham restaurant in Europe. It is a one-off: an inimitable conjunction of talents, enthusiasms and family histories. The practice of architect Richard Rogers has designed – and then re-designed – the stylish site that now sports a wood-fired oven that is champion for pizzas, breads and roasts. Rogers's wife Ruthie and her friend Rose Gray are the martinet cooks able to spot a blemish on a leaf of Swiss chard at 100 metres. The philosophy (if that is what you call it) behind the menu is the best of ingredients – tame and wild – interfered with to the point of transformation but not much further. Thus you might get chubby sardines or turbot steak on the bone, roasted in the wood oven and enhanced just with herbs. The chargrill, the other popular cooking method, might sear a butterflied leg of lamb to be served with salsa verde and an oven-cooked dish of potatoes, pancetta and sage; or brand a tranche of wild salmon to be served with new season's green beans and basil mayonnaise. When it comes to dessert, owners of '*The River Cafe Cook Book*' who failed to make their chocolate nemesis hang together can eat the perfected version here. The food is for the most part sublime – the holiday cooking of your dreams – until, come 11pm when the place must close, you find yourself in Hammersmith. Service sometimes lacks the zest of the specially imported Sicilian lemons.

THE LOSS OF the annotations trumpeted in the 1995 edition of the Guide is still keenly felt. A straightforward, unilluminating list of Vini Rossi and Bianchi is not helped by an innate bias towards, admittedly good, northern Italian wines. The lemon zest La Segreta Bianco from Sicily (£14.50) demonstrates positive modern wine-making techniques; otherwise you are rooted in Pinot Grigio country, hardly the cutting edge of vinicultural fashion. If you are crazy about Sangiovese, try Eugenio Campolmi's savoury Vigneto Le Contessine from Bolgheri, or Querciabella's awesome Chianti Classico. Unfortunately, a succession of poor vintages in Italy means that even average wines are commanding high prices, so grab the '90s and '91s while they last. Dessert wines — seven by the glass — are worth sampling. I am informed by a reliable source that there is a reserve wine list bristling with goodies that can be asked for. Why do they not publish it?

Royal China   £15–35

13 Queensway W2 (221 2535)

+ *dim-sum; steamed eel with black-bean sauce*
- *queueing for dim-sum at weekends; the nightclub decor*

When you see on the menu braised sliced abalone with vegetable at £80, you know know you are somewhere where the Chinese like to eat. Royal China is for serious lovers of Chinese food not because it is overall especially expensive — abalone is a rare commodity now — but because to get the best from the restaurant it is wise to eschew conventional ordering. The above-mentioned steamed eel with black-bean sauce; whitebait omelette with chives; braised duck with superior sauce; Empress chicken (half or whole); braised asparagus with egg and garlic sauce; and hot pots taken from the list entitled 'Chef's Favourites' are just some ideas. The emphasis in the menu is on seafood. Dim-sum (served until 5pm) is considered by those in the know to be the best in London. If Putney is handier than Bayswater, there is a Royal China at 3 Chelverton Road SW15 (0181-780 1520), but Queensway seems to have the edge in cooking.

Open
Every day
Hours
12.00–11.00pm
(Sun 11.00am–
10.00pm)
Credit cards
AmEx, Mastercard,
Visa, Switch,
Diner's, Delta
Service charge
12.5%
Set-price lunch
£22, £28
**Nearest tube
station**
Queensway
Map 6

Open
Mon-Fri & Sun

Hours
12.00-3.00pm,
5.30-11.30pm

Credit cards
AmEx, Mastercard,
Visa, Switch,
Diner's, Delta

Set-price lunch
£15.95 & £19.95

**Nearest tube
station**
High Street
Kensington

Map 2

Royal Garden Hotel – The Tenth

 £40

2–24 Kensington High Street W8 (361 1910)

+ *a hotel restaurant that almost manages to fly free*
− *a potentially great view lost at night*

The top- (tenth-)floor restaurant that has emerged from the revamp of the Royal Garden Hotel has some of the weak points of an hotel restaurant – including costly but crass interior design – but, in its pricing policy for both food and wine, and in the lively modernity of the cooking, it almost comes across as the independent entity its PR people attempted to establish. Chef is Paul Farr, who has worked at The Crillon in Paris, and at Claridge's and Mezzo (q.v.). The last is immediately apparent in the composition of the dishes, which boldly go hither and thither for ingredients and influences while, importantly, bright ideas are underpinned by tutored technique. Tested dishes that triumph include crab and saffron pudding soufflé (more soufflé than pudding) with watercress butter sauce; tartare of scallop and tuna with lime and ginger; roasted lobster and monkfish with coconut and galingale broth (particularly fine); and breast of guinea fowl with parsnips and sage (homely in the best sense of the word). Side dishes, which are not really needed in terms of quantity but appeal on the grounds of quality, are caramelized carrots with thyme, Swiss chard, polenta chips and Maté Fame potatoes with mushrooms. However, making the lemon curd hot for lemon meringue tart proves a duff idea, and pineapple crème brûlée with garam masala and fried cookie ribbons seems a step too far in the direction of incorporating savoury spices into desserts. The à la carte list kicks off with 'soup with a view'. Unfortunately, soup of the evening is denied the vista of Kensington Gardens and Hyde Park, because the restaurant's designer has lit the interior so that the windows reflect back an image of the restaurant and its lighting scheme – one feature being coloured, illuminated panels that change like tepid traffic lights from shades of pink to apricot to green. Perhaps it looked promising on the drawing-board. To which someone should quickly return.

Royal Lancaster Hotel – Nipa Thai Restaurant

 £35

Lancaster Gate W2 (262 6737)

+ *the list of chef specialities*
- *hotel pricing*

In the somewhat unlikely setting of a sprawling, faceless, modern hotel is this authentic Thai restaurant. It is located in a small dining-room overlooking Hyde Park, its interior lined with intricately carved wooden panels. That Nipa Thai is not a sop to a transient international clientele is to some extent conveyed by the list of specialities on the long menu, and by the gravitas in the service. As is customary in Thailand, the chefs are women. Head chef Nongyao Thoopchoi has the reassuring demeanour – and something of the uniform – of a hospital sister. Dishes that she considers her stars are choo chee kung nang (fried king prawns in red curry); kai jiew nuea poo (Thai omelette with crab meat); and kao klok kapi (steamed rice flavoured with shrimp paste, served with sweet pork, shallots and hot chillies). The omelette has a crisp, thin skin and a tangible amount of crab. The rice assembly is served as a heap of rice surrounded by the other elements presented separately and left for the customer to mix, providing variation and diversion within the one dish. Other items that I can recommend are kao krieb pak moh (steamed dumplings of transparent dough, cradling vigorously seasoned minced chicken studded with chopped peanuts and slicked with sugar, and served with dipping sauce, chillies and fresh herbs); kaeng mussaman nuea (a long-cooked beef curry based on a dark, complex roasted curry paste, with notes of tamarind, galingale and cardamon all discernible); and yam won sen (a glass-noodle salad with shrimps and chillis, where fiery spicing contrasts with slippery texture to nice effect). Unfortunately, a hotel location adds to the prices. One way round this is via the set-price menus, particularly as – if ordered by a party of four – one person eats free; although, as usual, the interesting dishes are offered à la carte. The wines are wildly overpriced.

Open
Lunch Mon-Fri,
dinner Mon-Sat
Hours
12.00-2.00pm,
6.30-10.30pm
Credit cards
AmEx, Mastercard,
Visa, Switch,
Diner's
Set-price lunch
£10.50
Set price dinner
£22-25
**Nearest tube
stations**
Lancaster Gate,
Paddington
Map 6

RSJ £29

Open
Lunch Mon-Fri,
dinner Mon-Sat
Hours
12.00-2.00pm,
6.00-11.00pm
Credit cards
AmEx, Mastercard,
Visa, Switch,
Diner's
Service charge
10%
Set-price lunch
£15.95
**Nearest tube
station**
Waterloo
Map 3

13a Coin Street SE1 (928 4554)

+ *a definitive wine list*
– *definitive (i.e. frigid) air-conditioning*

According to meteorologists, in 50 years' time at the current rate of global warming we will be producing Vouvrays in Virginia Water and Bourgeuils in Boreham Wood. If you are looking for a restaurant that currently combs treasures from the Loire region, then RSJ is your destination. Sandwiched between the South Bank concrete-arama and various Waterloo office developments, the restaurant spans three floors, the first-floor dining-room being the most pleasant with its sunny daffodil-yellow walls. First courses were uninspired: a salad of avocado, citrus fruit, fresh crab and citrus dressing lacked focus, and a terrine of rabbit confit was too dry, needing more pork fat. Roast fillet of beef, mushroom, spinach, gnocchi and red-wine sauce was a good wholesome piece of meat. There is a fondness for flavoured oils, which might be employed more sparingly. One menu contained rabbit with a tarragon-mustard sauce, a dish featuring simultaneously in Le Pont de la Tour (q.v.) and The People's Palace (q.v.) and thus confirming that, on the South Bank, bunnies are the chickens de nos jours.

LOIRE IS ALL about Sauvignon, right? Wrong. Chenin Blanc, which shares top billing with Riesling in the pantheon of modern wine prejudice, is the king. This list concentrates on these unfashionable glories of the Loire, on Vouvrays aged through the decades into densely textured, honeyed marvels, on mineral-edged Savennières with steely sophistication, on Quarts de Chaume and on Bonnezeaux noble-rotted wines produced in misty microclimates, their fierce acidity softened by time, exhibiting a cornucopia of exotic fruit flavours. Try Joel Gigou's white Jasnières from a recently revived appellation which was described to me as 'like biting into a salty Granny Smith'. On the red front there is much to admire in the Cabernet Franc, the 17 Chinons and the 14 Bourgeuils, all from good years and top producers. Nigel Wilkinson's tasting notes are properly informative: he reminds us quite correctly that Loire sweet wines are best enjoyed with cheese.

Rules   £29

35 Maiden Lane WC2 (836 5314)

+ *late-lunch offer of any first and main course for £7.95*
- *the staff's electronic ordering pads — a sort of gameboy to order game*

Rules (established in 1798) serves good old-fashioned tucker in the type of venue where, as a shiny-faced schoolboy, your maiden aunt might take you (to Maiden Lane) during the hols to give you a slap-up lunch. Specializing in customary furred and feathered game, seasonal rarities abound: snipe, woodcock and ptarmigan are all roasted to order. If it flies or scurries and is game, you'll probably find it here. Starters include smoked-haddock soufflé, stilton and walnut tart, and smoked pheasant with pear chutney. Puddings are seasonal, English and fattening. Waiters wear starched aprons and service is silver. Although the atmosphere has relaxed over the last few years, it is still metaphorically plush and regally purple. Piquancy is added to the sauce of the meal if you can throw yourself into the experience of the place and transport yourself back a century or two.

Open
Every day
Hours
12.00-11.30pm
(Sun 12.00-10.30pm)
Credit cards
AmEx, Mastercard, Visa, Switch, Delta, Diner's
Set-price dinner
£14.95 (pre-theatre)
Nearest tube stations
Charing Cross, Covent Garden
Map 4

Sabai Sabai   £23

270–2 King Street W6 (0181-748 7363)

+ *well-presented food*
- *Saturday night crowd Thai-ing one on*

This is a Thai restaurant with a certain style; it is not The Blue Elephant (q.v.), but then it is not a transformed workmen's caff or pub annexe either. The pricing lies between these extremes. A family-run operation, the restaurant has a loyal following among local 30-somethings. All the usual Thai favourites are on offer, from tom yam kai (hot-and-sour chicken soup) to green and red curries. Prawn dishes, either charcoal-grilled or in a variety of guises, are enduringly popular with regulars.

Open
Lunch Mon-Sat, dinner every day
Hours
12.00-2.30pm, 6.00-11.30pm
Credit cards
AmEx, Mastercard, Visa, Switch, Delta, Diner's
Set-price lunch
£7.95
Set-price dinner
£35
Nearest tube station
Ravenscourt Park
Map 1

Saigon £22

Open
Mon-Sat
Hours
12.00-11.30pm
Credit cards
AmEx, Mastercard,
Visa, Delta, Diner's
Service charge
10%
Set-price lunch
£15.75
Nearest tube
stations
Piccadilly Circus,
Leicester Square,
Tottenham Court
Road
Map 5

45 Frith Street W1 (437 7109)

+ *happiness is the accomplishment of the perfect rice pancake*
- *Vietnamese wrap music*

Y ou can't miss Saigon: it's right next door to Ronnie Scott's,
and it could do with an atmosphere transfusion from same.
Exemplifying the best aspects of Vietnamese, which has echoes
of Chinese, Thai and colonial French influences, this is cooking
that has a lightness of touch all its own. There is green papaya
salad with finely shredded carrot and roasted peanuts, and a
nuoc mam dressing derived from chilli, garlic, rice vinegar, lime
juice and oil. Wind dried duck sausages with bamboo shoot and
water chestnut are for you to assemble in crisp lettuce leaves.
Wrapping little parcels of food in filo thin rice paper is not so
much an art form as a religion: try to achieve the oriental
harmony – the yin and the yang – between soft and crunchy,
sweet and spicy, hot and cold. Portions are slender, as if in
respect to a Zen philosophy that only by achieving hunger will
you understand it.

Saint Bar & Restaurant £32

Open
Dinner Mon-Sat
Hours
Mon-Thurs
5.30pm-1.00am,
Fri-Sat 5.30pm-
2.00am
Credit cards
AmEx, Mastercard,
Visa, Switch,
Diner's, Delta
Set-price lunch
£13.50
Nearest tube
station
Leicester Square
Map 5

8 Great Newport Street WC2 (240 1551)

+ *hands-across-the-sea cooking is well-handled*
- *everyone there is likely to be younger, thinner and hipper
  than you*

T he owners of this basement bar and restaurant near Leicester
Square aimed to attract the young and hip who find most
restaurants too formal an environment. They succeeded. The
crowd that gathers treats the place as a club, as, rather
disconcertingly, does the person taking reservations, who
enquires when you ring for a table whether you are a member.
However, it is worth brazening your way over this hurdle for the
sake of the Pacific Rim food prepared by chefs Kerwin Browne
and Neale White. Pacific Rim may be the culinary hot phrase of
the mid-'90s, but it is often just an excuse for a formless hotch-
potch of ideas, enthusiasms and the latest fashionable
ingredients. Browne and White, who have worked at Fulham
Road and Delicious Blue respectively, know their onions – or
scallions, as they might put it – and handle a menu that
juxtaposes French, Japanese and Eastern-inspired dishes with
aplomb. The menu kicks off with a section called 'Amuse',
comprising small dishes that give a taste of pleasures to come,
or provide delicate ballast while drinking. Examples are sushi of

marinated salmon and oriental pickled vegetables; charred squid, olives and samphire on toasted bread; and potted shrimps with sweet cucumber salad. Further menu divisions come under headings of salads and noodle soups, as well as starters, entrées and desserts. Carpaccio of kangaroo is something that you might want to skip, although honey-roasted pork belly with chilli and coriander chutney is appealing (but for the intrusion of red peppers), while rock oysters are well-accessorized by horseradish cream and crisp bacon. A fillet of beef with rocket, salsa verde and a Pinotage jus was predicated on a fine piece of meat. The one disappointment in a test meal was the miso soup with udon noodles and Chinese roast duck. Miso soup is usually reliable – even out of a packet – but somehow this broth tasted even more commercially manufactured than that. Music (live and recorded) is a prominent presence in the evenings, but the relatively sedate lunchtime at Saint is a useful retreat in the garish area. Staff are savvy and efficient in that way you find in the USA. Even if you have neglected to let your hair devolve into dreads, have allowed your tum to become too pillowy to bare and have made the mistake of growing older than 26, they treat you well.

St John   £27

26 St John Street EC1 (251 0848/4998)

+ *brainy use of brawn; the refreshingly plain dining-room*
- *school mince*

There is never any likelihood of buying a pig in a poke at St John. The menu is graphically frank and exhibits a delight in all manifestations of nature, red in tusk and trotter, such as the brutal-sounding skewered ox heart and leeks; roast bone marrow and parsley salad; jellied ox tail; and bloodcake (a variant of black pudding) and eggs. Sometimes there is a danger of teetering into self-parody, as in the unadorned duck leg and greens, or in the matter-of-fact mushrooms on toast. This is the ultimate in frill-free cooking: no sauce, no garnish, just artful heartiness. Minor details are, however, attended to with care – accurately cooked vegetables, expertly dressed salads and so forth – although pig, from nose to tail, in all its splendour, is the house speciality. Tongue, liver and belly are respectively anatomized, and even ears are crisped to garnish a pea soup. Desserts feature a tart, a trifle, something chocolatey, and a pudding: for example, brandy and vanilla pudding with raspberry sauce. A swift butcher's at the wine list reveals an all-French affair. Sticking to the rustic regionals or the mid-price clarets will bring ample reward. The waiters are well-groomed, and have the unerring ability to catch your eye when necessary.

Open
Lunch Mon-Fri, dinner Mon-Sat
Hours
12.00-3.00pm, 6.00-11.30pm; bar menu Mon-Fri 11.00am-11.00pm
Credit cards
AmEx, Mastercard, Visa, Switch, Diner's, Delta
Nearest tube stations
Farringdon, Barbican
Map 3

St Quentin £35

Open
Every day
Hours
12.00-3.00pm,
7.00-11.30pm
(Sun 12.00-
3.30pm, 6.30-
11.00pm)
Credit cards
AmEx, Mastercard,
Diner's, Visa,
Switch, Delta
Service charge
12.5%
Set-price lunch
£10
**Nearest tube
stations**
South Kensington,
Knightsbridge
Map 2

243 Brompton Road SW3 (589 8005)

+ *patisserie*
- *smoke gets in your eyes (of the Gitanes variety)*

From the top of the menu to the toe of the wine list, from the interior dark-panelled wood shelves, brass railings, mirrored walls to the studious decorum of the white-aproned waiters and the chic society of the customers who dwell in the arrondisements of Au Sud de Kensington or Pont de Chevalier, St Quentin is French to its roots. The emphasis is on haut bourgeois cooking, so choose from classics like omelette aux fines herbes; jambon persillé; foie gras terrine; magret de canard; tripes à la mode; a traditional cassoulet; a short list of fish dishes and various cuts of lamb or beef. The plainer flesh and fowl dishes are expertly rendered, the style of cooking sympathetic to the quality of the ingredients, a simplicity appealing to those who rather mistrust the vogue for mix and match.

Salloos £35

Open
Mon-Sat
Hours
12.00-2.30pm,
7.00pm-11.15pm
Credit cards
AmEx, Mastercard,
Visa, Switch,
Delta, Diner's
Service charge
12.5% service
Cover charge
£1.50 per person
Set-price lunch
£16.50
Set-price dinner
£25
**Nearest tube
stations**
Hyde Park,
Knightsbridge
Map 2

62–4 Kinnerton Street SW1 (235 4444)

+ *the quality of the meat dishes*
- *bossy service*

It is generally agreed that this family-owned restaurant with links to Lahore serves truly excellent Pakistani food. The quality of the ingredients used and the care and attention taken in spicing and marinating produces superb tandoori cooking, definitive karahi assemblies, unusual specialities such as haleem Akbari (shredded lamb cooked with lentils, spices and whole wheat berries) and superior rice cooking (whether pulao or biryani). Cavils are not usually about food but about prices: for example, £7.50 for a vegetable dish based on okra. A reduction in the 'optional' service charge from 15% to 12.5% this year is a minor concession that the management has made; the cover charge of £1.50 per person still stands. It is certainly worth experiencing the heights to which northern Indian food can be raised. You just have to bite the bullet – as they might say in Pakistan – and pay.

San Lorenzo Fuoriporta £30

Worple Mews SW19 (0181-946 8463)

+ *where to see the players if you didn't get your centre-court seats*
- *£2 cover charge; prices generally*

This is the country retreat (fuoriporta meaning 'outside the city walls') of the Knightsbridge San Lorenzo. The Wimbledon branch is run by Mara and Lorenzo Berni's son Ghigo and his wife Angela (an ice-cream specialist), and it is Ralph Lauren to Knightsbridge's Karl Lagerfeld. On Sundays the mood becomes distinctly family, which is particularly pleasant when the weather allows outdoor eating. Pizzas have thin, crisp bases with generous toppings. Grilled main courses of fish and meat tend to be garnished with rocket. Something called Robespierre sauce adds a bit of interest. Prices are expressed in pennies (for example, crostino al pomodoro e basilico at 650p) but this, as you might imagine, does not mean that the pounds take care of themselves. Staff are good-humouredly attentive and genuinely fond of children.

Open
Every day
Hours
12.00-3.00pm,
7.00-11.00pm
Credit cards
AmEx, Mastercard,
Visa, Switch,
Diner's, JCB
Cover charge
£2 per person
Nearest tube station
Wimbledon

Savoy Grill £60

The Savoy Hotel, The Strand WC2 (0171-836 4343)

+ *a palpable feeling of power eating*
- *not much fun if you don't have a title*

Captains of industry, politicians, newspaper editors and celebrities of stage and screen do indeed dine here, making obtaining reservations for hoi polloi a long, drawn-out affair. Dinner is easier than lunch, and it is worth noting the offer of the pre-theatre menu of three courses including coffee for £29.75, served until 7pm (dessert and coffee can be consumed post-theatre). Daily specials include farmhouse sausages with creamed potatoes at Monday lunch; steak-and-kidney pudding on Tuesday; and roast duck with aromatic vegetables for Friday dinner. Seasonality is respected and celebrated, not only in game and native oysters but also in vegetables. Come here for nostalgia, to consume old-fashioned dishes that young upstart restaurants fail to deliver – flamed lamb's kidneys, omelette Arnold Bennett, roast suckling pig, roast rib of beef with inflated Yorkshire pudding – and understand what was once meant by service.

Open
Lunch Mon-Fri,
dinner Mon-Sat
Hours
12.30-2.15pm,
6.00-11.15pm (Sat
11.30pm)
Credit cards
AmEx, Mastercard,
Visa, Switch,
Delta, Diner's
Nearest tube stations
Embankment,
Covent Garden
Map 4

Savoy River Restaurant £55

Open
Every day
Hours
12.00-2.30pm,
6.00-11.15pm
Credit cards
AmEx, Mastercard,
Visa, (Switch &
Delta if with Visa),
Diner's
Service charge
Table d'hôte menu
price, service
charge of 7%
Set-price lunch
£27.50
Set-price dinner
£32.90 Sun-Thurs
& £39.50 Fri & Sat
**Nearest tube
station**
Embankment
Map 4

(Address as above)

+ *dinner–dancing...*
- *...on the Titanic*

As we go to press, there is notice of changes in 'the menu concept' at the River Restaurant. Anton Edelmann is still in control of the Anglo-French menu, with its necessary luxuries but also with its acknowledgement of how appetites and diets have changed, and with its seasonally inspired recipes. Dishes of the day continue to be offered in addition to the à la carte, but the new pricing structure means that any dish can be ordered in the relaxing knowledge of the facts that at lunch two courses are £25.75 and three courses £32.50; while at dinner two courses are £29.75 and three courses £37.50. Of course, your state of relaxation is somewhat dependent on the health of your bank account. A view of the Thames is a privilege granted to only a few. Service will bow and scrape if that is what you require. The River Restaurant is indelibly old-fashioned – the sort of experience that was once handed down from father to son.

THIS IS A competent list, lighter than some hotel behemoths, but still religiously pursuing the holy – albeit not wholly – claret grail. When I see that Château Mouton Baron Phillipe 1985 is fetching £94 here, I feel that customers are being led like *moutons* to the slaughter. No more anachronistic than other compositions of the same ilk, to damn with faint praise, and the odd nod given to contemporary producers (Torres, Mitchelton) seems like token topicality.

Scotts £34

Open
Lunch Mon-Fri,
dinner Mon-Sat
Hours
12.00-3.00pm,
5.30-11.30pm
Credit cards
AmEx, Mastercard,
Visa, Switch,
Delta, Diner's, JCB
Service charge
12.5%
Cover charge
£1.50
Set-price lunch
£15 & £18

20 Mount Street W1 (629 5248)

+ *revamped interior*
- *owned by a public company*

At the time of going to press this historic English fish restaurant and oyster bar (originally established 1891 just off Piccadilly Circus) is undergoing radical re-furbishment with the aim of creating a 200-seater restaurant, an oyster terrace and a basement piano bar. It is destined to be open mid-November but, as almost everyone knows to their cost, builders and destiny often don't mix. The head chef is Mark Holmes, at 27 a mere stripling compared to some, like head waiter Giuseppe Gargana who has been working at Scotts since the year before

Holmes was born and Maria Kolliari, in charge of the cloakroom, who has already put in 35 years faithful service. The new owners, Group Chez Gerard Ltd, have already gone some way to ameliorating what had become ridiculously high prices and they hope to lose the reputation Scotts had developed as being a trap for unwary American tourists and return the restaurant to Londoners keen on a stylish fish supper.

HERE IS A wide selection of the classics, plumped up with four pages of wines from around the world. Although the intention to recognize areas outside Burgundy and Bordeaux is laudable, to lump French, Italian, South African and Australian wines together willy-nilly militates against quick and easy selection. Curiouser and curiouser is the balance: there are more wines from the region of Chablis than from Beaujolais and Burgundy, and there are more rosés from Israel than Spanish wines on the entire list (i.e., one).

Set-price dinner
£18 & £15 (pre-theatre)
Nearest tube stations
Bond Street, Green Park
Map 3

Searcy's Brasserie £33

Library Floor, The Barbican Centre, Silk Street EC2 (588 3008)

+ *chef Richard Corrigan transforming contract catering*
- *he never promised to stay for long*

Like most chefs, Richard Corrigan would like to have a place of his own; perhaps by the time you read this he will have succeeded. At the time of writing — after his stint at Fulham Road restaurant for which he attracted a Michelin star, and his startling transformation of Cafe East 15 at Hackney Stadium dog track into a destination restaurant — he is bringing a long-awaited and well-reviewed production of The Kitchen to The Barbican. More than most, this arts' centre has disappointed and frustrated its visitors with the catering arrangements, but Corrigan's culinary energy and espousal of home-grown and some homely ingredients, treated with respect and ingenuity, has brought a new audience to the second-floor restaurant for a drama in three courses: this might be poached ox tongue, roast beetroot and shaved horseradish; roast scallops, crispy squid, turnips and chilli; and baked rice pudding with prunes and Armagnac. Not only theatre-, film- and exhibition-goers are attracted, but also business people and residents of the Barbican estate. There is nothing mealy-mouthed about Corrigan's cooking. Dishes such as casserole of pig's head, veal kidneys and new-season carrots, and grilled rump of Angus beef with snail butter and field mushrooms have not been scared off the menu. But he can also tread lightly, as with a salad of Cornish crab, artichoke and mimosa vinaigrette; steamed fillets of brill with

Open
Lunch Sun-Fri, dinner Mon-Sat
Hours
12.00-3.00pm, 5.00pm-12.00am (Sun pre-theatre only)
Credit cards
AmEx, Mastercard, Visa, Switch, Delta, Diner's
Set-price lunch £17.50
Set-price dinner £20.50
Nearest tube stations
Moorgate, Barbican
Map 1

tomato butter, artichoke and tarragon; citrus fruit salad; and chocolate and orange sorbet. Promises have been made to improve the corridor-like, institutional dining-room. Food in Corrigan's style continues to be offered at Hackney Stadium, and doubtless he has trained a brigade in his ways to continue the good work at The Barbican. In the other restaurants and cafes in the Centre, the catering company of Digby Trout is making strides forward with what is on offer.

755 £30

755 Fulham Road SW6 (371 0755)

+ *a young couple go it alone*
- *drawing-room decor*

Open
Lunch Tues-Sun,
dinner Mon-Sat
Hours
12.30-2.30pm,
7.30-11.00pm
Credit cards
AmEx, Mastercard,
Visa, Switch, Delta
Set-price lunch
£10, £18
**Nearest tube
station**
Parsons Green
Map 1

Alan and Georgina Thompson, chef-proprietors of 755 (previously Fleurie), which is to be found a long way down Fulham Road, met while working at Turner's (q.v.). They must have liked the decor there, as they have used the same designer for their new restaurant's interior, with shades of the same colours – blue and yellow – for fabrics, carpet and paint. It seems a loyal but rather unoriginal decision. Between leaving Turner's and starting up his own place, Thompson worked briefly at Pied à Terre (whose former chef Richard Neat now offers strong competition a few blocks down at Fables [q.v.]), and at Kensington Place (q.v.). He summarizes his style of cooking as 'modern British with foreign influences': something of a tautology, as I thought modern British meant that it had foreign influences. Dishes that Thompson describes as his specialities are seared scallops with apple purée and parsnip crisps; crab sausage with aïoli; roast quail with a truffle mousse and lentils (all first courses); and steamed Dover sole with mussels and saffron. The crab sausage, although somewhat Findus in appearance, was rewarding in both vivid flavour and juicy texture, and the accompanying aïoli did not pull its punches. Other items liked included smoked haddock with hollandaise and tomato, and a pear tarte Tatin with cinnamon ice cream. There can be a retrograde British element in the clientele, who might well choose to start with smoked salmon and go on to fillet steak with wild-mushroom sauce. The disposition of ingredients on plates, with their blobbing and dribbles of garnish and sauce, seems quaintly old-hat and sometimes convoluted to no interesting end. The classic expertise of Turner's is lacking, but so is the new-wave vivacity of, say, Kensington Place. Set-price menus help to keep the bill appropriate to the experience.

Shaw's £40

119 Old Brompton Road SW7 (373 7774)

+ *commendable attention to detail, from bread to petits fours*
− *consider the lilies of the field, for they shall not be gilded*

Country-house cooking for parties in South Kensington? Shaw's is one of those nice, polite establishments with starched tablecloths, light beige walls and a menu of creations and contortions that seems not to belong in London. Pancakes of marinated salmon with coriander and lemon had salty pancetta to contend with, but that was as nothing compared with salmon and spinach roulade with tapenade and saffron sauce, where the extraneous ingredients re-enacted The Battle of The Fugitive Flavour. Another starter of millefeuille of asparagus and polenta with a tarragon and mushroom sauce had 'Masterchef' written all over it, a dish to plunge your fork into rather than eat. Consolation comes in the more prosaic-sounding dishes − minted-pea and sorrel soup, or crisp lamb's sweetbreads with parsley sauce and capers − and in the puddings, where expansive gestures are often more welcome: the Grand Marnier soufflé with mango sorbet, and the Queen of puddings, are exceptional.

Open
Lunch Mon-Fri, dinner Mon-Sat
Hours
12.00-2.00pm, 5.30-11.00pm
Credit cards
AmEx, Mastercard, Visa, Switch, Diner's
Set-price lunch
£15 & £18.50
Set-price dinner
£29.95 & £32.95
Nearest tube stations
Gloucester Road, South Kensington
Map 2

Simply Nico £34

48a Rochester Row SW1 (630 8061)

+ *Nico at knock-down prices*
− *supplements defeat the purpose of a set menu*

Although the master has sold up (to The Restaurant Partnership plc) the disciples cook the cleverly varied menu with sympathy and panache. Gutsy Gascon virtues are enrolled in a pressed ham terrine with parsley, apple chutney and celeriac; and salt cod fritters with rouille are a success due to the lightness of the batter and the pungency of the sauce. The refreshing absence of over-elaboration continues into the main courses, with poached guinea-fowl breast with a purée of lentils, and fillet of brill complemented by a sharp Provençal sauce. Foie gras comes in multifarious guises, such as in a creamy mousse with chicken livers, and pan-fried in its own right on a bed of spicy lentils. Menu prices include service, making them even more of a bargain. The wine list shows the same confident Catholicism as the cooking. Every wine merits its place, but you might wish to investigate the 'R' de Rieussec, one of the best examples of dry Sauternes.

Open
Lunch Mon-Fri, dinner Mon-Sat
Hours
12.00-2.00pm, 7.00-11.00pm
Credit cards
AmEx, Mastercard, Visa, Switch, Delta, Diner's
Nearest tube stations
Victoria, St James's Park
Map 1

Simpson's-in-the-Strand   £35

100 The Strand WC2 (836 9112)

+ *the history, the tradition, the decor; flying in the face of BSE*
- *the roast potatoes*

Open
Every day
Hours
12.00-2.30pm,
5.30-11.00pm
(Sun 6.00-
9.00pm)

Credit cards
AmEx, Diner's,
Mastercard, Visa
Service charge
12.5% (for 6 or
more)
Set price dinner
£10
**Nearest tube
station**
Charing Cross
Map 4

The Savoy Group would seem to have taken the decision to run Simpson's (established 1828) as an all-day theme park, starting with breakfast complete with '10 deadly sins', with lunch and dinner wrapped around a new afternoon-tea service featuring a knickerbocker glory. How fitting, that at my most recent visit Prince Edward should be lunching (set-price menu £22.50) in the first-floor Grand Divan Tavern. It's a Royal Carve-Up? The surroundings are unassailable and must gratify tourists. The roasts from the trolley are dependable (remember to tip the carver), but much else — such as leathery potatoes and flaccid cabbage — is just a cipher. Unless they know you or you are a prince of the realm, service can be off-hand.

Singapore Garden   £26

83 Fairfax Road NW6 (328 5314)

+ *Nonya cooking*
- *companions who cry: 'Oh, let's drink grass jelly'*

Open
Every day
Hours
12.00-2.45pm,
6.00-10.45pm
(11.15pm Fri &
Sat)
Credit cards
AmEx, Mastercard,
Visa, Switch,
Diner's, Delta
Service charge
12.5% optional
Set-price lunch
£5.50 & £8
Set price dinner
£16
**Nearest tube
station**
Swiss Cottage
Map 1

Owned and run by the Lim family with Mrs Lim in the kitchen, this lively Swiss Cottage neighbourhood restaurant attracts custom from far and wide, including from abroad. The two areas on the long menu to address first are the clipped-on list of specials and the back page of Malaysian and Singaporean dishes. From the specials, try wok-fried pork dumplings with a vinegar and ginger dip; spicy chicken wings which are a credit to the species; the rich and combative black-pepper and butter crab; and braised duck imbued with star anise. Kang kong blachan from the Malaysian section demonstrates what blacham (prawn paste) and chilli can do for a vegetable: in this case, Chinese spinach. Noodle assemblies such as fried kway tiow, ho jien (oyster omelette) and the soothing Hainanese chicken rice provide good underpinning to spirited spicing in other dishes.

Smokey Joe's Diner   £10 BYO

131 Wandsworth High Street, SW18 (0181-871 1785)

+ *For Joe, every night is Friday night*
- *sometimes slapdash cooking*

Joe (real name Charlie Phillips) works hard, flirting and cooking. His chat brings the customers back, as does his jerk chicken and pork, available for take-away or to eat in at picnic-style tables. Lapses in service are easily forgiven in the light of Joe's big smile, but you are likely to get your order piecemeal: served when it is ready, dish by dish. Caribbean and soul-food specials are scrawled on the blackboard. Best bets are daily fish specials, BBQ spare ribs and jerk anything. Great taped calypso and reggae music adds to the party spirit. Late at night the diner is crammed with a clubbing crowd; during the day it is for families and office workers with soul.

Open
Every day
Hours
12.00-3.00pm,
6.00-10.30pm
Credit cards
None
Cover charge
Lunch 40p per
person, dinner £1
per person
**Nearest tube
stations**
East Putney,
Wandsworth Town
Map 1

Snow's on The Green   £28

166 Shepherd's Bush Road W6 (603 2142)

+ *news flash: Snow rains flavours in sunny restaurant*
- *the more variables in the dish, the more variable the results*

Baby lavender trees on every table and posters of Provence on the sunflower-yellow walls leave you in no doubt that Sebastian Snow's cooking will take you for a picturesque spin on the page before leading you over a palatine assault course. Flavours can be described as rumbustious: anchovy fritters come with fiery aïoli; while foie gras, fried egg and balsamic vinegar is destined to be the Brook Green version of builder's breakfast. There is also a genuine mixed grill for those with demotic inclinations. For a refined beginning to the meal, the layered terrine of mozzarella, courgette and tomato, served chilled, is a reminder that not everything need be salty. Tarte Tatin with vine tomatoes, olive tapenade and goat's cheese is an up-market pizza, while pot-roast pork belly with morels and soy and broad-bean fricassée shows oriental scrupulosity in the accuracy of the meat cooking and in the amalgamation of textures. Finish off with polenta cake with clotted-cream ice cream.

Open
Every day
Hours
12.00-3.00pm,
7.00-11.00pm
(Sun 10.00pm)
Credit cards
AmEx, Mastercard,
Visa, Switch,
Delta, Diner's
Set-price lunch
£12.50 & £15.50
**Nearest tube
station**
Hammersmith
Broadway
Map 1

Sofra Restaurant £25

Open
Every day
Hours
12.00pm-12.00am
Credit cards
AmEx, Mastercard,
Visa, Switch,
Diner's, Delta
Service charge
12.5%
Cover charge
£1.50 per person
Set-price lunch
£8.45
Set-price dinner
£9.95
**Nearest tube
station**
Green Park
Maps 3 & 4

18 Shepherd Street, Shepherd Market W1 (493 3320);
36 Tavistock Street WC2 (240 3773)

+ *true commitment to healthy food and good value*
− *crowds stretch kitchen- and waiting-staff capabilities*

Owner Hseyin Ozer is a good advertisement for the success of the Sofra 'healthy-eating' regimen. His growing empire currently stands at six outlets, including the two large restaurants in Shepherd Market and Covent Garden. His concern with the quality of the product makes it very good value indeed. A set meze menu delivers 11 items (salads, diced and spiced meat and poultry dishes, iman bayildi, tabbouleh and borek) for £8.45 or £9.95 per person. There is an inexpensive 'Light Lunch/Dinner' menu for £5, including houmus or a parsley salad to start, and main courses such as lamb fillet with oregano or chicken casserole. The à la carte menu is strong on grilled and baked lamb, and chicken dishes, all of which use good-quality meat. Queues form outside both branches, but are dealt with quickly.

Soho Soho £35

Open
Lunch Mon-Fri,
dinner Mon-Sat
(rotisserie every
day)
Hours
12.00-2.30pm,
6.00-11.30pm
(rotisserie 12.00-
12.45pm, 5.00-
11.00pm Sun)
Credit cards
AmEx, Mastercard,
Visa, Switch,
Delta, Diner's
Service charge
12.5% (first floor
only)
Cover charge
£1.50 per person
Set-price dinner
£15.25 & £17.95
**Nearest tube
station**
Leicester Square
Map 5

11–13 Frith Street W1 (494 3491)

+ *a whiff of Provence*
− *sometimes so-so*

Restaurateurs have a propensity for cashing in on middle-class cultural signifiers. In Frith Street, a culture dedicated to the dissemination of olive oil and balsamic vinegar has taken root. With Soho Soho, the Chez Gerard (q.v.) group has latched on to the Provençal-song-and-sunburnt-mirth myth and themed a successful restaurant around it. This, then, is the Nice end of the street. Food can evoke a sense of place as we trawl our spoons through an authentically highly spiced, if not traditionally composed, soupe de poissons de Marseille. Red mullet, skin iridescent, with fennel purée and anchovy and orange sauce, delivers the flavour it promises on the page. Roasted peppers with aubergine caviar further evince the sunny nature of the cuisine. There is more than a cursory nod to other regions in the adroit handling of meat dishes: calf's liver, wild boar, lamb and côte de boeuf are all well-cooked. Downstairs in the Rotisserie, expect Toulouse sausages and mash, pastas, salads, grills and noise.

Sonny's £29

Open
Lunch every day,
dinner Mon-Sat

Hours
12.30-2.30pm,
7.30-11.00pm
(cafe 10.00am-
4.00pm)

Credit cards
AmEx,
Mastercard, Visa,
Switch, Delta

Set-price lunch
£12

**Nearest tube/
railway station**
Hammersmith,
Barnes

Map 1

94 Church Road SW13 (0181-748 0393)

+ *Sunday lunch; set-price lunch; the wine list*
- *without a home in Barnes you may feel an outsider*

In last year's Guide we said that chef Redmond Hayward had been replaced by Anthony Demetre. Obviously we blinked for a moment because the chef is now Peter Harrison. However, through all the comings and goings the style of the kitchen retains its youthful Britishness and the restaurant its popularity. Dishes such as goat's-cheese polenta with grilled asparagus and field mushrooms; vegetable tempura with a soy-chilli dip; roast Trelough duck with summer vegetables and red-wine sauce; and elderflower jelly with shortbread and cream, are appealing and not overpriced. Cafe, delicatessen and large, light restaurant come together in a business that now includes The Phoenix Bar & Grill (q.v.) nearby. The owners have a canny knack of providing just what is wanted, including well-selected wines, many of them sold by the glass.

SOME OF THE most exemplary wine lists in London are comparative bantamweights. Whites feature the buttery attractions of Clos du Val Chardonnay; and there are also good examples of Sancerre, Bourgogne Aligoté and Pouilly-Fuissé, and, if funds are sufficiently elastic, Pierre Gaillard's rich, creamy Condrieu (£29.50), which needs to be sipped slowly because it improves strikingly in the glass. Highlights among the reds comprise the iodine-edged Firesteed Pinot Noir from Oregon; Pascal Granger's Black Forest gâteau of a Juliénas; and Château Meyney 1988, a brawny but ultimately rewarding Saint Estèphe, at the absurdly generous price of £24.50. Glug it while stocks last.

Spices £23

Open
Every day

Hours
12.00-2.30pm,
6.00-11.30pm

Credit cards
AmEx, Mastercard,
Visa, Switch, Delta

Set-price lunch
£5.95

**Nearest tube
station**
Paddington

Map 6

18 Chilworth Street W2 (706 8588)

+ *conventional Indian-restaurant food, cooked with care*
- *food colouring splashed in with gay abandon*

The Chilworth Street site that houses Spices has seen restaurant ventures come and go in brisk succession. However, this rather unimaginatively named Indian restaurant ought to be a stayer, as the quality of ingredients used overall and the particularity in spicing mark it out as well above average. Dishes take their time to arrive from the kitchen, suggesting that items are cooked or at least finished to order rather than being fished from some great melting pot. The prawns used are not the defrosted little comma-shaped creatures so beloved of Indian restaurants, but large, fresh specimens. Try them in a first course of king-prawn puri, or in the main course of king-prawn sagwala dry-cooked with shredded fresh spinach. Tandoori lamb chops are briskly seasoned and boldly charred. The section of balti dishes seems to exist just to catch a bandwagon should it be passing — especially given the fact that there is also a list of korai dishes (basically the same cooking mode). Again, however, assemblies are made somewhat special through the use of prime ingredients. The chef's recommendation of chicken dhakeshwari cooked with mango and ground almonds is only for those who like their food coloured a pillar-box red. The narrow ground-floor room is simple in design, the main visual diversion being provided by turquoise tablecloths over pink undercloths. Staff are gentle and attentive.

The Square £50

6–10 Bruton Street W1 (839 8787)

At the time of going to press The Square is in the process of relocating from King Street to the above address. The ownership, chef and manager remain the same, making it possible — based on a meal eaten just before the lights at King Street were switched off — to praise some particular dishes of chef Philip Howard that also delineate his style and approach: terrine of foie gras, summer truffles and guinea fowl; warm salad of rabbit with salsify and grain mustard; lemon and chive buttered lobster with oysters and Jersey royals; and thinly sliced veal with artichoke purée and fondant potato. Howard, who trained with the Roux brothers, Simon Hopkinson and Marco Pierre White has developed an assured touch of his own. His dishes invariably have some unexpected, pleasing detail or, as with the veal served as a neat, interleaved bundle of fine slices, cause you to look at an ingredient anew. The Bruton Street address may attract groovier customers than used to be found at The Square, which was a haven for American women of the desiccated sort.

St James (the original home of The Square) is the heart of fine wine, and this is a fine fine wine list — as wide as it is long. Unfortunately, to get that choice you undoubtedly pays your money. The white Nuits St Georges from Domaine de l'Arlot will cost you here £30 more than Odette's (q.v.) and a whopping £46 more than at 192 (q.v.). Why do the owners not use a sliding scale of mark-up to make more expensive wines more attractive to drink, rather than using the customers to subsidize the vanity

Open
Lunch Mon-Fri, dinner every day
Hours
12.00-3.00pm, 6.00-11.45pm (Sun 10.00pm)
Credit cards
AmEx, Mastercard, Visa, Switch, Delta, Diner's
Service charge
12.5% optional
Set-price dinner
£39.50
Nearest tube stations
Green Park, Bond Street
Map 3

of having a long list? Whichever, Burgundy and Bordeaux are long and strong and handsome, with solid support from the Australasian brigade and California: Moss Wood, Ata Rangi (New Zealand's best Pinot Noir), Shafer, Ridge and the intensely backward Rubicon of Niebaum-Coppola are worth experiencing. Mark-ups are typically unforgiving — comb the good selection of wines from the Rhône or from regional France for a touch of give in the take.

The Stamford £25

320 Goldhawk Road W6 (741 1994)

NOW THE BROOK

In the spring of 1996, many column inches of *The Spectator* were occupied by Nigella Lawson and Justin de Blank, plus various of their supporters and detractors, after Ms Lawson (now retired as *The Spectator*'s restaurant reviewer) described what she said was a disappointing meal eaten at a pub newly owned and run by Justin de Blank. The articles and correspondence raised a number of issues, one of which was whether it was fair for a reviewer to try a restaurant almost immediately upon its opening. Mr de Blank — he of the eponymous Elizabeth Street delicatessen (now no more) and a veteran of both hotel and corporate catering — claimed to be of the impression that reviewers waited until being told by a management that all was as it should be before visiting a new establishment: a patently absurd belief. However, putting my own oar in, I would say that any canny prospective restaurateur should purchase an A–Z, apprise himself of where London reviewers live, circle the immediate vicinities and avoid opening in them. The Stamford, another perfectly pleasant pub conversion (and considerably more handsome to look at than some), did not warrant a full-page review in a national journal — but then it is not far from Ms Lawson's house. The chef has changed since she reviewed the place, and he is also in fact a different chap to the one who was there when I reviewed The Stamford. However, knowing Justin de Blank — as I do — I would imagine he can ensure that the menu of fairly simple (some sweetly dated) dishes — such as cold plum-tomato and basil soup; deep-fried brie on green leaves with redcurrant sauce; steak aux poivres with Dauphinoise potatoes and mange-touts; and spinach-stuffed river trout with white-wine sauce and an almond potato cake — is well-enough executed. Desserts, which change daily, are listed on a blackboard, and I would risk a bet that they quite often

Open
Lunch every day, dinner Mon-Sat
Hours
12.00-2.30pm, 7.00-10.30pm
Credit cards
AmEx, Mastercard, Visa, Switch, Delta
Nearest tube station
Stamford Brook
Map 1

involve meringue. The Stamford provides the Ravenscourt Park/Stamford Brook area with an agreeable neighbourly venue for times when eating out seems preferable to staying in.

Star of India £35

154 Old Brompton Road SW5 (373 2901)

+ Reza the manager; Vineet the chef
– not getting a table on the first floor

Italianate frescoes, a jazz singer, recorded opera, a co-owner/manager who resembles all Bollywood stars (male and female) condensed into one slender package: this is not the average Indian restaurant. What makes Star of India (established in 1955) truly notable, though, is Vineet Bhatia's cooking and his informed and precise use of spices. A summer menu that favoured fish offered an extraordinary dish – taar machli nimbuwalli – based on fillets of zander in a sauce to which okra lent an eerie viscidity, while chillies, assorted mustard seeds, fresh lime leaves and coriander cut through any potential cloyingness. Large crabs cooked in the tandoor were another revelation. The definitive roganjosh is the one cooked here using meat on the bone. Try the vegetable dishes based on baby aubergines and on cashewnuts with beans and fresh coconut. Malai naan (tandoori-basked bread stuffed with soft cheese, onion and chillies) is irresistible. For dessert, see what happens when pineapple dusted with saffron and fennel seeds meets the caramelizing heat of the tandoor. And eat it with vanilla ice cream.

Open
Every day
Hours
12.00-3.00pm,
6.00pm-11.45pm
(Sun 7.00-
11.15pm)
Credit cards
AmEx, Mastercard,
Visa, Switch,
Delta, Diner's
Cover charge
£1 per person
Nearest tube
stations
Gloucester Road,
South Kensington
Map 2

Stephen Bull £32

5–7 Blandford Street W1 (486 9696)

+ Prices include VAT and vegetables (sic); the Irish soda bread
– monochromatic decor, matched by monochromatic clientele

Unlike so many meretricious operators who surf the latest trends, Stephen Bull espouses the idea that simplicity is a virtue and that gimmicks are to be eschewed. The menus are appealingly innovative, and there is a lightness of touch that relies on the uncomplicated use of seasonings and flavourings allied to good-quality raw ingredients. Among the starters, twice-cooked goat's cheese soufflé has justifiably become something of a standard: beautifully risen, moist and with a fine flavour, it makes you yearn to eat it twice. Braised rabbit with a pearl-barley risotto and lovage is a notable main

Open
Lunch Mon-Fri,
dinner Mon-Sat
Hours
12.15-2.30pm,
6.30-10.30pm
Credit cards
AmEx, Mastercard,
Visa, Switch
Nearest tube
stations
Bond Street, Baker
Street
Map 3

course, and the pan-fried calf's liver with beetroot confit and green-peppercorn sauce combines contrasting flavours to good effect. Wealthy local businessmen appreciate the dessert of warm pear and almond financier with lemon sauce, and Harley Street is conveniently close if the variations on a chocolate theme raise the blood-sugar level too high. The staff, who are mainly French, are sweet and relaxed, belying the apparent formality of the operation. A well-sourced wine list, with a strong bias towards Burgundy and Bordeaux, completes the picture.

Stephen Bull, Smithfields £25

69–71 St John Street EC1 (490 1750)

+ *watching oysters being shelled sharpens the appetite*
- *wrestling with the wrong end of the post-modern door to open it*

St John Street being well-endowed with meat restaurants, Stephen Bull has taken a different tack by adding a seafood bar to his establishment, which dispenses all manner of shellfish, cured salmon and sushi. The formula is evidently a winning one, judging by the way the city folk throng in at lunchtime. Although there is a strong emphasis on fish, in the rest of the menu first courses include chicken-liver parfait with fruit chutney; roast-garlic tartlet; and the panoply of smoked meats and cheeses called simply 'Delicacies from Spain'. The main course might feature grilled breast of duck with bok choy to provide an attractive non-piscine alternative. The meritorious wine list and cheerful waiting staff compensate for a slightly frenetic atmosphere (evenings are more laid-back).

Open
Lunch Mon-Fri, dinner Mon-Sat
Hours
12.00-2.30pm, 6.00-10.30pm (Sat 7.00-10.30pm)
Credit cards
AmEx, Mastercard, Visa, Switch
Nearest tube station
Farringdon
Map 3

The Stepping Stone £26

123 Queenstown Road SW8 (622 0555)

+ *winner of the Muscadet Most Sympathique Restaurant Award*
- *wobbly on oriental ideas*

The daily-changing menus at this busy neighbourhood restaurant announce the chefs as well as the dishes. Thus it might be that 'Malcolm, Tom, Beatrice and The Swedish Chef are cooking tonight'. All very egalitarian and matey, and, indeed, owners Gary and Emer Levy seem palpably concerned with the contentment and gratification of their customers. The modern British menu, with a bias towards fish, appears more

Open
Lunch Mon-Fri & Sun, dinner Mon-Sat
Hours
12.00-2.30pm, 7.00-11.00pm
Credit cards
AmEx, Mastercard, Visa, Switch, Delta, Diner's
Service charge
10% on parties of 6 and over
Set-price lunch
£10.50 & £13.50

Nearest tube/
railway station
Sloane Square,
Clapham
Common,
Queenstown Road
Map 2

reliable when it keeps out of oriental territories. Stir-fried vegetables and rice noodles in an acidic sauce swamped and ruined a dish of roasted chicken. On the other hand, a slice of duck-liver pâté served with hot buttered brown toast could not have been bettered. Mrs Levy is a fine patissière.

WHEN YOU SEE a front page that enumerates five Belgian beers, including the delightfully named Slag Lager, and a Pilsener from Parson's Green, you know that someone cares about the finer details of the drinks list. This impression is reinforced by 14 halves, including the lustrous Shafers from Napa valley; a Californian rosé made from the Mourvèdre grape; and Charlie Melton's dark-hued 'Rosé of Virginia', which is a rosé by any other name (i.e., it's a red). Whites include a dry, grapey Muscat from Piedmont; and Domaine de Joy, a barrel-fermented, lees-agitated Gros Manseng from Gascony with delicious honey-polished tones. Discrimination is equally evident in the reds: Conterno for Barbera, Weinert for Carrascal, Penley Estate for Shiraz and Rion for Nuits-St-Georges.

Stratford's £29

7 Stratford Road W8 (937 6388)

+ *what's your poisson? They order these things well in France — and in Earl's Court*
- *the charge of the heavy brigade: cover charge, 15% service charge, etc.*

Open
Every day
Hours
12.00-3.00pm,
6.00-11.00pm
(Sun 7.00-
10.30pm)
Credit cards
AmEx, Mastercard,
Visa, Switch,
Delta, Diner's
Service charge
15%
Cover charge
£1.50 per person
Set-price lunch
& dinner
£12
Nearest tube
stations
Earl's Court,
High Street
Kensington
Map 2

The sister restaurant of Lou Pescadou (q.v.) resides not far away in an attractive townhouse, and plays to a slightly more well-heeled Francophile audience. Fish is what they do, and they do it well. Palourdes (clams) steamed with thyme score more highly than watery moules marinière. Calamars Provençale, soupe de poisson lifted by a lambent flame of garlic, and Salade Stratford's (shelled crab, langoustine and flaked, marinated salmon on a crunchy assortment of diced and shredded vegetables), are good opening gambits. Then choose from half-a-dozen fish — sea bass, john dory, halibut, etc. — to be cooked as you will, either plainly grilled or roasted with garlic, and accompanied by a tomato and basil sauce or by beurre blanc. There are meat dishes for those who have wandered in unawares. Surroundings are seaside-bright.

The Sugar Club £34

32a All Saints Road W11 (221 3844)

+ *the frisson from the flavours*
- *£7.50 for a glass of champagne*

The young chef, New Zealander Peter Gordon, is beginning to get known outside food fashion-conscious London through his articles and recipes for a Sunday newspaper colour supplement. Although I tear them out, I'd rather go down to The Sugar Club (no membership required) partly because his brigade juggles with layers of flavour and patchworks of textures so very adeptly but also because it is such an agreeable, well-run, reasonably priced restaurant with wines that don't tend to grace the rack in my own kitchen. There are daring pairings within dishes but also relatively plain assemblies which can have as much impact, e.g. grilled scallops with sweet chilli sauce and crème fraîche; a whole artichoke with mustard and spring onion dressing; pan-fried monkfish, new potatoes and olives with almond pesto and watercress; biscotti with spiced mascarpone and papaya. But Gordon's hallmark is his ability to compare and contrast, as in a salad of spicy smoked pork, pickled bean sprouts, coriander, mint leaves and crisp shallots or a main course of roasted guinea fowl on braised fennel and leeks with couscous and truffle sauce. Vegetarians are well cared for. A perfect dessert for those who usually skip the course is a plate of biscuits and chocolates. The one cheese is carefully chosen and served with excellent bread made in-house. The ground floor is for smokers, the basement houses the open-plan kitchen, no-smoking tables and, outside, a pretty terrace. From my non-smoking point of view, it is the preferable place to sit. Waiters might easily be the customers and vice versa which is relaxing but does not impinge of the efficiency of service; no-one is ever asked who's the grey mullet?

Open
Every day
Hours
12.30pm-3.00pm,
6.30-11.00pm
Credit cards
AmEx, Mastercard,
Visa, Switch, Delta
Service charge
12.5% (for 6 or
more)
Set-price lunch
£12.50 & £15.50
**Nearest tube
station**
Westbourne Park
Map 6

Le Suquet £35

104 Draycott Avenue SW3 (581 1785)

+ *plateau de fruits de mer*
- *je m'en fiche service*

Pierre Martin, owner, is nowadays just a flying visitor to his South of France fish restaurant, and in his absence standards tend to waver. However, the atmosphere here is glamorous, with something of the Riviera of our fantasies invoked — oysters of all sizes, clams, mussels, langoustines and crab make a wonderful catch piled on to a huge cork platter; while prime fish

Open
Every day
Hours
12.30-2.30pm,
7.00-11.30pm
(Sun 12.30-
11.30pm)
Credit cards
AmEx, Mastercard,
Visa, Switch,
Diner's
Cover charge
£1 per person
Service charge
15%

Set-price lunch
£12
Nearest tube
station
South Kensington
Map 2

such as sea bass and gilt-head bream can be perfect when simply grilled (although the accompanying beurre blanc may be found wanting). Meat dishes such as poulet Basquaise or lapin aux pleurottes are provided for the perverse who come here not to eat fish. The bar is a nice place to toy with a dozen oysters when eating on your own. Le Suquet never closes, meaning that you could have a Christmas dinner of harengs pommes à l'huile followed by homard grillé – nice idea.

Open
Dinner Tues-Sun
Hours
6.00-10.30pm
Credit cards
Mastercard, Visa,
Switch, Delta
Set-price dinner
£14 & £25
Nearest tube
station
Willesden Green
Map 1

Sushi-Say ⭐new   £25

33b Walm Lane NW2 (0181-459 7512)

+ *a Tokyo-style sushi chef of many years' experience*
– *silly dolly decorations*

Katsuharu and Yuko Shimizu are the owners (chef and manager respectively), of this friendly Japanese restaurant. Katsuharu Shimizu, a venerable sushi chef, previously worked at the John Pawson-designed Wakaba (q.v.) in Swiss Cottage, where he was an impressive presence. Two-dinner sized and traditionally dressed, complete with Velcro hair and narrow rolled headband, he now seems happy to be running his own show in Willesden Green. His selection of sushi is broad-based and – importantly for the non-Japanese customer – well-described, including warnings to the unwary such as 'very salty' for ika shiakara ('part of squid prepared in traditional Japanese style'). The cognoscenti can dither between seaweed, jellyfish, turbot wing and salmon skin, but the novice or nervous should probably opt for a sushi selection such as nigiri toku, based on fairly familiar seafood. There are some interesting vegetarian options rolled in seaweed (nori), which include pickled radish, wild burdock and sticky soy beans, and okra, mustard cress, cucumber and spinach. Sashimi (raw fish) is fresh and frisky: the selection includes tuna (lean and fatty), salmon and turbot. The list of starters is long and fascinating: gyoza (dumplings) are notably fresh and light; chawan mushi (savoury egg custard with chicken and vegetables) is a sort of invalid food that immediately makes you feel better; and pumpkin, yam Japanese peas (fresh soy beans) and various treatments of beancurd combine healthiness and delectation. Main courses might be grilled fish or meat with teriyaki sauce, or tempura (fish and vegetables fried in feathery batter). Complete dishes based on rice, such as oyakodon (slices of chicken and vegetables cooked with special sauce and egg on rice) bring a meal to a satisfying and homely close. Sushi-Say is an eminently approachable local Japanese restaurant, but one also worth a detour.

Sweetings £32

39 Queen Victoria Street EC4 (248 3062)

+ *no bookings taken*
- *no credit cards taken*

Open
Lunch Mon-Fri
Hours
11.30am-3.00pm
Credit cards
None
Nearest tube station
Mansion House
Map 1

Many things fluctuate in the City but, thankfully, not Sweetings, a restaurant which in Victorian times would have been called a fish ordinary. Open weekday lunchtimes only, 11.30am sees the first customers anxious to find a place either at a counter or shared refectory table to enjoy West Mersea oysters, roll mops, smoked eel, dressed crab or a plate of environmentally unsound real turtle soup followed by the freshest of fish ranging from the cheaper plaice or haddock to the more luxurious (and expensive) halibut, turbot or Dover sole. New potatoes or mash is the best accompaniment, green vegetables and salads being a somewhat token gesture. Home-made English puddings – or sweets as they call them here – include baked jam roll, spotted Dick and steamed syrup pudding but a popular end to a meal is a savoury such as Welsh rarebit or roes on toast.

Tamarind £32

20 Queen Street W1 (629 3561)

+ *Atul Kochhar's north Indian cooking*
- *the unwelcoming entrance*

Open
Lunch Mon-Fri &
Sun, dinner every
day
Hours
12.00-3.00pm,
6.00-11.30pm
Credit cards
AmEx, Mastercard,
Visa, Switch,
Diner's, Delta
Service charge
12.5%
Set-price lunch
£16.50 (also
pre/post theatre)
Nearest tube station
Green Park
Map 3

A self-taught Bangladeshi cook and a trained Indian chef are worlds apart, and it is a pity that their output gets bracketed together in the category 'Indian restaurant' – it can lead to pejorative comments about 'pricey' meals that would not be perceived as such were the cuisine in question, say, French. Tamarind is a glitzy Mayfair restaurant serving complex cooking based on high-quality raw ingredients with the spicing, saucing, combinations, juxtapositions and cooking methods – notably marinating and the use of the tandoor – that define it as Indian. The menu has developed and lengthened this year. Among the first courses and tandoor-cooked kebabs, try jalpari chaat (a mixture of prawns and fish marinated in mint and coriander); murg kaleji masala (pan-fried, spiced chicken livers); changezi champen (lamb chops with a red-chilli and coriander crust); and jhinga-e-Khyber (prawns with sunflower and cardamom seeds, ginger and yoghurt). Among the curries, hari machli is an unusual dish of fish wrapped with crisp ribbons of spinach; khade masala ka gosht uses whole spices in a dry lamb dish. Vegetables are interesting. Consider cauliflower in onion sauce with shredded spinach and nuts, and steamed spinach and potatoes served as a purée with fennel and cardamom. The chef is proud of his dark, rich lentil dish, dhal bhukari. From the tandoor ovens visible behind a pane of glass come fabulous breads such as bhaharkani, a Mogul speciality made with saffron and fennel. Service has improved but tends towards obtrusiveness.

La Tante Claire £70

68 Royal Hospital Road SW3 (352 6045)

+ *all the elements of a grand meal working in harmony*
– *the dated wine list*

Open Mon–Fri
Hours 12.30–2.00pm, 7.00–11.00pm
Credit cards AmEx, Mastercard, Visa, Diner's
Set-price lunch £26
Nearest tube station Sloane Square
Map 2

In his relatively small Chelsea restaurant, Pierre Koffmann has achieved over the years an ideal balance of the various elements that contribute to a special meal: innovation and finesse in the cooking; comfort, flattery and diversion of surroundings; responsive, enthusiastic service; a knowledgeable sommelier; and a clientele that fits no one description, but is usually pursuing pleasure rather than business. Koffmann's upbringing in Gascony still informs his cooking, notably in the handling of foie gras and duck, rabbit, pigeon and venison. Galette de foie gras au Sauternes et échalotes roties is one of his self-styled specialities. However, the boy from farming country is also an artist, as can be observed in coquilles St Jacques à la planche sauce encre, in which feathery strokes with coral 'paint' on a black background feed the eye as well as teasing the palate. Terrific desserts include croustade de pommes caramelisées and soufflé aux pistaches et sa glace. Koffmann works a five-day week and chooses to stay firmly in the kitchen. Note the set-price lunch. It is of course a great bargain although, to see the three Michelin stars shining brightly, eat à la carte.

THIS YEAR MORE of an effort has been made to source 'house-style' wines, as the selection of 25 regional French wines affirms. Domaine de Coujan from the ancient grape variety Rolle tastes weirdly of lime-flavoured fruit pastilles; Domaine des Terriers is that rare thing – a good-quality Viognier from the Ardèche; Guilbert Alquier's smoky, pruny Faugères is one of the best around; and La Cuvée Mythique is a splendid Rhône blend from Languedoc. If you're straying outside the Rhône, Loire and Alsace, set the credit-card controls to overdrive: there are 84 clarets and 81 burgundies from tip-top vintages to choose from.

The Tate Gallery Restaurant   £32

Millbank SW1 (887 8877)

+ *entering through the trompe-l'oeil stone arch known as the
   Grotto of Gluttons; the wine list*
- *dingy lighting, pub glasses*

Open
Mon–Sat
Hours
12.00pm-3.00pm
Credit cards
AmEx, Mastercard,
Visa, Switch, Delta
**Nearest tube
station**
Pimlico
Map 1

Rex Whistler's allusive mural entitled 'An Expedition in
Pursuit of Rare Meats' is one of the attractions of The Tate
Gallery's basement restaurant. The wine list is another. Early in
1996 a new chef was engaged. Shaun Rowland, whose previous
job was at The Ivy (q.v.), styles his menus as modern British, a
definition that here seems to embrace Caesar salad; fettucine
with a tomato and coriander salsa; seared red mullet with
ratatouille and basil; and chocolate pecan tart with white-
chocolate ice cream. Traditional British — such as Cumberland
sausage and mash; liver and bacon; and summer pudding with
clotted cream — is also offered. The standard of preparation is
good enough, but somehow an institutional feeling still hangs in
the air here: you suspect that you might easily find a printed
sign warning you against enjoying yourself too much.
Sacrificing a few tables to make more space, and upgrading the
glassware and cutlery, would effect more of a transformation
than the gallery's conservation team has managed on the mural.

IT MAY NOT be art, but I know I like it. These knock-down
masterpieces are generally from the mid-'70s period, displaying
the signature value-for-money motif. Sidestep the Pomerols —
they lack the structure of their left-bank brethren — and apply
yourself to the châteaux favoured in the Médoc (d'Issan, Haut-
Bailly, Léoville-Barton and Gruaud-Larose, for example). Various
wines listed are considerably less expensive than they might be
sourced retail. A crisp £50 note will get you a bottle of Château
d'Issan '83 plus one of Château Beychevelle '78; meanwhile a
shockingly fruity Château Grand Puy Lacoste '85 (£24.50),
oozing with savoury blackcurrant aromas, will vie for your
aesthetic approval against anything on the walls, especially
when you are ploughing through your second bottle. The
remainder of the list is a concession to changes in
tastes, fashions and wine-making techniques: wines from St
Hallett, Thelema, Cape Mentelle, Ridge and a Viognier/
Chardonnay blend from Qupé are a breath of modernity among
the wonderful 'old masters'.

Open
Mon–Fri
Hours
11.30am–2.30pm,
6.00–9.30pm
Credit cards
AmEx, Mastercard,
Visa, Switch,
Diner's, Delta
Service charge
13%
Set-price lunch
£21
Set price dinner
£23
Nearest tube
station
Liverpool Street
Station
Map 1

Tatsuso   £50

32 Broadway Circus, Broadgate EC2 (638 5863)

+ *the best of traditional Japanese cooking*
– *the price you pay for the above*

There is a consensus that some of the best, classic Japanese cooking can be found at this City restaurant. Bypassing the ground-floor teppan-yaki grills, which have a self-limiting quality in terms of subtlety or discovery, go downstairs to the wood-panelled main restaurant. The price quoted above is somewhat notional, as set-price dinners alone range from £29 to £75 (with a lunchtime bento box available at £28). They have the advantage of providing a balance and harmony that you may not obtain by ordering à la carte; however, staff are helpful. The traditional virtues of Japanese food — freshness, refinement, modesty, allusiveness, artistry in presentation — are all in evidence, and the sushi and sashimi are irreproachable. The menu changes according to season, and there are always dishes of the day worth enquiring about.

Open
Every day
Hours
1.00–3.00pm,
6.00–11.00pm
Credit cards
AmEx, Mastercard,
Visa, Switch,
Diner's, Delta
Set-price lunch
£5.95
Set price dinner
£15.95
Nearest tube
station
Bayswater
Map 6

Tawana Thai   £23

3 Westbourne Grove W2 (229 3785)

+ *apparently Loyd Grossman's favourite Thai restaurant*
– *Loyd Grossman nibbling, quibbling, ruminating, etc.*

Owned and run by women, this Thai restaurant on the corner of Queensway and Westbourne Grove has a particularly agreeable atmosphere. Two first courses that have a refreshing lack of familiarity are moo sarong (minced pork wrapped in a skein of noodles before being deep-fried) and look chin ping (beef balls, bouncy from fine mincing, served with a hot-and-sweet sauce). Star of the main courses, served for two and worth having as a course apart is pla pae sa (seasonal fish — usually sea bass — steamed over stock flavoured with lemongrass, garlic, fresh chilli, salted plum and Thai celery). Forego phad Thai and try phad kuay teow kee mow goong (wide rice noodles with shrimp and basil leaves). There is an additional vegetarian menu with some excellent curries.

Thailand £25

15 Lewisham Way SE14 (0181-691 4040)

+ *Lao dishes; hot chilli sauces*
- *the small room can get stuffy*

There are only 25 seats in Khamkhong Kambungoet Herman's eccentrically decorated front room of a restaurant, so booking is essential – especially if New Cross is not your patch. Any effort it takes to reach the restaurant is well-rewarded by the authentic and adventurous Thai food, with particular reference to the dishes from Laos. One to try is the country dish known as lap (hot-and-sour minced pork, beef or chicken served as a complete dish with spiced rice balls, which are eaten wrapped in lettuce leaves). Other Lao dishes should be accompanied by sticky rice, which you mould with your fingers and use like bread to mop up the last vestiges of fragrant juices. When mussels are available, try them in a powerful curry sauce. Beers and wines are augmented by an astonishing array of single-malt whiskies.

Open
Dinner Tues-Sat
Hours
6.00-10.30pm
Credit cards
Mastercard, Visa
Set price dinner
£20
Nearest railway stations
New Cross,
New Cross Gate
Map 1

33 St James's £50

33 St James's Street SW1 (930 4272)

+ *discovering there is life after Masterchef*
- *cover charge; supplements; no vegetarian main courses*

Derek Johns, one of the owners of this restaurant which in present-day St James's suddenly seems all the more interesting for its lack of fashionability, won Masterchef 1993. His day job is as a dealer in old masters. Some 'old master' still-lives painted by Paul Howard Karslake are one of the decorative features of the dining-room carved out of a former branch of The Abbey National Building Society. Chef Sean Davies recently worked in an hotel. Inviting you to cogitate, ruminate, expectorate, mutilate, Johns and Davies offer you dishes such as smoked salmon gazpacho; crab tortellini with curry oil and fresh apple juice (not dissimilar to a creation of Bruno Loubet at nearby L'Odeon [q.v.]); salad of caramelized sweetbreads with white asparagus; seared scallops, braised vegetables and garlic snails; spit-roasted baby chicken with salsify and tarragon. As you might infer, the anthem is never leave a good thing alone. Some of the desserts seem like the party pieces of Dame Edna Everage, for example, rhubarb and walnut ravioli with caramelized rhubarb broth, and hazelnut and malt bombe with oven-dried bananas. But as Dame Edna might say, there's a place in this world for everybody.

Open
Lunch Mon-Fri,
dinner Mon-Sat
Hours
12.15-3.00pm,
6.00-11.30pm
(last orders
10.45pm)
Credit cards
AmEx, Mastercard,
Visa, Switch
Service charge
12.5%
Cover charge
£1 per person
Set-price lunch
£16.95
Nearest tube stations
Green Park,
Piccadilly
Map 3

Open
Lunch Mon-Fri &
Sun, dinner every
day
Hours
12.30-2.30pm,
7.30-11.00pm
Credit cards
AmEx, Mastercard,
Visa, Switch,
Delta, Diner's
Set-price lunch
£12.50 & £15.50
Set-price dinner
£29.50
Nearest tube
station
South Kensington
Map 2

Turner's £55

87–9 Walton Street SW3 (584 6711)

+ *old-fashioned values*
– *subliminal muzak*

Bluff Brian Turner, popping up on TV morning, noon and afternoon, still finds time to put in plenty of appearances at this comfortingly genteel`restaurant decorated in Giverny shades of yellow and blue. He is clearly an able teacher as, although head chefs – currently Charlie Curran – come and go, the style of cooking doesn't waver, nor does the menu undergo much revision. Careful, classic treatment of unchallenging cuts would seem to be the guiding spirit. Perhaps the most raunchy dish is seared calf's kidney on a bed of celeriac with a grain-mustard sauce or, as the menu also puts it, rognons de veau rôti à la purée de celeri-rave. Prices are high – although it should be noted that tax and service are included – making lunchtimes (when the living is cheaper) and Sunday lunch (a relaxed event celebrating Yorkshire pudding and attended by friends/regulars) particularly attractive.

Open
Dinner Mon-Sat
Hours
7.00-10.30pm
(11.00pm Fri/Sat)
Credit cards
Mastercard, Visa,
Switch, Delta
Service charge
10% optional
Set-price dinner
£9.95 & £14.75
Nearest tube
station
Brixton
Map 1

Twenty Trinity Gardens £25

20 Trinity Gardens SW9 (733 8838)

+ *three-course menu at £9.95 Monday–Thursday*
– *quite hard to find*

Correct French cooking from competitively priced set menus continues, but the husband-and-wife team who own this longstanding restaurant are also branching out into some Moroccan dishes and occasional Moroccan nights (Abdel Baha is French Moroccan), which will be worth investigating. The charm of their colourful, comfortable conservatory room, his welcome, and her menus – for example, vichyssoise, Toulouse sausage with lentils and then clafoutis for £9.95; or salade Lyonnaise, coq au vin et riz pilaf, and then tarte au pruneaux et Armagnac for £14.75 – make it particularly welcome in an area that is not overburdened with good restaurants.

Two Brothers Fish Restaurant £21

277/303 Regent's Park Road N3 (0181 346 0469)

+ fish and chips plus
- Finchley Road goes on for longer than Tennyson's brook

That this restaurant was good enough to calm the correspondent who thought it was on the Primrose Hill Regent's Park Road and finally arrived at Two Brothers by cab owing a huge fare to find a queue at the door, is tribute to the food and service. Chips that are cut each day and very fresh fish keenly filleted or fried on the bone are the staple, accompanied by mushy peas, cucumber, ketchup and tea. But if you prefer, take oysters, grilled Dover sole and a bottle of Chassagne Montrachet. The man (or, less likely, woman) who could round off either meal with a Knickerbocker Glory deserves to be stood the cab fare back home. Note, there are no bookings taken.

Open
Tues-Sat
Hours
12.00-2.30pm,
5.30-10.15pm
Credit cards
AmEx, Mastercard,
Visa, Switch
Nearest tube station
Finchley Central
Map 1

Union Cafe & Restaurant £26

96 Marylebone Lane W1 (486 4860)

+ breakfast is worth getting up late for; creative drinks list
- an indefinable aura of worthiness

A number of dishes might have been adapted from The Body Shop formulae: fresh carrot, beetroot and ginger juice would make a revivifying skin tonic, whereas a mint and coconut laksa could be applied as a cooling face-mask. Although you may glimpse a Vogue-ish wafer-thin model crunching through a beautiful and healthy vegetable salad with avocado, garlic flowers, coriander and lime, this would be to miss the point of the place, where the evangelical desire to use the highest-quality ingredients (free-range eggs, bacon and sausages from Heal Farm, corn-fed chicken), allied to virtues of home-baking (bread, muffins, biscotti), fleshes out the balance of the menu. Spicy, refreshing soups may be followed by chicken and fish served with fresh vegetables, herb-laced salad leaves and either a pesto or a good yolky hollandaise. A between course includes Scottish oak-smoked salmon with watercress and fresh horseradish, or a plate of Neal's Yard cheeses if you are in a mood more picky than peckish. Desserts are simple and simply wonderful, leading one to pose the question: why is it that the most puritanical establishments seem to make the most sinfully delicious puddings?

Open
Mon-Fri
Hours
10.00am-10.00pm
(last orders lunch
3.30pm)
Credit cards
Mastercard, Visa,
Switch, Delta
Service charge
12.5%
Nearest tube station
Bond Street
Map 3

Open
Lunch Tues-Sat,
dinner Mon-Sat
Hours
12.00–2.15pm,
6.00–10.15pm ;
Sat 12.00–3.00pm,
Fri & Sat 5.30–
10.15pm
Credit cards
None
Nearest tube
stations
Angel, Highbury &
Islington
Map 1

Upper Street Fish Shop £14 BYO

324 Upper Street N1 (359 1401)

+ *peerless in the upper house of fish 'n' chips*
- *hi, cholesterol!*

Being fryers for three generations has enabled the Conways to come close to discovering the perfect formula for fish and chips. This is an ideal neighbourhood bistro, with plain wood-panelled walls hung with mirrors. A congenial atmosphere allows you to bring your own bottle (Oddbins is conveniently nearby) or, if you want to be truly ethnic, ask for a pot of tea with some bread and butter on the side. Plaice, haddock and cod are enveloped in light, golden batter with chunky chips, and may be supplemented with side orders of mushy peas, pickled onions and so forth. The house special is halibut; otherwise fish lasagne, grilled snapper and Dover sole are proficiently done, and the starters of fish soup and smoked-salmon pâté are legends in their own lunchtime. If you finish your main course, you are allowed a sweet.

Open
Mon-Fri
Hours
12.00–3.00pm,
6.00–11.00pm
Credit cards
AmEx, Mastercard,
Visa, Diner's
Cover charge
£1.50 per person
at lunch
Set price dinner
£14.95
Nearest tube
station
Oxford Circus
Map 5

Vasco & Piero's Pavilion £28

15 Poland Street W1 (437 8774)

+ *the family ownership; the quirkiness; the tortelloni*
- *large parties can dominate*

Vasco Matteucci and his son Paul (Piero, alas, is in the trattoria in the sky) run a singular, pleasingly old-fashioned restaurant serving food that has moved with the times. The history of the Pavilion goes back to the late, lamented Academy Cinema on Oxford Street, where the tented theme originated in Angus McBean's design. Lunch and dinner provide a different clientele, the evening crowd being wooed with an extremely good value £14.95 three-course menu. Antipasti — including roasted vegetables and a nice frittata; homemade pastas; marinated herrings on potatoes; grilled fish and meat; and authentically low-key desserts — are its backbone. Now that Soho proper has been colonized, it is streets like Poland Street and restaurants like this that give a flavour of the good old days.

Il Vicolo £25

3–4 Crown Passage, Pall Mall SW1 (839 3960)

+ *the location; fresh fish dishes*
- *occasional longueurs in service*

The typeface on the menu and, to some extent, the dishes offered (insalate Caprese, pollo al limone) prime you for the never-mind-the-quality-feel-the-length-of-my-pepper-mill experience, but Giacomo (manager) and Alfredo (chef) offer something much better than that. Dishes of the day, mainly centred on fish, and details in the garnishes – such as the endives braised with sweet-sour balsamic vinegar, which are served with grilled spicy sausages – lift the experience. Pastas are good: for example, orecchiette with broccoli and spaghetti with fresh clams, as well as the cooking of veal, reveal a true Italian hand at the stove. If you have never discovered Crown Passage, it is worth doing so – and stopping by here for a meal. Lunch is hectic, evenings quieter.

Open
Mon–Fri
Hours
12.00–3.00pm,
6.15–10.15pm
Credit cards
AmEx, Mastercard,
Visa, Switch, Delta
Cover charge
£1.20 per person
Nearest tube station
Green Park
Map 3

Villandry Dining Rooms £24

89 Marylebone High Street W1 (224 3799)

+ *eat good food, buy good food*
- *cramped and crowded at peak hours*

This is a delicatessen – particularly strong on breads and cheeses – which also acts as cafe and restaurant. The dining-room at the back has the air of a schoolroom; sitting in the shop is a bit like stopping to eat in somebody's hallway, but it makes the quality of food delivered all the more impressive. The daily-changing menu offers healthy and delicious soups such as celeriac with celeriac crisps or cream of fennel with a watercress purée; imaginative salads such as avocado with lime, caramelized bacon and toasted sourdough bread; notably light savoury tarts (quiche would be the wrong word); fish dishes along the lines of escabeche of sole with roasted fennel; cunning meat dishes such as roasted duck served with a shallot and honey sauce, pearl barley and delicately cooked pears; delectable desserts, the moist chocolate cake being a favourite. Wines are well chosen but pricey. Villandry is moving to bigger premises down the High Street but no-one seems to know quite when.

Open
Lunch every day
except Sun,
dinner only once
a month
Hours
12.30–3.00pm
Credit cards
AmEx, Mastercard,
Visa, Switch,
Diner's, Delta
Nearest tube station
Baker Street/Bond
Street
Map 3

Open
Mon-Sat
Hours
12.00-2.30pm,
6.00-11.30pm
Credit cards
AmEx, Mastercard,
Visa, Switch,
Diner's, Delta
Service charge
12.5%
Set-price lunch
£20
**Nearest tube
station**
Hyde Park Corner
Map 2

Vong  £36

Wilton Place SW1 (235 1010)

+ *the perfect culinary marriage of France and the Orient*
− *Jean-Georges is sometimes missed*

The transformation of the restaurant Le Perroquet at The Berkeley Hotel into Vong at the close of 1995 was one of the more dramatic events in catering of the last few years. Jean-Georges Vongerichten (a native of Alsace, who once worked briefly in London as Louis Outhier's chef when Outhier was consultant at The Grosvenor House Hotel) moved on to work in New York where, after a stint at Drake Swissotel, he opened the restaurants Jo-Jo and Vong. By this time he had built on to his classic French training − some of it with Paul Haeberlin at the Auberge de L'Ill − a commitment to lightness and healthiness, and a mission to explore and exploit Asian spicing. A fascination with foods of the East had begun during time spent working at The Oriental Hotel in Bangkok, and continued in Singapore and Hong Kong. The fusion of French and Thai at Vong is not the careless rambling and scrambling of self-styled eclectic chefs, but an informed upping of the ante in both traditions. For anyone who likes Thai food (more or less everyone, I should have thought), it is simply the best of both worlds. Consider lobster and daikon roll with rosemary-ginger dip; dumplings of chicken and foie gras served with truffle dipping sauce; steamed John Dory with cardamom, cabbage and cress; dusted aromatic veal chop with kumquat chutney; figs baked in port and Chinese honey, with cumin-vanilla ice cream; and warm Valrhona chocolate cake and caramel-sesame ice cream (sensational). This is oriental food filtered through French sensibility, and thus incorporates no raw garlic or dried fish to introduce strident and fusty notes. When Vongerichten himself is in residence in Knightsbridge, the cooking is sublime. His chef, New Yorker Tom Dimarzo, mostly upholds standards but they can occasionally wobble. The site that once did service as a watering hole for debs and their mothers has been transformed by the design team of Keith Hobbs and Linzi Coppick, and its own entrance on Knightsbridge gives the restaurant a stylish identity quite separate from that of the hotel. Inside, pleasing details in art, ceramics, textures, reflections, flowers and the spices on titillating display complement the seductive dishes. Service is polished. A felicitous coincidence is the way in which the Alsace wines on the list enhance and are enhanced by the food.

Vrisaki Kebab House £18

73 Myddleton Road N22 (0181-889 8760)

+ *unpretentious food and fun*
- *can become a bit 18–30*

Open
Mon–Sat
Hours
12.00-3.00pm,
6.00-11.30pm
Service charge
10%
Nearest tube
station
Wood Green

A small parade of shops sits like an island in a sea of houses, and among the shops you find Vrisaki. On the face of it an unpromising location, and with a façade that seems to signal only a take-away operation, when you visit the 125-seater restaurant in the two long rooms at the rear of the premises it always seems to be full. To get the most from Antonio Andrea's food you should go at about 9pm with as large a group as you can muster, and order the seasonally-changing 30-dish mezedes. This will include good things (such as butterbeans, field mushrooms, dressed crab and sheftalia), and not-so-good things (tuna mush and cauliflower in salad cream). On balance though, you'll have a great party.

Wagamama £14

10a Lexington Street W1 (580 9365); 4 Streatham Street WC1 (323 9223)

+ *quick, delicious, nourishing noodles*
- *bleak design; back-to-school, noisy refectory atmosphere*

Open
Every day
Hours
12.00-11.00pm
(12.00-10.00pm
Sun)
Credit cards
Mastercard, Visa,
Switch
Nearest tube
stations
Tottenham Court
Road, Leicester
Square
Map 4 & 5

The formula is the same in Lexington Street as at the original Streatham Street – and it's a winner. Even with the competition in the Soho area, lunchtime queues snake down narrow Lexington Street. A mobile drinks waiter initiates the event and, once inside, the sideshow of a huge, steamy, clattering open kitchen keeps you entertained. This is not so much a noodle bar, more a people's food factory. The 'kaizen' philosophy of stressing constant improvement and assessment is impressive, with staff seemingly truly concerned about prompt service and customer enjoyment. At this Soho branch, as well as the ramen- (noodle-) based soups and pan-fried noodle and rice assemblies, yakitori and tempura are offered: yasai tempura (a mix of interesting vegetables in a light and lacy batter) is one to try. Raw juices (mango, apple, cucumber and tomato) are recommended, but there is wine and sake should you want to dent your own kaizen.

Wakaba £35

Open
Dinner Mon-Sat
Hours
6.30pm-10.45pm
Credit cards
AmEx, Mastercard,
Visa, Diner's
Service charge
10%
Set-price lunch
£23.60-£33
Nearest tube
station
Finchley Road
Map 1

122a Finchley Road NW3 (586 7960)

+ *John Pawson's design...*
- *...is becoming a period piece*

A curve of opaque glass is how this Japanese restaurant presents itself. Once inside it, the gritty reality of Finchley Road and its traffic takes on an ethereal quality you would never have dreamed possible. It is instant vindication of minimalist design. However, just as nicks and scratches on once-pristine surfaces confer a dated air, so the high prices for sushi, sashimi and the rest seem out of kilter with the way Japanese restaurants are developing. I would not be surprised if sushi lovers had followed sushi master Katsuharu Shimizu from here to his own more reasonably priced establishment Sushi-Say (q.v.) The decor there, featuring Japanese dollies, would have John Pawson fainting clean away. The preparation and cooking is of a high standard, and the menu is laid out in a manner easy to deal with. If they closed the credit-card slips – given that service charge is included – it would help.

The Waterloo Fire Station £25

Open
Every day
Hours
12.30-2.30pm
6.30-11.00pm
(pre-theatre 6.00-
7.00pm)
Credit cards
AmEx, Mastercard,
Visa, Switch,
Delta, Diner's
Service charge
10% (for 5 or
more)
Set-price lunch
£9.95; party
menus £13.50 &
£16.50
Nearest tube
station
Waterloo
Map 3

150 Waterloo Road SE1 (620 2226)

+ *fun in a desolate area*
- *food runs out*

Chef Dan Evans has gone to The Anglesea Arms (q.v.) but the style lives on: chefs flying by the seat of their pants; dishes dicing with dangerous spicing; staff running to keep up, but items (chalked on a blackboard) often running out before the evening has ended. The huge space, once a real fire station, is very basically furnished although, as there is a no-bookings policy, you may find your table – when you get one – furnished with some people you have never met. Obviously you must go here in the right mood and either young or young at heart, but the price is reasonable – as are prices in the bar, which occupies half the premises – and there is an appealing bran-tub quality to the picking of your order. For example, you will be luckier ending up with polenta-crusted halibut than with duck and beansprout fritters. However, desserts usually dry your eyes over any disappointments.

West Zenders £26

4a Upper St Martin's Lane WC2 (497 0376)

+ *for after-theatre Chinese*
- *classic modern design is sadly compromised*

Despite a certain amount of deliberate graffiti applied by the owners to Rick Mather's original unfussed, three-storey steel-and-glass design, the building still holds allure and suggests gastronomic excitement waiting inside. The offer of 'The Zen Experience' – a list of about 60 dishes from the various Zen restaurants, from which the customer can choose all he or she wants for £18.80 – has these days a somewhat ironic quality since ownership of the outlets seems a moveable feast; the managers and chef from here are, at the time of writing, running Pearl of Knightsbridge (q.v.) However, recent reports of the cooking suggest that it is competent enough for the price and, presumably, seemingly the more competent the more appetite you can muster. Peking, Cantonese, Szechuan and modern Hong Kong dishes are offered, and there are some items – such as spring-onion cake, stir-fried venison and what are described as designer noodles – that are not run-of-the-mill.

Open
Every day
Hours
12.00-2.45pm,
6.00-11.15pm
Credit cards
AmEx, Mastercard,
Visa, Switch,
Diner's, Delta
Service charge
12.5%
Set-price lunch
£10.80
Set price dinner
£18.80
Nearest tube station
Leicester Square
Map 5

White Tower £32

1 Percy Street W1 (636 8141)

+ *Mary and George*
- *changes to the layout of the ground floor*

Dutifully I tried a meal in the first-floor restaurant at this historic address, recently bought by Roy Ackerman's Restaurant Partnership plc, but the promised duck press was out-of-order – permanently it would seem – and I sat feeling miserable and guilty that I had betrayed my allegiance to Mary Dunne and George Metaxas – mercifully still working on the ground floor – who have between them been The White Tower for the past decade and worked there for close on four decades. So my advice remains the same in this guide as in previous editions: book a table on the ground floor, order the mixed pâtés – Pâté Diana (based on chicken and duck livers) and taramasalata – and follow by sharing an Aylesbury duckling farcie à la Cypriote, reserving it ahead just to be sure. For dessert? Greek yoghurt and honey, followed by Greek delight or halva with coffee. Relax in the privacy and warmth of the wonderfully dated, cluttered space. Upstairs rooms may be hired for private parties.

Open
Lunch Mon-Fri
Hours
12.00-3.00pm,
6.00-11.00pm
Credit cards
AmEx, Mastercard,
Visa, Switch,
Diner's
Service charge
12.5% optional
Cover charge
£2 per person
Set-price lunch
£12.50
Set price dinner
£15.50
Nearest tube station
Tottenham Court
Road
Map 4

Wilson's £25

Open
Lunch Mon–Fri &
Sun, dinner Mon–
Sat
Hours
12.30–2.30pm,
7.30–10.00pm
Credit cards
AmEx, Mastercard,
Visa, Switch, Delta
Service charge
12.5%
Nearest tube
station
Hammersmith
Map 1

236 Blythe Road W14 (603 7267)

+ *Scottish accents, including malt whiskies*
− *a request from another table for the bagpipes*

Staff wear tartan ties but usually draw the line at tartan troosers. The owners' heritage is apparent in details of the decoration of this friendly, idiosyncratic bistro − stag's antlers looming out from the wall, for example − but the menu is only mildly themed. You could, and perhaps should, start with finnan haddock pudding with a spinach and bacon salad, and move on to a dish of which the restaurant is proud: rack of lamb with haggis crust and a red-wine, garlic and rosemary sauce. However, a south-of-the-border order might be cold-smoked mackerel with a fresh rhubarb coulis, followed by sautéed breasts of wood pigeon glazed with a vinaigre de Cabernet Sauvignon. Desserts include athol brose (whisky whipped with cream, oats and heather honey), with strawberries and framboise and lemon posset. The set-price menu seems to have been abandoned, but prices remain generally very reasonable.

Wiltons £50

Open
Sun–Fri
Hours
12.00pm–2.15pm
6.00pm–10.15pm
Credit cards
AmEx, Mastercard,
Visa, Switch,
Delta, Diner's
Service charge
£1.00
Set-price lunch
£19.75 (Sunday
only)
Nearest tube
station
Green Park
Map 3

5 Jermyn Street SW1 (629 9955)

+ *there'll always be a Wiltons?*
− *stiff service and even stiffer prices*

An institution for the past 250 years, this St James's fish restaurant populated in the main by a white, male, mature, upper-class clientele may nowadays strike some as having an air of The Last Chance Saloon. The food provides solace. It is comfortingly plain and, by the way, based on absolutely first-rate ingredients. A dozen oysters, followed by a thick tranche of poached turbot, a savoury such as angels on horseback and some fresh raspberries is an unassailably good meal even if it sets the recipient back close on a bus conductor's weekly wage. Items you seldom see these days like turtle soup and sherry trifle survive on the menu. The nannies who serve have had their uniforms softened somewhat but they still expect you to finish your greens before pudding is served. Order of precedence is engraved in the manager's mind and it is unlikely anyone be given a booth − known as a Pullman − unless the booking can be cross-referenced to Debrett.

Wodka £30

12 St Alban's Grove W8 (937 6513)

+ *blinis, pierogis, caviar and vodka*
- *as spirits get high, the noise gets you down*

There has long been a Polish restaurant on this site: Chez Krysztof, a key émigré hangout in the '50s and '60s, was owned by the father of the current proprietor Jan Woroniecki. Eastern Europe is enjoying a renaissance among young travellers. Indoctrination can begin here with the list of 30 vodkas and eaux de vie, and with the rugged delights of dishes such as golabki (cabbage stuffed with pork and wild rice); warm smoked eel with sautéed potatoes; and zrazy of venison filled with wild mushrooms. Vegetable dishes such as puréed beetroot, carrots with honey and sesame, and braised white cabbage are excellent. Note the daily-changing two-course set lunch for £9, featuring dishes such as salad of wild-boar ham with figs, and grilled wild rabbit with herbs and garlic.

Open
Lunch Mon-Fri,
Dinner every day
Hours
12.30-2.30pm,
7.00-11.15pm
Credit cards
AmEx, Mastercard,
Visa, Switch,
Diner's
Set-price lunch
£9 & £12
Nearest tube station
High Street
Kensington
Map 2

Yoisho £18

33 Goodge Street W1 (323 0477)

+ *few non-Japanese*
- *few non-Japanese*

This softly lit bar-restaurant serves mainly Japanese businessmen who arrive singly to sit at the bar, or in boisterous groups for a post-office binge. Is it a coincidence that the pickled-cabbage dish kimchi, originally from Korea – which has a reputation for keeping hangovers at bay – is a speciality here? The long list of small dishes, which now seems properly translated, are well worth dipping into for about £5 a go, and grills are good too. Unusually for Japanese cuisine, there are no set menus; instead you eat a little, then order more. For authentic, robust food and a less hectic pace, Yoisho has the edge over the better-known (among Westerners) Ikkyu (q.v.) around the corner.

Open
Dinner every day
Hours
6.00-10.30pm
Credit cards
None
Service charge
10%
Nearest tube station
Goodge Street
Map 4

Open
Mon-Sat
Hours
12.00-2.30pm,
7.00-11.00pm
Credit cards
AmEx, Mastercard,
Visa, Delta
Set-price lunch
£14.50 & £17.50
Set-price dinner
£18.50, £22.50 &
£25.50
Nearest tube
station
Knightsbridge
Map 2

Zafferano £35

15 Lowndes Street SW1 (235 5800)

+ *un-greedy prices for the area and for the superior Italian food; the wine list*
- *nearly every table is the worst table in the room*

Chef Giorgio Locatelli has gone from strength to strength in the short time since opening here in early 1995. His cooking style seems not so much connected to a region as to an innate talent and good judgement. Pastas — from a simple trenette al pesto to a more robust and complex orecchiette with turnip tops and chilli, or pappardelle with broad beans — are masterful. Seafood is innovative: namely, monkfish with walnuts and capers; and chargrilled eel with a herb crust. The Belgravia location does not inhibit Locatelli from offering roast rabbit with Parma ham and polenta. Desserts — especially the ices and sorbets — have become a course not to be missed. Peaches with a bitter-almond granita, and Sardinian fried pecorino pastries with honey and undersweetened rich vanilla ice cream, are superb. Service can wear a far-away air. There is talk of a more casually styled Soho branch opening.

Open
Every day
Hours
12.15-3.30pm,
6.30pm-11.15pm
(Sun 10.45pm)
Credit cards
AmEx, Mastercard,
Visa, Switch,
Delta, Diner's
Service charge
15%
Cover charge
£1 per person
Set-price lunch
£28
Set price dinner
£35 & £42
Nearest tube
station
Green Park
Map 3

Zen Central £50

20–2 Queen Street W1 (629 8089)

+ *proper Peking duck*
- *over-the-top pricing*

Lobster priced at £22.50 a pound and Dover sole at £15 a pound (a pound not a kilo) give an idea of the cavalier attitude to cost displayed by this Mayfair restaurant. However, once that is swallowed the quality of cooking, and also of service, is high. The menu lists mostly familiar, undaunting dishes, but reassuringly includes double-boiled supreme shark's fin and whole abalone (at £80 and £70 for two), showing that Chinese custom is commonplace. Should you want to push the boat out for a party, roasted whole Kwantung suckling pig can be ordered (with 24 hours' notice), at a price to be negotiated. Even when shunning luxurious ingredients and choosing the path less travelled — for example, sea-spiced lamb slices; hand-cut pork with dried shredded scallops; baked rice with duck meat and shrimps wrapped in lotus leaves — a meal here will still seem expensive, especially when you notice the 15% 'gratuity' that is added on.

ZenW3 £28

83-84 Hampstead High Street NW3 (794 7863)

+ *zen and the art of restaurant consistency*
- *becoming zenophobic towards Hampstead's fashion victims*

A certain spirituality attaches to the architecture of this Hampstead restaurant with its clean geometric lines, bold use of steel and glass, two-storey tree and waterfall running down the bannisters. It was Rick Mather's first — and arguably best — showcase for the light, creative MSG-free cooking which characterizes Zen restaurants. Plump dumplings, soft-shelled crab, steamed sea bass with ginger, the wrapping dishes involving a meat/fish/poultry combination with julienned raw vegetables parcelled in rice paper and dipped in tangy sauce, prawns sizzling from the wok, sea-spice aubergine (one of several good vegetarian dishes), and imaginative seasonal specials which draw on produce not so often used in Chinese restaurants, are reliably good. Clever marinading, sharp spicing and quickfire assembly of fresh ingredients encourage dynamic and subtle contrasts. The palate registers fugitive sensations of sweetness and spice, textures soft and crunchy, temperatures hot and cold; the cooking zings as it yins and yangs. The young staff are notably smiley and efficient.

Open
Every day
Hours
12.00-11.30pm
(11.00pm Sun)
Credit cards
AmEx, Mastercard,
Visa, Switch,
Diner's, Delta
Service charge
12.5%
Set-price lunch
£11.50
Set price dinner
£26.50
**Nearest tube
station**
Hampstead
Map 1

Ziani £35

45 Radnor Walk SW3 (351 5297)

+ *a kitchen happy to comply with requests*
- *preferential treatment for neighbours and old Ziani hands*

A lmost forgotten in the rush for newer, bigger and flashier restaurants, Ziani is like an old friend: comfortable (if cramped), unchallenging and reliable. Its inspiration is the Veneto. Prices are reasonable and the decor sunny and bright. Pastas are simple, but several stand out: gnocchi with a ragoût of wild rabbit; penne rustica (sautéed with wild-boar sausages, aubergine and tomato); and cannelloni filled with seafood. Main dishes hold no surprises, although the zuppa di pesce is generously stocked, and baked sea bass cheaply priced at £10. The Sunday-brunch crowd brings children and newspapers for the £12.50 brunch bargain.

Open
Every day
Hours
12.30-2.45pm
(3.15pm Sun),
7.00-11.30pm
(10.30pm Sun)
Credit cards
AmEx, Mastercard,
Visa, Switch,
Diner's, Delta
Service charge
£1.25 per person
Set-price lunch
£12.50
**Nearest tube
station**
Sloane Square
Map 2

Zoe   £29

Open
Mon-Sat
Hours
12.00-2.30pm,
6.30-11.30pm
(cafe 11.30am-
11.30pm)
Credit cards
AmEx, Mastercard,
Visa, Switch,
Diner's, Delta
Set-price lunch
£11.00
Set price dinner
£8.50
Nearest tube
station
Bond Street
Map 3

3–5 Barrett Street, St Christopher's Place W1 (224 1122)

+ *refuge from Oxford Street*
- *avoid the more arcane dishes at peak times*

Were Zoe a compass, its needle would be spinning in all directions simultaneously, since its frenzied global menu aspirations pinpoint this as being Worral-Thompson's ultimate laboratory of garnishes. Eclectic Mediterranean dishes are given a further twist with the introduction of an extra ingredient, the qualification being that you have to map your meal around the ingredients unless you are partial to double doses of balsamic vinegar, or you harbour an irresistible passion for peanut sauce (three dishes), gorgonzola (three), fennel (several), to name but a few repeat performers. Sometimes the desire for swashbuckling alliteration contributes towards culinary illiteracy.

Indices

The Capital Hotel
  Restaurant SW3
Chez Bruce SW17
Chez Gerard W1
Chez Nico W1
Connaught Dining
  Room & Grill W1
The Criterion W1
La Dordogne W4
Élena's L'Étoile
L'Estaminet WC2
The Fat Duck, Bray,
  Berks
Le Gavroche W1
The Green Olive W9
Hyde Park Hotel — The
  Restaurant SW1
Interlude de Chavot W1
The Lobster Pot SE11
Lou Pescadou SW5
Maison Novelli EC1
Mange 2 EC1
McClements,
  Twickenham
Mon Petit Plaisir W8
Mon Plaisir WC2
Monsieur Max,
  Hampton Hill
Le Muscadet W1
L'Oranger SW1
Le Palais du Jardin WC2
Le P'tit Normand SW18
St Quentin SW3
Stratfords W8
Le Suquet SW3
La Tante Claire SW3
Turner's SW3
Twenty Trinity Gardens
  SW9

GREEK
Cafe O SW3
Beotys WC2
Kalamaras Mega and
  Micro W2
Lemonia NW1
Vrisaki Kebab House
  N22
The White Tower W1

GRILLS
Butler's Wharf Chop
  House SE1
Cafe Med W11
Cantina del Ponte SE1
Clarke's W8
Christophers American
  Grill WC2

Gaucho Grill W1
Grill St Quentin SW3
Museum Street Cafe
  WC1
Phoenix Bar & Grill
  SW15
The Popeseye W14
Quaglino's SW1
Randall & Aubin W1
The River Cafe W6

INDIAN
Babur Brasserie SE23
Bengal Clipper SE1
Bombay Brasserie SW7
Brilliant Restaurant,
  Southall
Cafe Spice Namaste E1
Chutney Mary SW10
Gitanjli-Mayfair W5
Great Nepalese NW1
  (Nepalese)
Lahore Kebab House E1
  (Pakistani)
Ma Goa SW15
Malabar W8
Old Delhi W2
La Porte des Indes W1
Red Fort W1
Salloos SW1 (Pakistani)
Spices W2
Star of India SW5
Tamarind W1

INDIAN VEGETARIAN
Chutneys NW1
Kastoori W17
Mamta SW6
Mandeer W1
Rani N3 & Richmond
Rasa N16

ITALIAN
L'Accento W2
Alba EC1
Al San Vincenzo W2
L'Altro W11
Assaggi at
  The Chepstow W2
L'Arte W1
Bice W1
Caffe Italia SE3
Cantina del Ponte SE1
La Capannina W1
Caraffini SW1
Cento 50 W11
Cibo W14
Daphne's SW3
De Cecco SW6

Del Buongustaio SW15
Dorchester Hotel Bar W1
Emporio Armani
  Express SW1
Enoteca Turi SW15
La Famiglia SW10
La Finezza SW1
Florians N8
Formula Veneta SW10
Il Goloso SW10
The Halkin Hotel
  Restaurant SW1
L'Incontro SW1
Little Italy W1
Luna NW1
Olivo SW1
Oliveto SW1
Orsino W11
Orso WC2
Osteria Antica Bologna
  SW11
Osteria le Fate SW3
The Red Pepper W9
Riva SW13
The River Cafe W6
San Lorenzo Fuoriporta
  SW19
A Tavola NW8
Il Vicolo SW1
Vasco & Piero's Pavilion
  W1
Zafferano SW1
Ziani SW3

IRISH
O'Conor Don-Ard-Ri
  Dining Room W1

JAPANESE
Ajimura WC2
Arisugawa W1
Gonbei WC1
Inaho W2
Ikkyu W1 & WC2
Kulu Kulu W1
Mitsukoshi SW1
Moshi Moshi Sushi EC2
Sushi Say NW2
Tatsuso EC2
Wagamama WC1 & W1
Wakaba NW3
Yoisho W1

KOREAN
Bu-San N7
Jin W1

LEBANESE
Al Bustan SW1
Al Hamra W1

THE MAGHREB
Adam's Cafe W12
Agadir W2
Bruno Soho W1
Laurent NW2
Twenty Trinity Gardens
  SW9

MIDDLE EASTERN
Ali Baba NW1
Alounak W2 & W14
Ebla W6
Istanbul Iskembecisi N16
Sofra W1 & WC2

PACIFIC RIM
The Collection SW3
Cucina NW3
Granita N1
Mezzonine W1
Saint W1
The Sugar Club W11

PUBS
The Abingdon W8
The Anglesea Arms W6
The Cow W2
The Chapel NW1
The Eagle EC1
The French House
  Dining Room W1
The Havelock Tavern
  W14
The Lansdowne NW1
The Peasant EC1
Prince Bonaparte W2

SCANDANAVIAN
Anna's Place N1
The Causerie —
  Claridge's W1

SPANISH
Albero & Grana SW3
Cambio de Tercio SW5
La Copita W12
Meson Bilbao NW6

SRI LANKAN
Prince of Ceylon N4

THAI
Bahn Thai W1
Bangkok SW7
Blue Elephant SW6
Chada Thai SW11
Esarn Kheaw W12
I-Thai W2 (Italian-Thai)
Mantanah Thai SE25
Royal Lancaster Hotel
  Nipa Thai W2
Sabai Sabai W6

Tawana W2
Thailand SE14
Vong SW1

VIETNAMESE
Saigon W1

RESTAURANTS BY AREA

BAKER STREET
Muscadet

BANKSIDE
Oxo Tower Restaurant

BARBICAN/FARRINGDON
Alba
Le Cafe du Marché
Maison Novelli
East One
The Eagle
Mange 2 Restaurant
The Peasant
Quality Chop House
Searcy's
St John
Stephen Bull, Smithfields

BARNES
Riva
Sonny's

BATTERSEA
B Square
Chada Thai
Ransome's Dock
The Stepping Stone

BAYSWATER
Amazonas
Four Seasons
Kalamaras Mega/Micro
Mandarin Kitchen
Royal China
Tawana

BELGRAVIA
Al Bustan
Ebury Wine Bar
The Halkin Restaurant
Oliveto
Olivo

BERKSHIRE
The Fat Duck

BLOOMSBURY
Alfred
Chiaroscuro
Museum Street Cafe
Wagamama

BRIXTON
Twenty Trinity Gardens

CAMDEN TOWN
Blakes
Belgo Noord
Luna Restaurant

CHELSEA
Bar Central
Browns Restaurant &
   Bar
The Canteen
Caraffini
Chutney Mary
La Famiglia
La Finezza
Monkeys
Osteria le Fate
La Tante Claire
Ziani

CHINATOWN
China City
Fung Shing
Harbour City
Ikkyu of Chinatown
The Immortals
Mr Kong
Poons

CHISWICK
The Chiswick
La Dordogne
Oliver's Island

CITY
Cafe Spice Namaste
Imperial City
Lahore Kebab House
Moshi Moshi Sushi
Sweetings
Tatsuso

CLAPHAM
Osteria Antica Bolgna

COVENT GARDEN
Ajimura
Belgo
Bertorelli's
Le Cafe du Jardin
Calabash
Christopher's
   American Grill
Detroit
L'Estaminet
Euten's
The Ivy
Mon Plaisir
Orso

Le Palais du Jardin
The Poetry Cafe
Rules
Saint
Sofra
Westzenders

CROUCH END
Les Associés
Florians

EALING
Gitanjli-Mayfair

EARLS COURT
Cambio De Tercio
Lou Pescadou

EDGWARE ROAD
The Chapel
Mandalay

EUSTON
Chutneys
Great Nepalese

FINCHLEY
Two Brothers Fish
   Restaurant
Rani

FINSBURY PARK
The Captain
Humming Bird

FITZROVIA
Arisugawa
L'Arte
Chez Gerard
Elena's L'Etoile
Ikkyu
Interlude de Chavot
Pied-à-Terre
Mandeer
White Tower
Yoisho

FOREST HILL
Babur Brasserie

FULHAM
Brady's
The Blue Elephant
Fables
Mamta
Montana
755

GOLDERS GREEN/FINCHLEY
Laurent
Quincy's

GREAT PORTLAND STREET
Nico Central

HAMMERSMITH
Anglesea Arms
The Brackenbury
Ebla
Havelock Tavern
Popeseye Steak House
The River Cafe
The Stamford
Sabai Sabai Thai
Wilson's

HAMPSTEAD
Cucina
ZenW3

HAMPTON
Monsieur Max

HENDON
Prince of Ceylon
Gourmet Garden

HOLLAND PARK
Belvedere
Chez Moi
The Halcyon Hotel –
   The Room
Orsino

HOLLOWAY
Bu-San

HYDE PARK
Chez Nico
Dorchester Grill Room
Dorchester Bar
Dorchester Oriental
   Restaurant

ISLINGTON
Anna's Place
Bar Central
Euphorium
Frederick's
Granita
Kavanagh's
Upper Street Fish Shop

KENNINGTON
The Lobster Pot

KENSINGTON
The Abingdon
Alounak
Arcadia
Boyd's Restaurant
Cibo
Clarke's
Downstairs At 190
Bistrot 190
Kensington Place
Launceston Place

TOWER BRIDGE/
BUTLERS WHARF
The Apprentice
Bengal Clipper
Blue Print Cafe
Butlers Wharf Chop
  House
Cantina Del Ponte
Le Pont De La Tour

VICTORIA
Joyful
Simply Nico

VICTORIA PARK
Frocks

WANDSWORTH/TOOTING
Brady's
Chez Bruce
Kastoori Restuarant
Smokey Joe's Diner

WATERLOO
Bar Central
Livebait
Waterloo Fire Station

WEST END
Brown's Restaurant & Bar
The Cafe at Sotheby's
Maze
Nicole's
The Square

WESTBOURNE GROVE
Agadir
Alounak

WESTCOMBE PARK
Caffe Italia

WESTMINSTER
The Atrium
Auberge de Provence

WILLESDEN GREEN
Sushi-Say

WIMBLEDON
San Lorenzo Fuoriporta

WOOD GREEN
Vrisaki Kebab House

UNDER £20 PER
PERSON

Adam's Cafe W12
Ali Baba NW1
Alounak W2 & W14
Bangkok SW7
Brady's SW5 & SW18
Brilliant Restaurant,
  Southall

Caffe Italia SE3
Calabash WC2
The Captain N4
The Chapel NW1
Chutneys NW1
La Copita W12
Cork & Bottle Wine Bar
  WC2
The Crescent SW3
Great Nepalese NW1
Green Cottage NW3
The Havelock Tavern
  W14
Ikkyu of Chinatown WC2
Istanbul Iskembecisi N16
Kalamaras Micro W2
Kastoori SW17
Kulu Kulu W1
Lahore Kebab House E1
Mandalay W2
Mandeer W1
Moshi Moshi Sushi EC2
  & EC4
Patio W12
Rasa N16
Royal China W2
Smokey Joe's Diner SW18
Upper Street Fish Shop
  N1
Vrisaki Kebab House N22
Wagamama W1
Yoisho W1

£20–£40 PER
PERSON

The Abingdon W8
L'Accento W2
Agadir W2
Ajimura WC2
Alastair Little W1
Alastair Little
  Lancaster Rd W11
Alba EC1
Albero & Grana SW3
Al Bustan SW1
Alfred WC2
Al Hamra W1
Al San Vincenzo W2
L'Altro W11
Amazonas W2
Andrew Edmunds W1
The Anglesea Arms W6
Anna's Place N1
The Apprentice SE1
Arcadia W8
Arisugawa W1

L'Arte W1
L'Artiste Assoiffé W11
Assagi, The Chepstow W2
Les Associés N8
A Tavola NW8
Atelier W1
Atlantic Bar & Grill W1
The Atrium SW1
Auberge de Provence
  SW1
L'Aventure NW8
The Avenue SW1
Babe Ruth's E1
Babur Brasserie SE23
Bahn Thai W1
Bank WC2
Bar Central N1, SW3 &
  SE1
Belgo Centraal WC2
Belgo Noord NW1
The Belvedere W8
Bengal Clipper SE1
Bentley's W1
Beotys WC2
Bertorelli's WC2
Bibendum Oyster Bar
  SW3
Bice W1
Bistrot 190 SW7
Blakes NW1
Bleeding Heart Restau-
  rant & Wine Bar EC1
The Blenheim NW8
The Blue Elephant SW6
Blue Print Cafe SE1
Blues Bar & Bistro W1
Bombay Brasserie SW7
Boyd's W8
The Brackenbury W6
Brasserie du Marché aux
  Puces W10
Browns Restaurant &
  Bar W1 SW3 & WC2
Bruno Soho W1
B Square SW11
Bu-San N7
Butlers Wharf Chop
  House SE1
The Cafe at Sotheby's
  W1
Cafe dell'Ugo SE1
Cafe du Jardin WC2
Le Cafe du Marché £30
Cafe Fish SW1
Cafe Med W11
Cafe O SW3

Cafe Spice Namaste E1
Cambio de Tercio SW5
The Canteen SW10
Cantina del Ponte SE1
La Capannina W1
Le Caprice SW1
Caraffini SW1
Caviar House W1
Cento 50 W1
Chada Thai SW11
The Chesterfield
  Restaurant W1
Chez Bruce SW17
Chez Gerard W1
Chez Moi W11
Chiaroscuro WC1
China City WC2
Chinon W14
The Chiswick W4
Christopher's American
  Grill WC2
Christophe's SW10
Chutney Mary SW10
Cibo W14
Claridge's – The
  Causerie W1
Coast W1
The Collection SW3
The Cow Dining Room
  W2
The Criterion – Marco
  Pierre White W1
Cucina NW3
Daphne's SW3
De Cecco SW6
Del Buongustaio SW15
Dell'Ugo W1
Detroit WC2
The Dorchester Bar W1
La Dordogne W4
Downstairs at 190 SW7
Drones, Pont Street SW1
The Eagle EC1
East One EC1
Ebla W6
Ebury Wine Bar SW1
Elena's L'Étoile W1
Emporio Armani
  Express SW3
Enoteca Turi SW15
Esarn Kheaw W12
L'Escargot W1
L'Estaminet WC2
Euphorium N1
Euten's WC2
Fables Restaurant SW6

La Famiglia SW10
The Fat Duck, Bray, Berks
Feng Shang NW1
The Fifth Floor SW1
Fina Estampa SE1
La Finezza SW1
Florians N8
Formula Veneta SW10
Foundation SW1
Four Seasons W2
Frederick's N1
French House Dining Room W1
Frocks E9
Fung Shing WC2
The Gate W6
Gaucho Grill W1
Gay Hussar W1
Gilbert's SW7
Gitanjli-Mayfair W5
Il Goloso SW10
Gonbei WC1
Gourmet Garden NW4
Granita N1
The Green Olive W9
Green's Restaurant & Oyster Bar SW1
Green Street W1
Grill St Quentin SW3
Harbour City W1
Hilaire SW7
Humming Bird N4
Ikkyu W1
The Immortals W1
Imperial City EC3
Inaho W2
L'Incontro SW1
The Ivy WC2
Jason's W9
Jimmy Beez W10
Jin W1
Joyful SW1
Kalamaras Mega W2
Kartouche SW10
Kavanagh's N1
Kensington Place W8
The Lansdowne NW1
Launceston Place W8
Laurent NW2
Lemonia NW1
Little Italy W1
Livebait SE1
The Lobster Pot SE11
Lou Pescadou SW5
Luna NW1

Magno's Brasserie WC2
Ma Goa SW15
Maison Novelli EC1
Malabar W8
Mamta SW6
Mandarin Kitchen W2
Mange 2 EC1
Mantanah Thai SE25
Maze W1
McClements, Twickenham
Meson Bilbao NW6
Le Metro SW3
Mezzo W1
Mezzonine W1
Ming W1
Monkeys SW3
Mon Petit Plaisir W8
Mon Plaisir WC2
Monsieur Max, Hampton Hill
Montana SW6
Mr Chow SW1
Mr Kong WC2
Le Muscadet W1
Museum Street Cafe WC1
Nico Central W1
Nicole's W1
O'Conor-Don-Ard-Ri Dining Room W1
L'Odéon W1
Odette's NW1
Ognisko SW7
Old Delhi W2
Oliver's Island W4
Oliveto SW1
Olivo SW1
192 W11
L'Oranger SW1
Orsino W11
Orso WC2
Oslo Court NW8
Osteria Antica Bolgna SW11
Osteria le Fate SW3
Oxo Tower Restaurant SE1
Le Palais du Jardin WC2
Palio W11
Pearl of Knightsbridge SW1
The Peasant EC1
The People's Palace SE1
Le P'tit Normand SW18
The Pheonix Bar & Grill SW15

Poetry Cafe WC2
Poissonerie de l'Avenue
Poons WC2
The Popeseye W14
La Porte des Indes W1
Prince Bonaparte W2
The Prince of Ceylon NW4
Quaglino's SW1
Quality Chop House EC1
Quincy's NW2
Randall & Aubin W1
Rani N3 & Richmond
Ransome's Dock SW11
Red Fort W1
The Red Pepper W9
Riva SW13
Royal China W2
Royal Garden Hotel – The Tenth W8
Royal Lancaster Hotel – Nipa Thai Restaurant W2
RSJ SE1
Rules WC2
Sabai Sabai W6
Saigon W1
Saint Bar & Restaurant WC2
St John EC1
St Quentin SW3
Salloos SW1
San Lorenzo Fuoriporta SW19
Scotts W1
Searcy's Brasserie EC2
755 SW6
Shaw's SW7
Simply Nico SW1
Simpsons-in-the-Strand WC2
Singapore Garden NW6
Snow's on the Green W6
Sofra W1 & WC2
Soho Soho W1
Sonny's SW13
Spices W2
The Stamford W6
Star of India SW5
Stephen Bull W1
Stephen Bull's Bistro & Bar EC1
The Stepping Stone SW8
Stratford's W8
The Sugar Club W11
Le Suquet SW3

Sushi-Say NW2
Sweetings EC4
Tamarind W1
Tate Gallery Restaurant SW1
Tawana Thai W2
Thailand SE14
Twenty Trinity Gardens SW9
Two Brothers Fish Restaurant N3
Union Cafe & Restaurant W1
Vasco & Piero's Pavilion W1
Il Vicolo SW1
Villandry Dining Rooms W1
Vong SW1
Wakaba NW3
The Waterloo Fire Station SE1
West Zenders WC2
White Tower W1
Wilson's W14
Wodka W8
Zafferano SW1
ZENW3 NW3
Ziani SW3
Zoe W1

OVER £40 PER PERSON

Aubergine SW10
Bibendum SW3
Cafe Royal Grill Room W1
The Capital Hotel SW3
Chez Nico at Ninety Park Lane W1
Clarke's W8
The Connaught Restaurant & Grill Room W1
The Dorchester Grill W1
The Dorchester Oriental Restaurant W1
Le Gavroche W1
Greenhouse W1
Halcyon Hotel – The Room W11
The Halkin Restaurant SW1
Hyde Park Hotel – The Restaurant Marco Pierre White SW1
Interlude de Chavot W1
Leith's W11

Mitsukoshi W1
Pied-à-Terre W1
Le Pont de la Tour SE1
The Ritz Restaurant W1
The River Cafe W6
Savoy Grill WC2
Savoy River Restaurant
WC2
The Square W1
La Tante Claire SW3
Tatsuso EC2
33 St James's SW1
Turner's SW3
Wiltons SW1
Zen Central W1

RESTAURANTS WITH LAST ORDERS AFTER 11.30PM

Agadir W2
Ali Baba NW1
A Tavola NW8
Atlantic Bar & Grill W1
The Avenue SW1
Bar Central N1 SW3 &
SE1
Bistrot 190 SW7
The Blue Elephant SW6
Blues Bistro & Bar W1
Bombay Brasserie SW7
Cafe du Jardin WC2
The Canteen SW10
Le Caprice SW1
China City WC2
Christopher's American
Grill WC2
Criterion Marco Pierre
White W1
Dell'Ugo W1
Detroit WC2
La Famiglia SW10
Gaucho Grill W1
Istanbul Iskembecisi
N16
The Ivy WC2
Kartouche SW10
Kalamaras Mega &
Micro W2
Kensington Place W8
Lahore Kebab House E1
Little Italy W1
Lou Pescadou SW5
Maison Novelli EC1
Maze W1
Mezzo W1
Mezzonine W1

Ming W1
Mr Chow SW1
Mr Kong WC2
Orso WC2
Le Palais du Jardin WC2
La Porte des Indes W1
Quaglino's SW1
Ransome's Dock SW11
(Sat)
Rasa N16 (Fri & Sat)
Saint Bar & Restaurant
WC2
Sofra W1 WC2
Soho Soho W1
The Square W1
Star of India SW5

RESTAURANTS SERVING SUNDAY BRUNCH

L'Artiste Assoiffé W11
Assagi at The Chepstow
W2
A Tavola NW8
L'Aventure NW8
The Avenue SW1
Bistrot 190 SW7
The Blenheim NW8
The Blue Elephant SE1
Bombay Brasserie SW7
Butlers Wharf Chop
House SE1
Cafe at Sotheby's W1
Le Caprice SW1
Christopher's American
Grill WC2
Chutney Mary SW10
Coast W1
Daphne's SW3
Frocks E1
Florians N8
Gaucho Grill W1
Gilbert's SW7
The Green Olive W9
Harbour City W1
Jimmy Beez W10
Kartouche SW10
Kavanagh's N1
Luna NW1
Montana SW6
Osteria Antica Bologna
SW11
Palio W11
Pheonix Bar & Grill
SW15
Le Pont de la Tour SE1

La Porte des Indes W1
Quality Chop House
EC1
Ransome's Dock SW11
Searcy's Brasserie EC2
755 SW6
Smokey Joe's Diner
SW18
The Waterloo Fire
Station SE1

RESTAURANTS WITH LIVE MUSIC

Agadir W2
Amazonas W2
Arisugawa W1
Atlantic Bar & Grill W1
The Atrium SW1
The Avenue SW1
Babur Brasserie SE23
Blues Bistro
& Bar W1
Bombay Brasserie SW7
Brilliant Restaurant,
Southall
Le Cafe du Jardin
WC2
Cafe Fish SW1
Cafe O SW3
Cafe du Marché EC1
Calabash WC2
Cambio de
Tercio SW5
Le Caprice SW1
The Chesterfield Hotel
Restaurant W1
Claridge's –
The Causerie W1
Ebla W6
Euten's WC2
Fina Estampa SE1
The Halkin SW1
L'Incontro SW1
Jimmy Beez W10
Jin W1
The Lexington W1
Mezzo W1
Montana SW6
The O'Conor Don Ard-Ri
Dining Room W1
L'Odéon W1
Oslo Court
Restaurant NW8
Oxo Tower Brasserie
SE1
Palio W11

Patio W12
Pont de la Tour SE1
Quaglino's SW1
The Ritz Restaurant W1
Riva SW13
Royal Garden Hotel –
The Tenth W8
Saint Bar & Restaurant
WC2
Savoy River
Restaurant WC2
Sofra Restaurant W1 &
WC2
Soho Soho W1
Star of India SW5
Il Vicolo SW1
Wilson's W14

RESTAURANTS WITH NO MUSIC

Ajimura WC2
Alastair Little W1
Alastair Little Lancaster
Road W11
Alfred WC2
Andrew Edmunds W1
Anglesea Arms W6
Arcadia W8
A Tavola NW8
Atelier W1
Auberge de Provence
SW1
Aubergine SW10
Babe Ruth's E1
Bangkok SW7
Bank WC2
Belgo Centraal WC2
Belgo Noord NW1
Beotys WC2
Bertorelli's WC2
Bibendum SW3
The Bleeding Heart EC1
The Blenheim NW8
The Blue
Elephant SW6
Blue Print Cafe SE1
Bombay Brasserie SW7
The Brackenbury W6
Butlers Wharf Chop
House SE1
Claridge's – The
Causerie W1
Capannina W1

The Capital Hotel SW3
The Captain N4
Caraffini SW1
Cento 50 W11
The Chapel NW7
The Chesterfield
  Restaurant W1
Chez Bruce SW17
Chez Moi W11
Chez Nico at Ninety
  Park Lane W1
Chiaroscuro WC1
China City WC2
The Chiswick W4
Chutney Mary SW10
Cibo W14
Clarke's W8
Connaught Grill and
  Restaurant W1
The Cow W2
Criterion Marco Pierre
  White W1
Daphne's SW3
Dorchester Grill Wl
Dorchester Oriental
  Restaurant W1
La Dordogne W4
East One EC1
Elena's L'Étoile W1
Euphorium N1
Fables SW6
La Famiglia SW10
Fifth Floor SW1
La Finezza SW1
Foundation SW1
Frederick's N1
French House
  Dining Room W1
Le Gavroche W1
Gay Hussar W1
Gilbert's SW7
Gitanjli-Mayfair W5
Gonbei WC1
Granita N1
Green Cottage NW3
Green's Restaurant &
  Oyster Bar SW1
Grill St Quentin SW3
Hilaire SW7
Ikkyu W1
Ikkyu of Chinatown W1
Interlude de Chavot W1
The Ivy WC2
Jason's W9
Joyful SW1
Kulu Kulu W1
Lahore Kebab House E1

The Lansdowne NW1
Launceston Place W8
Laurent Restaurant NW2
Leith's W11
Livebait SE1
Lou Pescadou SW5
Malabar W8
Mamta SW6
Mandalay W2
Mandeer W1
Maze W1
Ming W1
Monkeys SW3
Mon Petit Plaisir W8
Monsieur Max,
  Hampton Hill
Moshi Moshi Sushi EC2
  & EC4
Mr Kong WC2
Museum Street Cafe
  WC1
Nico Central W1
Nicole's W1
L'Odéon W1
Odette's NW7
Olivo SW1
Oliveto SW1
192 W11
L'Oranger SW7
Orsino W11
Oxo Tower Restaurant &
  Brasserie SE1
People's Palace SE1
Phoenix SW15
Pied-à-Terre W1
Poetry Cafe WC2
Poissonerie de
  L'Avenue SW3
Poons WC2
La Porte des Indes W1
Prince of Ceylon NW4
Quality Chop House EC1
Rani N3 & Richmond
The River Cafe W6
Royal Garden Hotel -
  The Tenth W8
RSJ SE1
Rules WC2
St John EC1
St Quentin SW3
Salloos SW1
Savoy Grill WC2
Shaws SW1
Simpson's-in-the-Strand
  WC2
Sonny's SW13

Spices W2
The Square W1
Stephen Bull W1
Stephen Bull, Smith-
  fields EC1
The Stepping Stone SW8
The Sugar Club W11
Sushi-Say NW2
Sweetings EC4
La Tante Claire SW3
Tate Gallery SW1
33 St James's SW1
Twenty Trinity Gardens
  SW9
Two Brothers Fish
  Restaurant N1
Turner's SW3
Upper Street Fish Shop
  N1
Vasco & Piero's Pavilion
  W1
Villandry Dining Rooms
  W1
Vong SW1
Vrisaki N22
Wagamama W1
White Tower W1
Wiltons SW1
Ziani SW3
Zoe W1

RESTAURANTS THAT BAN SMOKING OR WITH NO-SMOKING AREAS

*denotes restaurant with
a no-smoking room

Agadir W2
Ajimura WC2
Arcadia W8
A Tavola NW8*
The Atrium SW1
Auberge de Provence
  SW1*
Babe Ruth's E1
Babur Brasserie SE23
Beotys WC2
Bertorelli's WC2
The Blenheim NW8
The Blue Elephant SW6
Bombay Brasserie
  SW7
Brilliant Restaurant,
  Southall*
The Cafe at Sotheby's
  W1

Capannina W1*
The Captain N4
Cento 50 W11
The Chapel NW1
Chesterfield
  Restaurant W1
Chiaroscuro WC1
China City WC2
Chutney Mary SW10
Clarke's W8*
La Dordogne W4*
East One EC1
Fables Restaurant
  SW6*
Foundation SW1
Frederick's N1*
Grill St Quentin SW3
Ikkyu of Chinatown W1
Jimmy Beez W10
Kulu Kulu W1
Leith's W11
Mamta SW6
Mandeer W1*
McClements,
  Twickenham
Ming W1*
Moshi Moshi Sushi EC2,
  EC4
Museum Street Cafe
  WC1
Nicole's W1
L'Odéon W1
192 W11
Orsino W11
Orso WC2
People's Palace SE1
Poetry Cafe WC2*
La Porte des Indes W1
Prince of Ceylon NW4
Rani N3 & Richmond*
Red Fort W1
Royal Garden Hotel –
  The Tenth W8
RSJ SE1
St Quentin SW3
Scott's W1
Searcy's Brasserie EC2
Sonny's SW13
Spices W2
Stephen Bull's Bistro &
  Bar EC1
The Stepping Stone
  SW8*
The Sugar Club W11
33 St James's SW1
Twenty Trinity
  Gardens SW9

Turner's SW3
Two Brothers Fish
  Restaurant N3
Union Cafe W1
Villandry Dining Rooms
  W1*
Vong SW1
Vrisaki N22*
Wagamama W1*
Zoe W1

RESTAURANTS WITH PRIVATE ROOMS

L'Accento W2
Adam's Cafe W12
Alastair Little W1
Albero & Grana SW3
Alfred WC2
Ajimura WC2
Alba EC1
L'Altro W11
Arcadia W8
Arisugawa W1
L'Artiste Assoiffé W11
A Tavola NW8
Atlantic Bar & Grill W1
The Atrium SW1
Babe Ruth's
Bank WC2
Belgo Centraal WC2
Belgo Noord N1
Bentley's W1
Beotys WC2
Bice WC2
The Bleeding Heart EC1
The Blenheim NW8
Blues Bistro & Bar W1
The Blue Elephant SW6
Brady's SW5 SW18
Brasserie du Marché aux
  Puces W10
Brilliant Restaurant,
  Southall
B Square SW11
Café du Jardin WC2
Cambio de Tercio SW5
Capannina Restaurant
  W1
Capital Hotel SW3
The Caviar House W1
The Chapel NW1
Chesterfield Restaurant
  W1
Chez Bruce SW17
Chez Nico W1
Chiaroscuro WC1

China City Restaurant
  WC2
Chinon W14
Christopher's American
  Grill WC2
Chutneys NW1
Chutney Mary SW10
Claridge's – The
  Causerie W1
Coast W1
Connaught Hotel W1
La Copita W12
Cork & Bottle Wine Bar
  WC2
Daphne's SW3
Dell'Ugo W1
The Dorchester –
  Oriental Restaurant W1
La Dordogne W4
Downstairs at 190 SW7
Ebla W6
L'Escargot W1
L'Estaminet WC2
Euphorium N1
Fables SW6
Fina Estampa SE1
La Finezza SW1
Florians N8
Formula Veneta SW10
Frederick's N1
Frocks E1
Fung Shing WC2
Gaucho Grill W1
Le Gavroche W1
Gay Hussar W1
Gonbei WC1
Green Cottage NW3
The Green Olive W9
Green's Restaurant &
  Oyster Bar SW1
Grill St Quentin SW3
The Halkin Restaurant
  SW1
The Halcyon – The
  Room W11
Harbour City W1
Hilaire SW7
Ikkyu W1
Ikkyu of Chinatown W1
L'Incontro SW1
Interlude de Chavot W1
I-Thai W2
The Ivy WC2
Jimmy Beez W10
Kalamaras Mega &
  Micro W2
Kulu Kulu W1

Launceston Place W8
Leith's W11
Lemonia NW1
The Lexington W1
The Lobster Pot SE11
Lou Pescadou SW5
Maison Novelli EC1
Malabar W8
Mandeer W1
Mange 2 EC1
Ming W1
Mon Plaisir WC2
Monsieur Max,
  Hampton Hill
Mitsukoshi W1
Mr Chow SW1
L'Odéon W1
L'Oranger SW7
Ognisko SW7
Orsino W11
Osteria le Fate SW3
Le Palais du Jardin WC2
Palio W12
The Phoenix SW15
Pied-à-Terre W1
Poetry Cafe WC2
People's Palace SE1
Le P'tit Normand SW18
Poissonerie de l'Avenue
  SW3
Poons WC2
La Porte des Indes W1
The Prince Bonaparte
  W2
Quaglino's SW1
Quincy's NW2
Rani N3
Royal China W2
RSJ SE1
Rules WC2
Saigon W1
St John EC1
St Quentin SW3
San Lorenzo Fuoriporta
  SW19
Savoy Grill WC2
Savoy River Restaurant
  WC2
Scotts W1
755 SW6
Singapore Garden NW6
Soho Soho W1
Snows on the Green W6
Spices W2
The Square W1
The Stamford W6

Star of India SW5
Le Suquet SW3
Sushi-Say NW2
Tatsuso EC2
Tawana Thai W2
33 St James's SW1
Vasco & Piero's Pavilion
  W1
Villandry Dining Rooms
  W1
Vrisaki N22
Il Vicolo SW1
The Waterloo Fire Sta-
  tion SE1
Westzenders W12
White Tower W1
Wiltons SW1
Wodka W8
ZenW3 NW3

RESTAURANTS WITH TABLES OUTSIDE

* denotes restaurant
  with a garden or
  courtyard

The Abingdon W8
L'Accento W2*
Alastair Little W11
Alfred WC2*
Al Hamra W2
L'Altro W11
Amazonas W2
Andrew Edmunds W1
Anglesea Arms W6
Anna's Place N1*
Arcadia W8
L'Arte W1
A Tavola
L'Aventure NW8
Babur Brasserie SE23
Bahn Thai W1
The Belvedere W8*
Bistro 190*
Blakes NW1
The Bleeding Heart*
Blue Print Cafe SE1
The Brackenbury W6
Brasserie du Marché W10
B Square SW11*
Butler's Wharf Chop
  House SE1
Le Cafe du Jardin WC2
Cafe Fish SW1
Caffe Italia SE3*
Cafe Med W11

Cafe O SW3
Cafe Spice Namaste E1*
Cambio de Tercio SW5
Cantina del Ponte SE1
Caraffini SW1
The Chapel NW1*
Chez Gerard W1
Chiaroscuro WC1
Chinon W14*
The Chiswick W4
Christoph's SW10
Chutney Mary SW10*
Cibo W14
Clarke's W8*
Cork & Bottle Wine Bar WC2
Daphne's SW3*
Dell'Ugo W1
La Dordogne W4
The Eagle EC1
Elena's L'Etoile W1
Euphorium N1*
Euten's WC2
La Famiglia SW10*
The Fat Duck, Bray, Berks*
La Finezza SW1
Formula Veneta SW10*
Fredericks*
Frocks E1*
The Gate W6*
Gilbert's SW7
Il Goloso SW10
Gourmet Garden NW4*
The Green Olive W9*
Halcyon Hotel – The Room W11*
The Halkin SW1*
Havelock Tavern W14*
Jason's W9*
Jimmy Beez W10
Joyful SW1
Kalamaras Mega & Micro W2
Kavanagh's N1
The Lansdowne NW1*
Lemonia NW1*
Little Italy W1
Livebait SE1
Lou Pescadou SW5*
Maison Novelli EC1
Mange 2 EC1
Maze W1
Mon Petit Plaisir W8
Monsieur Max, Hampton Hill

Odette's NW7*
Ognisko SW7*
Oliver's Island W4
192 W11
L'Oranger SW1*
Osteria Antica Bologna SW11
Oxo Tower Restaurant & Brasserie NW7
Le Palais du Jardin WC2
Palio W11
La Poissonerie de L'Avenue SW3
Popeseye Steak House W6*
Le Pont de la Tour SE1
Randall & Aubin W1*
Ransome's Dock SW11*
Ritz Restaurant W1*
River Cafe*
RSJ SE1
Riva SW13
St John EC1
San Lorenzo Fuoriporta SW19*
Scotts W1
755 Restaurant SW6*
Shaws SW1
Singapore Garden NW6
Sofra W1 & WC2
Soho Soho W1
The Stamford W6*
The Sugar Club W11*
Le Suquet SW3
The Phoenix SW15
The Red Pepper W1
Twenty Trinity Gardens SW9
The Waterloo Fire Station W1
White Tower W1
Zafferano SW1
Zoe W1*

RESTAURANTS WITH WHEELCHAIR ACCESS

(this list only includes restaurants with wheelchair access to the lavatory as well as the restaurant)

Albero & Grana SW3
The Apprentice SE1
Atlantic Bar & Grill W1

The Atrium SW1
Auberge de Provence SW1
The Avenue NW8
Babe Ruth's E1
Bahn Thai W1
Bank WC2
Bar Central N1 SW3 & SE1
Belgo Centraal WC2
Belgo Noord NW1
Beotys WC2
Bibendum Oyster Bar & Restaurant SW3
Bice W1
The Blue Elephant SW6
Blue Print Cafe SE1
Blues Bistro & Bar W1
Bombay Brasserie SW7
Brilliant Restaurant, Southall
Butlers Wharf Chop House SE1
Cafe Royal Grill W1
Cafe Spice Namaste E1
The Canteen SW10
Capital Hotel SW3
Claridge's – The Causerie W1
Cento 50 W11
Chada Thai SW11
Chez Nico W1
The Chiswick W4
The Collection SW3
The Connaught Restaurant & Grill W1
Criterion Marco Pierre White W1
Detroit WC2
Dorchester Bar Grill & Oriental Restaurant W1
East One EC1
Emporio Armani Express SW3
Esarn Kheaw W12
The Fat Duck, Bray, Berks
Fifth Floor SW1
Florians N8
Gitanjli-Mayfair W5
Green's Restaurant & Oyster Bar W1
The Halkin SW1
Humming Bird N4
Hyde Park Hotel – The

Restaurant Marco Pierre White SW1
Imperial City EC3
I-Thai W2
Jason's W9
Kalamaras Mega & Micro W2
Kartouche SW10
Kensington Place W8
Lemonia NW1
Livebait SE1
Maison Novelli EC1
Mezzo W1
Moshi Moshi Sushi EC2
Museum Street Cafe WC1
L'Odéon W1
Ognisko SW7
Oliver's Island W4
Olivo SW1
Oxo Tower Brasserie & Restaurant SE1
Le Palais du Jardin WC2
People's Palace SE1
The Phoenix SW15
The Poetry Cafe WC2
Le Pont de la Tour SE1
The Prince Bonaparte W2
Prince of Ceylon NW4
Quaglino's SW1
The River Cafe W6
Royal Garden Hotel – The Tenth W8
Royal Lancaster Hotel – Nipa Thai W2
Saint Bar & Restaurant WC2
Savoy Hotel – River Restaurant WC2
Searcy's Brasserie EC2
Soho Soho W1
St John EC1
The Square W1
Sushi-Say NW2
La Tante Claire SW3
Tate Gallery Restaurant SW1
Vong SW1
Wakaba NW3
The Waterloo Fire Station SE1
ZenW3 NW3
Ziani SW3